MONOGRAPHS ON THE PHYSICS AND CHEMISTRY OF MATERIALS

General Editors

WILLIS JACKSON H. FRÖHLICH N. F. MOTT
E. C. BULLARD

MONOGRAPHS ON THE
PHYSICS AND CHEMISTRY OF MATERIALS

General Editors

WILLIS JACKSON   H. FRÖHLICH   N. F. MOTT
E. C. BULLARD

This series is intended to summarize recent results in academic or long-range research in materials and allied subjects, in a form that should be useful to physicists in universities and in Government and industrial laboratories

---

EXPERIMENTAL
TECHNIQUES IN
LOW-TEMPERATURE
PHYSICS

BY

GUY KENDALL WHITE

OXFORD
AT THE CLARENDON PRESS
1959

Oxford University Press, Amen House, London E.C.4

GLASGOW NEW YORK TORONTO MELBOURNE WELLINGTON
BOMBAY CALCUTTA MADRAS KARACHI KUALA LUMPUR
CAPE TOWN IBADAN NAIROBI ACCRA

PRINTED IN GREAT BRITAIN
AT THE UNIVERSITY PRESS, OXFORD
BY VIVIAN RIDLER
PRINTER TO THE UNIVERSITY

PREFACE

Iт is not very many years since most low-temperature physicists —those doing research on physical properties at the temperatures of liquid helium or liquid hydrogen—were trained in the techniques of this particular field at one of the comparatively few centres of low-temperature research such as Leiden, Berlin, Berkeley, Oxford, Cambridge, Toronto. Today, with the advent of increased research grants, defence contracts, and Collins helium liquefiers, many physicists in many laboratories around the world wish to carry out physical investigations in the low-temperature range and are faced with problems of designing cryostats, filling them with liquid helium, maintaining and measuring various temperatures. Often these problems are not very difficult, but nevertheless the technical information and published experience which may help to solve them are spread over a wide range of years and journals. There appears to be a need for a book which gives details of this information, including physical data for the technical materials used in cryostat design, methods of measuring and controlling temperatures, and associated problems. This book is an attempt to meet this need.

In a first flush of enthusiasm I hoped to include the full technical details of many operations, for example the winding of a countercurrent heat exchanger, but soon realized that lack of space made this impossible. Some chapters, notably those dealing with gas liquefaction and magnetic cooling, are merely brief discussions of the principles involved with examples and references to more detailed work. They are intended not only to give continuity to the subject-matter and to introduce those not familiar with the subject to the principles and the literature but also to act as a guide for anyone wishing to design a liquefier or adiabatic demagnetization cryostat; these are both subjects to which complete books could be devoted and recent reviews by Daunt, Collins, Ambler and Hudson, and de Klerk, and earlier books by Ruhemann, Keesom, Casimir, and Garrett cover these subjects far more competently than I could hope to do. Any reader wishing for a more complete survey of low-temperature physics, its scope and its achievements rather than its techniques, should prefer the texts of E. F. Burton, H. Grayson Smith, and J. O. Wilhelm (*Phenomena at the Temperature of Liquid Helium*, Reinhold, 1940), L. C. Jackson (*Low Temperature Physics*, Methuen, 2nd edn. 1948), or C. F. Squire (*Low Temperature Physics*, McGraw-Hill, 1953).

I would like to acknowledge my debt of gratitude to the late Sir Francis Simon for his kindness and patience when I started the study of low-temperature physics; he asked me, as one of his students, to design and build a Linde helium liquefier. I hope this book is rather more successful than my first effort at solving the problems of helium liquefaction.

In preparing this book I have been helped considerably by various friends who have read and criticized individual chapters: these include my colleagues Drs. T. H. K. Barron, J. S. Dugdale, D. K. C. MacDonald, F. D. Manchester, and S. B. Woods of the Division of Pure Physics (National Research Council), Dr. J. A. Morrison of the Division of Pure Chemistry (National Research Council), Dr. H. Preston-Thomas of the Division of Applied Physics (National Research Council), and Dr. R. P. Hudson of the National Bureau of Standards in Washington.

As will appear throughout the text many publishers and learned societies have kindly granted permission for the reproduction of figures which originally appeared in their books and periodicals. The facilities and the co-operation of such sections of the National Research Council as the Central Drafting Office, Duplication, and the Typing Pool have been of great assistance.

Finally, I am happy to thank Dr. M. T. Elford for his help in the proof-reading of this book.

G. K. W.

Ottawa, Canada
July 1957

CONTENTS

PART I

GENERAL

CHAPTER I

PRODUCTION OF LOW TEMPERATURES

1. Isentropic cooling

Introduction

SINCE the entropy or degree of disorder of a system at constant volume or constant pressure is a monotonically increasing function of temperature, any process of cooling may be regarded as one of ordering or entropy reduction. In the words of Simon, a refrigerator is a form of 'entropy-squeezer'. This 'squeezing' is possible since entropy S is a function of other variable parameters as well as temperature, e.g. $S = S(T, X)$ where the parameter X is a physical property of the system which can be varied within limits so as to change the entropy.

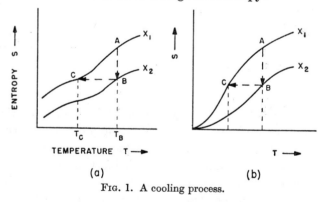

(a)   (b)

FIG. 1. A cooling process.

Figure 1 (*a*) shows that when X is altered isothermally from X_1 to X_2 the entropy is reduced. By further varying X from X_2 to X_1 under isentropic conditions, a lowering in temperature from a temperature T_B to temperature T_C is achieved; an isentropic change is adiabatic since $\Delta S = \int dQ/T$. The process is a reversible one and therefore by the second law of thermodynamics is the most efficient means of cooling, in terms of the external work required. From Figure 1 (*a*) it would seem possible, in principle at least, to cool the system to the absolute zero of temperature by a limited number of such steps as $A \to B \to C$. However, if the situation is as depicted in Figure 1 (*b*), this is no longer the case; that 1 (*b*) is correct, rather than 1 (*a*), is implied by the third law of thermodynamics, which in the form due to Simon (1930, 1956) states: 'at absolute zero the entropy differences disappear between all those states of a system which are in internal thermodynamic equilibrium'.

The equivalence of this statement to the alternative statement that 'it is impossible by any procedure, no matter how idealized to reduce the temperature of any system to the absolute zero in a finite number of operations', has been demonstrated by Guggenheim and is strongly suggested by Figure 1 (*b*). However, we still have a means of lowering the temperature—even if not to absolute zero—at our disposal and in practice such methods have been widely used. Associating the parameter X with the pressure p applied to a gas or with the magnetic field H applied to an assembly of magnetic dipoles, the principles of gas cooling by isothermal compression and adiabatic expansion, and of magnetic cooling by isothermal magnetization and adiabatic demagnetization are exemplified.

Examples

In the single-expansion helium liquefier (Simon, 1932) shown schematically in Figure 2, helium gas is compressed isothermally into chamber 1 to a pressure of 100 atmospheres; a temperature of about 15° K is maintained, heat being transferred through the medium of helium exchange gas in the space 2 to a bath of liquid hydrogen boiling under reduced pressure in the dewar vessel 3. Thus the initial temperature $T_B \simeq 15°$ K; in practice T_B may be lowered to 10° K by reducing the pressure above the evaporating hydrogen to well below its triple-point pressure. Then the exchange gas is removed from 2 and the compressed helium in chamber 1 is expanded through the valve V to a pressure of 1 atmosphere, so that the gas remaining in the chamber is adiabatically cooled to the final temperature T_c (equal to the liquefaction temperature); a substantial fraction of the chamber is left filled with liquid helium. The importance of the metal chamber 1 having a heat capacity small in relation to the gas is paramount, and is easily realized with helium gas at about 10° K, but would not be the case for compressed air at 200° K, for the heat capacity of the containing pressure vessel at this higher temperature would be considerable.

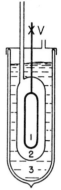

The desorption helium liquefier first discovered by Simon in 1926 and developed further by Mendelssohn (1931) is very similar. In this the inner container is partially filled with activated charcoal and the process $A \to B$ of Figure 1 is simply the isothermal adsorption of helium gas to a pressure of 1–5 atmospheres on the charcoal, the heat of adsorption being removed

FIG. 2. Schematic diagram of the Simon expansion liquefier.

via exchange gas to the liquid-hydrogen bath. This is followed by an adiabatic desorption or pumping away of the adsorbed helium gas during which the temperature of the remaining gas, charcoal, and the container fall toward or to the liquefaction temperature.

The suggestion that a process of ordering by a magnetic field could be applied to an assembly of weakly interacting magnetic dipoles, as in a paramagnetic salt, and that a subsequent adiabatic demagnetization would cause cooling, was made independently in 1926 by Debye and Giauque. Within a few years Giauque and MacDougall (1933), de Haas, Wiersma, and Kramers (1933), and Kurti and Simon (1935) verified this experimentally; Figure 3 illustrates the process schematically. A pill of a paramagnetic salt (gadolinium sulphate in Giauque's early experiments) is magnetized in a field of a few kilo-oersteds at a temperature of about 1° K, the heat of magnetization being transferred through helium exchange gas to the pumped liquid helium in the surrounding dewar vessel. After removal of the exchange gas, the magnetic field is reduced and the temperature of the salt pill falls. There is a further analogy with the expansion liquefier in that for appreciable cooling to occur, the lattice vibrational specific heat at 1° K of the salt pill must be small in comparison with the 'magnetic heat capacity', i.e. with the

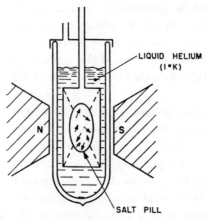

FIG. 3. Schematic diagram of the magnetic cooling process.

thermal energy of the disoriented magnetic ions; if this were not so, the reduction in the entropy on magnetization would be small in comparison with the total entropy of the crystal lattice.

2. Isenthalpic cooling

Introduction

The discovery, nearly a century ago, by Joule and Thomson that a gas undergoes a temperature change when it expands slowly through a porous plug, has been widely applied to gas refrigeration. The cooling on adiabatic expansion discussed in § 1 is a property of the perfect gas—in which attractive or repulsive forces are zero—and occurs for real gases at all temperatures by virtue of their performing 'external' work. However, the Joule–Thomson effect for any real gas depends both in magnitude and sign on the temperature and is zero for a perfect gas at all temperatures. This effect is sometimes called an 'internal work' process because the temperature change is determined by the change in energy of gas when the average separation between the gas molecules is increased.

In the Joule–Thomson process a gas undergoes a continuous throttling or expansion as it is driven by a constant pressure p_1 on one side of the expansion valve (or porous plug) and expands to a lower pressure p_2 on the other. Considering a fixed mass of gas passing the valve, it can easily be shown that the total heat or enthalpy $H = U + pV$ is unchanged in passing from state 1

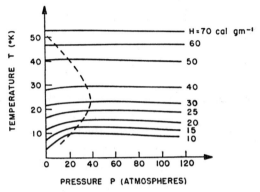

Fig. 4. Isenthalpic curves of helium.

(pressure p_1) to state 2 (pressure p_2); U is the internal energy per unit mass and V is the volume.

Since $dH = 0$ such a process is called isenthalpic.

Performing such a throttling experiment for helium we should obtain a set of values of T_2—the temperature after expansion— lying on a smooth curve. If T_1—the temperature before expansion—is below the so-called inversion temperature, such curves have a maximum as seen in Figure 4. The locus of the maxima encloses a region within which the differential Joule–Thomson coefficient

$$\mu = \left(\frac{\partial T}{\partial p}\right)_H$$

is positive and hence a cooling results on expansion.

We may show:

$$dH = \left(\frac{\partial H}{\partial p}\right)_T dp + \left(\frac{\partial H}{\partial T}\right)_p dT,$$

therefore

$$\left(\frac{\partial T}{\partial p}\right)_H = -\left(\frac{\partial H}{\partial p}\right)_T \Big/ \left(\frac{\partial H}{\partial T}\right)_p$$

$$= -\frac{1}{C_p}\left(\frac{\partial H}{\partial p}\right)_T$$

or, since $dH = dU + p\,dV + V\,dp = T\,dS + V\,dp,$

$$\left(\frac{\partial T}{\partial p}\right)_H = -\frac{1}{C_p}\left[T\left(\frac{\partial S}{\partial p}\right)_T + V\right]$$

$$= \frac{1}{C_p}\left[T\left(\frac{\partial V}{\partial T}\right)_p - V\right]$$

and this vanishes for the perfect gas since $pV = RT$.

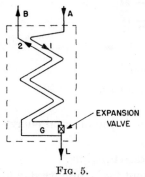

Fig. 5.

This isenthalpic process is important as it forms the final stage for nearly all 'circulation' liquefiers ('circulation' liquefiers exclude the Simon expansion and desorption liquefiers). Such a final stage, including expansion valve and heat interchanger, is shown schematically in Figure 5, where compressed gas at pressure p_A, temperature T_A, and enthalpy H_A per gram enters at A. After expansion the gas (state p_B, T_B, H_B) leaves through the interchanger at B and liquid L (state p_L, T_L, H_L) collects at L.

If the liquefaction efficiency is denoted by $\mathscr{E}$, then since the process is isenthalpic

$$H_A = \mathscr{E}H_L + (1-\mathscr{E})H_B,$$

therefore the efficiency $\mathscr{E} = (H_B - H_A)/(H_B - H_L)$.

Heat interchanger

So far the heat interchanger has not been mentioned, but it plays a vital role in determining the liquefaction efficiency as it determines T_B and therefore the enthalpy H_B. The exchanger efficiency, η, is usually defined as the ratio of the actual heat transferred from stream 1 to stream 2, to the total heat available for transfer.

As $\eta \to 1$, $T_B \to T_A$.

If $\eta = 0$, i.e. if there is no interchanger, then $T_B = T_G$ (where T_G is the temperature of the gas immediately after expansion), and so $H_B = H_G$.

For liquefaction to occur we require $T_G = T_L$, therefore $H_G = H_L + \lambda$, where λ is the latent heat, and so, for $\mathscr{E} \geqslant 0$, we should require $H_A \leqslant H_L + \lambda$ if $H_B = H_G$ ($\eta = 0$). For example, in the case of helium, $H_L + \lambda \simeq 7$ cal/g. The necessity that H_A be less than 7 cal/g would require that T_A should be less than about 7·5° K (from the enthalpy diagram for helium). Since this is clearly too low a temperature to reach by the use of any other liquid refrigerants, and difficult but not impossible by the use of a helium expansion engine, it is desirable to have an efficient interchanger.

In the case where the interchanger is 100 per cent efficient, i.e. $\eta = 1$, we may write $H_B = H_B^0$ and $\mathscr{E} = \mathscr{E}_0$.

Then
$$\mathscr{E}_0 = \frac{H_B^0 - H_A}{H_B^0 - H_L} \quad \text{for } \eta = 1.$$

It is easily shown in a practical case where $\eta < 1$ that

$$\mathscr{E} = \mathscr{E}_0 - (1 - \eta)(1 - \mathscr{E}_0)\frac{H_B^0 - \lambda - H_L}{H_B^0 - H_L}.$$

Since generally $0 \cdot 8 < \eta < 1$, this can be reduced to a simpler form, $\mathscr{E} = \mathscr{E}_0 - \alpha(1 - \eta)$, where the factor $\alpha < 1$. Under the normal range of conditions met with in the final stage of a helium liquefier, α has a value in the vicinity of $0 \cdot 6$ so that it is necessary in designing an interchanger that its inefficiency $(1 - \eta)$ shall not be comparable with or greater than the maximum liquefaction efficiency $\mathscr{E}_0$ of the last stage, often called the Linde stage of the liquefier.

Figure 6 shows the liquefaction efficiency $\mathscr{E}_0$ for helium as a function of the pressure p_A and temperature T_A, assuming $\eta \simeq 1$; the curves have been calculated from enthalpy data for helium given by Keesom (1942) and Van Lammeren (1941).

Since $\mathscr{E}$ is a maximum when H_A is a minimum, the conditions for maximum efficiency of this liquefaction stage include that

$$\left(\frac{\partial H_A}{\partial p_A}\right)_{T=T_A} = 0.$$

It follows from

$$C_p \mu = \left(\frac{\partial H}{\partial T}\right)_p \left(\frac{\partial T}{\partial p}\right)_H$$

that $\mu = 0$ satisfies this condition.

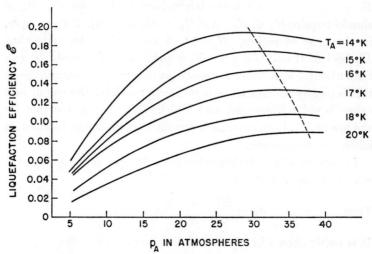

FIG. 6. Theoretical liquefaction efficiency of the Linde stage of a helium liquefier.

Thus the optimum entry pressure is a value of p_A lying on the inversion curve (see Figures 4 and 6).

Principles of a Joule–Thomson liquefier

Consider the schematic diagram (Figure 7) of a helium lique-fier which relies on Joule–Thomson cooling for its final or liquefaction stage. The hydrogen liquefier is similar in principle but is more simple as one cooling stage can be omitted.

C_1, C_2, C_3 are cooling stages, the final stage C_3 being the Joule–Thomson valve; X_1, X_2, X_3 are heat interchangers. The chief points that emerge are that:

(i) The cooling stage C_2, which may be liquid hydrogen or an expansion engine device, should be capable of producing an exit temperature for the gas stream of well below the inversion temperature and preferably $\leqslant 15°\,\mathrm{K}$ for high liquefaction efficiency.

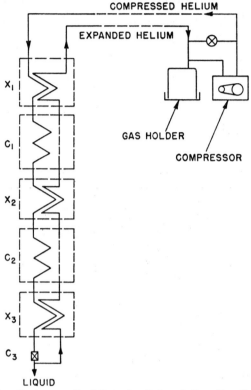

FIG. 7. A generalized flow circuit for a helium liquefier.

(ii) X_1, C_1, X_2 are all inessential in principle, but their form and efficiency determine the character of C_2; in practice C_1 may be either liquid air (or liquid nitrogen or oxygen) or an expansion engine.

(iii) C_1 should generally act as both a purifying and precooling stage, although these may be in separate units with the purifying part—a charcoal trap at liquid-air temperature —external to the main liquefier.

(iv) C_2, if it be a liquid-hydrogen cooling stage, may also be divided into two parts with a first part containing liquid hydrogen boiling under atmospheric pressure at 20·4° K and a second containing liquid hydrogen boiling under reduced pressure; such an arrangement considerably reduces the capacity required for the hydrogen pump.

A more detailed discussion of these considerations and the general methods of constructing such a liquefier will be given below in § 5, with the aid of the examples offered by some of the many liquefiers described in recent years.

In Table I are the Joule–Thomson inversion temperatures for some common gases and other data governing their suitability as refrigerant liquids.

TABLE I

Physical data for gases

Gas	Inversion temp. (°K)	Boiling-point (°K)	Critical temp. (°K)	Critical pressure (atm)	Triple-point (°K)	Triple-point pressure (mm Hg)
Helium (He³)	..	3·2	3·34	1·15	..	..
Helium (He⁴)	51	4·2	5·19	2·26	..	..
Hydrogen .	205	20·4	33·2	13·0	14·0	54
Neon . .	..	27·2	44·4	25·9	24·6	324
Nitrogen .	621	77·3	126	33·5	63·1	94
Argon .	723	87·4	151	48	83·9	512
Oxygen . '	893	90·1	154	50	54·4	1·2
Krypton .	..	121·3	210	54	104	..

3. Air liquefiers

Linde and Hampson

To the low-temperature physicist who either buys liquid nitrogen or oxygen commercially for 20, 30, or perhaps 50 pence per litre, or who draws freely on the output of a large central laboratory liquefier, a description of the principles involved in air liquefiers may seem out of place in this text. However, these principles serve to illustrate and introduce the various types of helium and hydrogen liquefiers, and to explain historically the terms such as Linde, Hampson, Claude, which are frequently applied to particular designs of liquefiers. Because of the higher temperatures involved they introduce the methods of liquefaction without the complexity of a precooling stage.

In the simple Linde air liquefier of Figure 8, a compressor, heat exchanger X, and expansion throttle V are the important features. In 1895, the same year as Linde first used this simple pattern for air liquefaction, Hampson developed his air liquefier, which used a similar flow circuit but a different design of

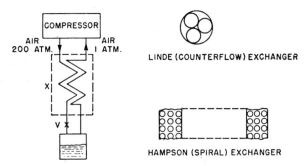

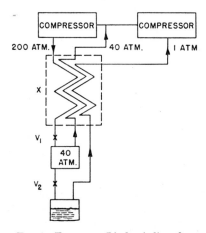

FIG. 8. Simple Linde air liquefier and section views of Linde and Hampson heat exchangers.

FIG. 9. Two-stage Linde air liquefier.

heat exchanger. Linde employed a countercurrent heat exchanger (see Figure 8 and Chapter III) in which the two gas streams passed through concentric tubes. In the Hampson exchanger the high-pressure gas flows through a tube wound in a spiral pattern with the spiral enclosed in the annular space between two cylinders, and the returning low-pressure gas passes up this annular space past the spiral of tubing. Linde later improved the efficiency of his air liquefier by letting the gas expand in two stages (Figure 9), first through a valve V_1 from 200 to 40 atmospheres after which about 80 per cent of the gas returns through exchanger X to be recompressed; the remaining fraction is expanded through V_2 to 1 atmosphere. The resultant saving in work of compression improved the practical efficiency by about 100 per cent.

A further improvement occurred when Linde introduced a liquid ammonia precooling stage so that the compressed gas entered X at about $-48°$ C.

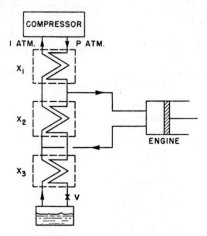

FIG. 10. Claude–Heylandt system of air liquefaction.

Claude

As the name Linde is invariably associated with the Joule–Thomson process of cooling, so Claude is associated with expansion-engine liquefiers, although in the later form used by Claude and also developed by Heylandt early in this century both an expansion engine and a Joule–Thomson valve were incorporated (Figure 10). Claude's first machines used simply isentropic expansion with liquid air being produced in the engine. However, the advantages of dividing the high-pressure stream and using Joule–Thomson expansion for the final liquefaction stage were considerable and this form has been used successfully over the years. Claude used a pressure of about 40 atmospheres and allowed 80 per cent of the gas to pass through the engine; Heylandt used 200 atmospheres, passed about 60 per cent through the engine, and dispensed with exchanger X_1. Thus in the Heylandt case gas enters the engine at room temperature which gives a somewhat higher operating efficiency.

The over-all operating efficiencies of the Linde and Claude systems are not very different and both are still widely used. Present-day developments in large-scale air liquefiers are largely concerned with the use of turbine expanders; the recent developments and references are given in the excellent review article by Daunt (1956) and by Davies (1949). While these are of little direct concern in this book, two other processes of air liquefaction, namely the Cascade process and the Phillips process, are of interest.

Cascade liquefiers

Pictet's first partially successful attempt to liquefy oxygen in 1877 used the cascade process, although the 'mist' of liquid which he produced was probably a result of adiabatic expansion plus cascade cooling rather than purely the cascade process itself. In this method a suitable gas A is liquefied at room temperature under pressure and then expanded to evaporate under atmospheric or under reduced pressure at a lower temperature; provided that this lower temperature is below the critical temperature of a second gas B, then this gas B may be liquefied likewise by isothermal compression; thus in stages the critical temperature of air may be reached. In Pictet's case gas A was sulphur dioxide and gas B was carbon dioxide. It is interesting to note that Keesom (1933) analysed the efficiency of a four-stage cascade process for air liquefaction using NH_3 (as gas A), C_2H_4 (B), CH_4 (C), and using N_2 (D) as the final stage; he found the efficiency to be higher than in the conventional Claude or Linde processes.

Keesom chose his refrigerants so that no liquid had to evaporate at a pressure less than 1 atmosphere (Table II) in order to get appreciably below the critical temperature of the next gas.

TABLE II

Keesom's cascade process

	Condenser temp. (°K)	Condenser press. (atm)	Evap. temp.	Evap. press.
$A = NH_3$	298	10·2	240	1
$B = C_2H_4$	242	19	169	1
$C = CH_4$	172	24·7	112	1
$D = N_2$	114·6	18·6	..	..

However, the use of such a process for helium or hydrogen lique-faction seems unlikely in view of the critical temperatures shown in Table I and the limited choice of refrigerants available for cooling in the range below 50° K.

Phillips

The process developed by the Phillips Company in Eindhoven also has no direct application in helium or hydrogen liquefaction —at least at the present time—but offers a very convenient means of supplying liquid air in a small machine of relatively low cost. Developed from the Stirling hot-air engine, it has been described by Kohler and Jonkers (1954); the principles are illustrated schematically in Figure 11.

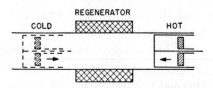

FIG. 11. Schematic illustration of the Phillips
air-liquefaction process.

On the right-hand side gas is compressed isothermally by the relative motions of a piston and 'cylinder' or, in effect, the out-of-phase motion of two pistons. These are then moved to the left-hand side on which expansion occurs; so that the cooling effect of the expansion is cumulative, the gas is forced through a regenerator—a type of heat interchanger which acts as a thermal reservoir and is therefore suitable for discontinuous flow processes—as the two pistons move from side to side.

The gas (helium or hydrogen) employed as the working substance is in a closed circuit and air is simply condensed from the atmosphere on the 'cold' head, corresponding to the left-hand side of the diagram, once the liquefaction temperature is reached; this machine supplies liquid air at about 5 l/hour and may fulfil a demand in small laboratories where the operation of a large air liquefaction plant is impracticable.

4. Expansion - engine helium liquefiers

Kapitza

The first successful helium liquefier which used an expansion engine rather than liquid hydrogen for precooling was that of Kapitza (1934) which operated in the Mond Laboratory, Cambridge, for nearly two decades. Figure 12 indicates the flow circuit in which helium gas, compressed to about 30 atmospheres, is precooled by liquid nitrogen, after which the majority of the gas is expanded in the engine *E* and returns through the heat exchangers *C*, *B*, and *A*. The minor fraction of compressed gas (about 8 per cent) passes on through exchangers to a Joule–Thomson expansion valve 4.

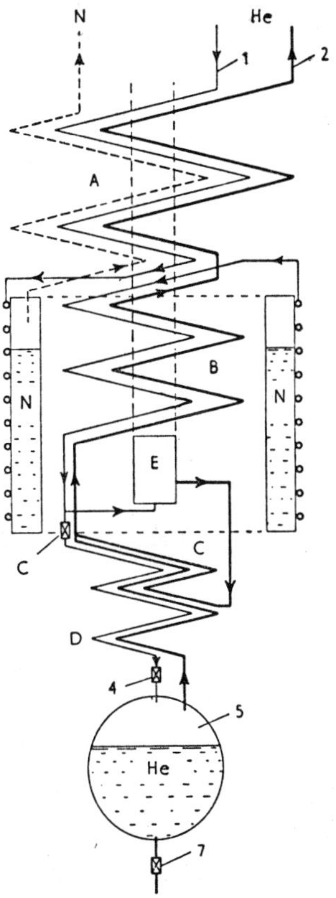

While this exemplifies the general principles of helium liquefaction

Fig. 12. Arrangement of heat exchangers and cooling stages in the Kapitza liquefier (after Kapitza, 1934).

discussed above (§ 2 and Figure 7), it is also a direct development of the Claude process of air liquefaction with the addition of the liquid nitrogen precooling. Kapitza used an unlubricated engine with a clearance of about 0·002 in. between the piston and cylinder, the small gas loss past the piston serving as a lubricant. The part of the liquefier below the nitrogen vessel is surrounded by a radiation shield thermally anchored to the liquid-nitrogen container, and the whole assembly is suspended in a highly evacuated metal vessel. This liquefier produced about 1·7 l/hour at an overall liquefaction efficiency of 4 per cent and was only recently superseded in the Mond Laboratory by the higher capacity liquefier designed by Ashmead (1950).

Collins

Closely related in principle of operation to Kapitza's liquefier is that developed by Professor Collins (1947; see also Latham and

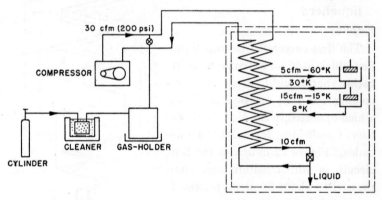

FIG. 13. Simplified flow circuit of a Collins helium liquefier.

McMahon, 1949) at the Massachusetts Institute of Technology. This liquefier and its commercial development by the Arthur D. Little Corporation has contributed to the present wide development of low-temperature research and to the familiar references to the two eras of low-temperature physics as 'before and after Collins'. As illustrated in the flow diagram of Figure 13 there is one obvious difference from the Kapitza model, in that there are two expansion engines, the first acting in place of the liquid-nitrogen cooling stage used by Kapitza. Other important features are:

(i) A very hard nitrided nitro-alloy steel for the engines allows the use of a very small clearance (0·0004 in.) between piston and cylinder wall and reduces the gas leakage to a negligible amount, without causing appreciable wear on either piston or cylinder.

(ii) In the heat exchanger (Plates I *a* and I *b*,† facing p. 32) the high-pressure helium at about 14 atmospheres flows down through copper-finned cupro-nickel tubes of $\frac{1}{4}$ in. diameter, and the low-pressure gas returns past these fins through the annular space between two cylindrical walls: the finned tubing is wound tightly on the inner slightly tapered cylinder and the outer jacket cylinder (similarly tapered) is forced up to cover the windings. A flexible cord is interwound with the exchanger tubing to force the return gas flow into more intimate contact with the copper fins, themselves solder-bonded to the cupro-nickel tubing. This exchanger is of high efficiency and gives a comparatively small pressure drop for the high helium flow rates used in this liquefier. The final section of the heat exchanger carrying about 10 cu. ft. of gas per minute to the expansion valve is a Linde concentric-tube interchanger and may be clearly seen in Plate II (between pp. 32–33).

(iii) In the Collins machine the piston and valve rods are always under tension rather than compression which allows the use of relatively thin stainless steel rods and makes the heat inflow through these small (Plate III) (between pp. 32–33).

(iv) Finally and most important from the maintenance viewpoint is the fact that the working parts are surrounded by an atmosphere of helium, rather than a high vacuum. The whole assembly enclosed by the heat exchanger fits inside a stainless steel dewar vessel and the possibility of serious vacuum troubles is considerably lessened by having the engines, helium flow tubes, and couplings, etc., in a static helium atmosphere; there is a change of temperature from about 295° K at the top to 4·2° K at the bottom, and into this region any small leakage of gas is of no great consequence. If operated from a 30 cu. ft./min compressor and if no liquid nitrogen is used, the liquefaction rate is 2–3 litres of liquid helium per hour. As frequently used, with liquid nitrogen flowing through the tubes which cool the radia-

† I am very grateful to Dr. Howard McMahon of Arthur D. Little, Inc., for photographs from which Plates I–III are taken.

tion shield (situated in the vacuum space around the lower half of the assembly), 4–5 l/hour are obtained. Also, by increasing the compressor capacity and running the engines more rapidly—

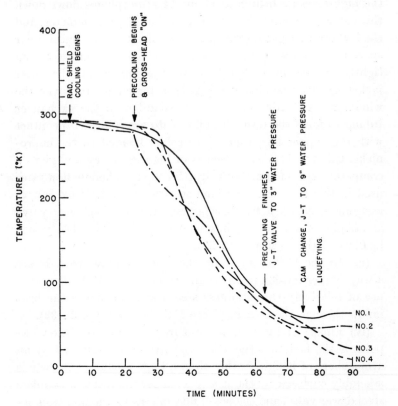

Fig. 14. Operating temperatures during cooling for a Collins helium liquefier (N.S.L. Mark II: Run 136 on 8 Jan. 1956, Sydney); thermocouples nos. 1 and 2 record inlet and outlet temperatures respectively at the first engine; nos. 3 and 4 record inlet and outlet temperatures at the second engine.

preferably accompanied by slight modifications to the cams in the crosshead—much higher liquefaction rates can be obtained.

Another important practical consideration is the time interval from the commencement of helium-gas circulation to the beginning of liquefaction. When liquid nitrogen is used for cooling the radiation shield, this period of time is about $2\frac{1}{2}$–3 hours. This time may be reduced considerably by slight modifications to the liquefier. During the initial cooling Mr. W. R. G. Kemp† and his colleagues (National Standards Laboratory, Sydney) lead part of the compressed helium gas through a coil immersed in a dewar of liquid nitrogen, then through a vacuum jacketed tube into the liquefier where it is expanded through a small needle valve into the outlet tube of the no. 2 engine. This precooling is continued for about 30 minutes and the total time required for liquefaction to commence is about 60 minutes. Figure 14 shows a graph of the temperatures at the inlets and outlets of no. 1 and no. 2 engines as a function of time and indicates when the precooling is stopped and when other adjustments may be made.

It is not profitable to discuss at great length the details of this liquefier as the commercially available models have adequate descriptive instructions with them; even with working drawings available, the labour and difficulty of constructing such a liquefier is fairly considerable. Both at the Radar Research Establishment in Malvern (England) and the National Standards Laboratory in Sydney such liquefiers have been built; the machine at Sydney has been operating successfully since early in 1951, but the making of such items as the heat exchanger, outer vacuum jacket, nitrided and lapped nitro-alloy pistons and cylinders, crosshead, and top plate, demand fairly extensive workshop facilities and considerable labour.

An interesting development in the field of expansion-engine liquefiers is that due to Long and Simon (1953) using a bellows engine. In their small-capacity helium liquefier, the cooling stages consist of a liquid-air bath and a bellows expansion engine. A serious disadvantage of this engine is the limited fatigue life of the bellows although this increases considerably as the temperature is reduced; under the conditions of operation in the Long and Simon liquefier, brass bellows had a life of about $\frac{1}{2}$ million cycles which is equivalent to about 60 hours of operation. Use of a different bellows material and a slightly decreased

† I am indebted to Mr. Kemp for his kindness in supplying details of these modifications and the temperature-time chart reproduced in Figure 14.

stroke might improve this considerably. So there is still the prospect of a helium liquefier which can be made in a laboratory workshop with limited facilities and which does not require liquid hydrogen for its operation.

5. A survey of hydrogen and helium liquefiers

Introduction

Bearing in mind that there are still Linde- and Simon-type liquefiers in operation in many laboratories, and that many more will probably be made, this section discusses some of these liquefiers. It is intended to present a representative collection, indicating the practical advantages and disadvantages of their construction and operation.

Apart from the ability of a liquefier to supply a demand for a liquefied gas, two major features which determine its value are ease of construction and ease of maintenance. Except in the case of an expansion-engine liquefier where engines and crosshead impose their own constructional difficulties, the major constructional problem is usually the heat exchanger and the primary maintenance problem that of keeping the heat leakage at a sufficiently low value. If the heat exchanger allows of relatively easy construction and assembly, and the high vacuum surrounding the liquefier is maintained without much labour, the liquefier should be a successful design. In small-capacity liquefiers this first requirement can be met with Linde-pattern exchangers and the second can often be satisfied by exposing as few as possible of the working parts to the high vacuum space, as is done in the Collins machine.

Another determining factor in liquefier design is the amount and pressure of the gas delivered by available compressors. This is particularly so in the case of hydrogen liquefiers where the optimum pressure for Joule–Thomson cooling is high—about 140 atmospheres. This has led to the construction of a number of successful small hydrogen liquefiers supplied from cylinders.

Small hydrogen liquefiers

The design principles and the expected performance of cylinder-operated hydrogen liquefiers have been discussed in

TABLE III

Hydrogen liquefaction percentage (after Starr, 1941)

Precooling temp. (°K)	Pressure (atm)	Efficiency of X		
		100%	90%	80%
77	150	18	14	9
	100	16	11	6
	50	10	5	−1
	25	4	−2	..
63	150	29	26	22
	100	26	22	18
	50	19	14	10
	25	8	3	−3
55	150	40	38	35
	100	37	35	32
	50	26	24	20
	25	12	8	3

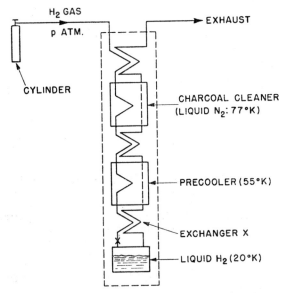

Fig. 15. Flow circuit of a small hydrogen liquefier.

detail by Starr (1941) who gave the figures shown in Table III
for the percentage liquefaction under various conditions of gas
pressure and precooling temperature. A schematic diagram of
Starr's suggested design is shown in Figure 15.

The isenthalps and the inversion curve for normal hydrogen are shown in Figure 16 from Woolley, Scott, and Brickwedde (1948). By comparison with data for helium (Figures 4 and 6) it is seen that much higher optimum operating pressures are required for hydrogen liquefaction; for example, a convenient

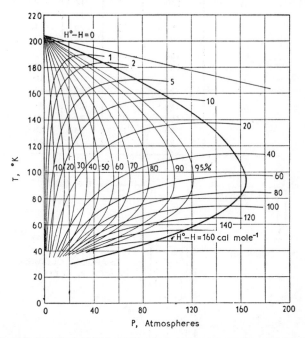

FIG. 16. Isenthalps (approximately horizontal curves) and inversion curve (heavy curve) for hydrogen (after Woolley, Scott, and Brickwedde, 1948). The light curves drawn roughly parallel to the inversion curve are lines at which the refrigeration is the marked percentage of 100 per cent on the inversion curve.

input temperature and input pressure for hydrogen gas entering the final stage of a Joule–Thomson liquefier might be 60° K and 130 atmospheres.

Figure 17 is a schematic diagram of the small hydrogen liquefier described by Ahlberg, Estermann, and Lundberg (1937). In this liquefier the liquid begins to collect, after about 30 minutes circulation, in the bottom of a glass dewar; the dewar serves as the thermal insulation so that the exchangers and solder joints are not exposed to the vacuum system but are in a static hydrogen atmosphere or in the liquid-nitrogen container.

Among other small hydrogen liquefiers which might be profitably studied by anyone concerned with design and construction are those described by Keyes, Gerry, and Hicks (1937), Fairbank (1946), and DeSorbo, Milton, and Andrews (1946).

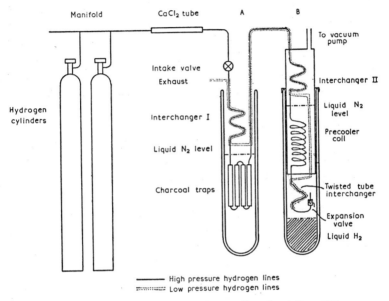

FIG. 17. A small-scale Linde hydrogen liquefier (after Ahlberg, Estermann, and Lundberg, 1937).

Large hydrogen liquefiers

Among the larger hydrogen liquefiers producing between 7 and 40 l/hour are those built at Leiden,† Berlin (Meissner, 1928), Oxford (Jones, Larsen, and Simon, 1948; also Croft and Simon, 1955), Zurich (Clusius, 1953), Bellevue (Spoendlin, 1954). These liquefiers, all of the Linde pattern, operate with an input pressure of 150–200 atmospheres, precooling temperature (i.e. entry temperature to the final Linde exchanger) of 63–66° K, and have

† Described in *de Modernisering van het Kamerlingh Onnes Laboratorium te Leiden* (1953): published through the N. V. de Bataafsche Petroleum Maatschappij.

a liquefaction efficiency in the range 22–30 per cent (cf. Table III, from Starr, 1941).

Figure 18 shows the circuit of the hydrogen liquefier at Oxford which has an output of some 20 l/hour. The gas is compressed from electrolytic hydrogen and led to the successive stages of (a) condensation cleaning, (b) charcoal cleaning and ortho-para conversion, and (c) liquefaction, which are housed in separate encased dewar vessels rather than having the whole unit inside one dewar. Incorporating a stage for partial conversion of the ortho-hydrogen into para-hydrogen within the flow circuit of the liquefier reduces the wastage by evaporation of liquid during the first few days of storage; this is discussed in more detail in Chapter II.

A larger capacity hydrogen liquefier is that of the National Bureau of Standards in Boulder, Colorado, with an output of about 350 l/hour of normal liquid hydrogen or 240 l/hour of para-hydrogen. As described by Johnson and Wilson (1955), the hydrogen gas passes successively through a 'Deoxo' purifier (palladium catalyst supported on silica gel), compressor, oil and water separator, refrigeration drier (cooled to below −100° C), and silica gel purifier (to adsorb N_2 and any remaining O_2); it then precools the refrigeration drier, and passes on into a Joule–Thomson liquefaction stage. For details of the methods of construction of these larger liquefiers, the reader should consult the original papers and in particular the comprehensive review by Daunt (1956) which gives more complete details of their performance and references to a number of other small hydrogen liquefiers.

Simon expansion helium liquefiers

The principle of operation of single-expansion liquefiers was discussed in § 1 above, and Figure 19 (Pickard and Simon, 1948) illustrates the dependence of percentage yield (i.e. percentage filling of the expansion vessel with liquid helium) on the pressure and temperature from which the expansion begins. While requiring a high-pressure helium supply together with liquid hydrogen, such a liquefier is itself of comparatively simple

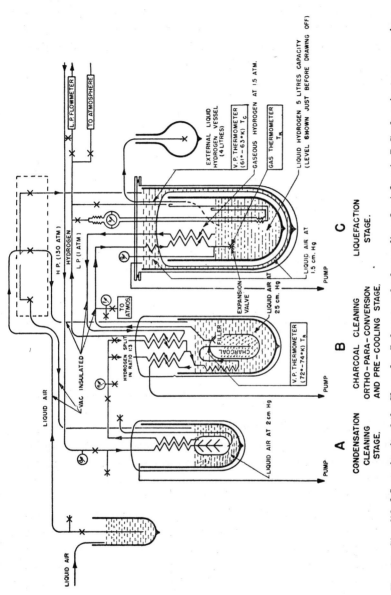

Fig. 18. Simplified flow circuit of the Clarendon Laboratory hydrogen liquefier (after A. J. Croft, private communication, 1957); safety blow-offs are not shown.

construction. Figure 20 gives a sectional view of the liquefier constructed by Croft (1952) which yields 1·2 litres per expansion from 95 atmospheres and 11° K and consumes about 5 litres of liquid hydrogen per expansion. As in the earlier liquefiers described by Cooke, Rollin, and Simon (1939), and Scott and Cook (1948), expansion takes place through a valve at the end

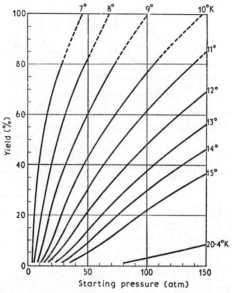

FIG. 19. Liquid-helium yield in the Simon expansion process (after Pickard and Simon, 1948).

of the transfer siphon and assists in precooling the siphon and the dewar into which the liquid is to be transferred. The liquid-hydrogen space G surrounding the Vibrac steel expansion vessel has a volume such that after reducing its temperature and the temperature of the steel vessel and contained helium to 11° K, very little hydrogen is left. Radial copper fins and copper braiding on the steel bottle assist thermal contact between the solid hydrogen and the inner vessel, reducing the time required for cooling the compressed helium. The applicability of this single-expansion system to situations where liquid hydrogen is available, but there is no high-pressure helium compressor, is demonstrated by the liquefier of Scott and Cook (1948); this operated successfully from a bank of cylinders and delivered 300–400 cm³ of liquid helium into an external dewar after each expansion. By judicious use of the bank of cylinders so that those cylinders at

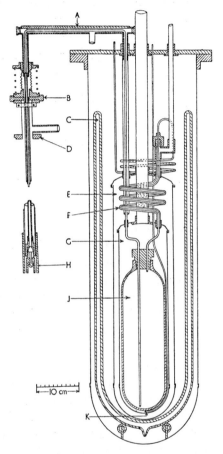

FIG. 20. Section of a Simon helium expansion liquefier (after Croft, 1952), E, vacuum space; F, heat exchanger; G, liquid-hydrogen space; H, outlet valve; J, helium bottle; K, extraction tube for the liquid-air precoolant.

lowest pressure supply the first helium to the cooling expansion vessel, and those at highest pressure are used at the end of the cooling stage, the full capacity of each cylinder may be gainfully employed.

While the small-capacity Simon helium liquefier has had an undoubted popularity at the Clarendon Laboratory, comparatively few have been constructed elsewhere and of these most have been operated from cylinders of compressed gas. A

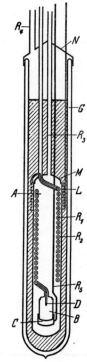

compressor suitable for delivering helium gas at over 100 atmospheres pressure is a rather uneconomical proposition when only called upon to supply one small liquefier. As a result the small Linde-type liquefier has been more commonly used, as it operates efficiently with an input pressure of 20–30 atmospheres and therefore can be supplied by a suitably modified commercial air compressor or from cylinders fitted with a pressure-reducing valve.

Linde helium liquefiers

Typical of the simplest and the earliest of these small Joule–Thomson–Linde liquefiers is that of Ruhemann (1930) (Figure 21). It has a small heat exchanger—a narrow copper tube R_1 inside a slightly larger German silver tube R_2—wound into a spiral and enclosed by the vacuum jacket A. The expansion valve D in Ruhemann's liquefier is adjusted by a small brass screw before attaching the vacuum jacket and the whole assembly is surrounded by a dewar of liquid hydrogen or

Fig. 21. Miniature Linde liquefier (after Ruhemann, 1930).

liquid air. This miniature liquefier yields about 40 cm³/hour of liquid helium or hydrogen and may be supplied from cylinders.

An example of the more usual type of liquefier in which the expansion valve can be continuously controlled from outside and in which a liquid air cooling stage is used, is that shown in Figure 22 (after Daunt and Mendelssohn, 1948). This liquefier may be easily constructed and assembled in three or four weeks by an experienced technician; it has a glass tail, attached by a copper-glass Housekeeper seal and Wood's metal joint to the brass vacuum jacket. Giving about 150 cm³ of liquid helium per hour with less than one hour starting time, this liquefier is very suitable for the visual observations on liquid helium for which it was intended. It has also served as a prototype for other small and larger liquefiers, e.g. the 1 l/hour liquefiers described by Dash,

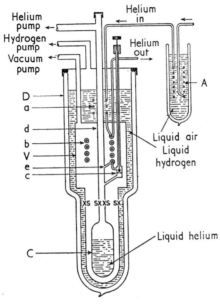

Fig. 22. Diagram of helium liquefier (after Daunt and Mendelssohn, 1948).

Cook, Zemansky, and Boorse (1950), Hercus and White (1951), Parkinson (1954), and Brewer and Edwards (1956); Figure 23 shows the Hercus and White liquefier, together with the cleaning-precooling stage and the transfer vessel. The Joule–Thomson liquefier at Ohio State University (Daunt and Johnston, 1949) with a production of 7·5 litres of liquid helium per hour and a liquid hydrogen consumption of 1·3 litres per litre of helium is a further example of the development. In this liquefier a Hampson-type heat exchanger is used to transfer heat from the incoming compressed gas to the low-pressure helium stream and to the evaporated hydrogen gas; this exchanger is designed to give a low pressure drop with the high flow rate used.

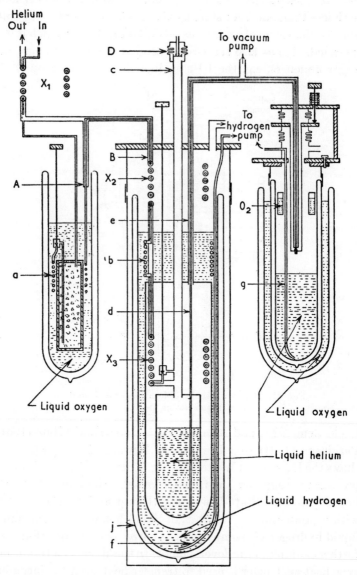

FIG. 23. Schematic diagram of helium liquefier with a precooling-cleaning stage and a transfer vessel (after Hercus and White, 1951).

Finally, the helium liquefier completed recently at the Clarendon Laboratory† is a good example of a large Linde helium
liquefier which can be used very successfully when adequate
supplies of liquid hydrogen are available. As shown in Figure 24
there are three distinct stages, only one of which, comprising
the final exchanger and liquid-helium chamber, is enclosed in a

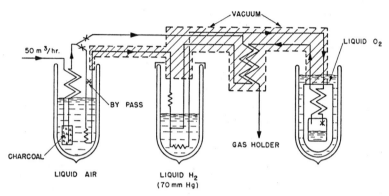

FIG. 24. The large Linde helium liquefier at the Clarendon Laboratory
(after A. J. Croft, private communication, 1957).

vacuum space. In the first liquid-air dewar, the helium gas is
purified by passing over charcoal and part of the helium stream
is precooled. The other part of the stream is precooled by the
returning cold helium gas; the incoming compressed helium is
then further cooled by liquid hydrogen (reduced to a pressure
of about 70 mm Hg, say 14° K) in the second dewar vessel before
entering the final Linde stage in the third dewar. With a two-
stage Reavell compressor 50 m³ of helium per hour are compressed to 27 atmospheres and the liquefier yields about 12 litres
of liquid helium per hour; the liquid hydrogen consumption is
approximately 1·5 litres of hydrogen per litre of helium.

Hydrogen–helium liquefiers

The combined hydrogen-helium liquefier is another development of interest in cases where Collins liquefiers are not economi-
cal and where it is not desired to have a separate hydrogen

† I am grateful to Dr. A. J. Croft for sending me details of this liquefier and
its performance.

liquefier. These have helium liquefaction as the main purpose, with hydrogen liquefaction merely as a necessary evil in the helium liquefaction process. The small-capacity hydrogen-helium liquefiers of Rollin (1936) and Schallamach (1943) used Joule–Thomson expansion at the liquid-hydrogen stage and Simon expansion at the liquid-helium stage. A more recent

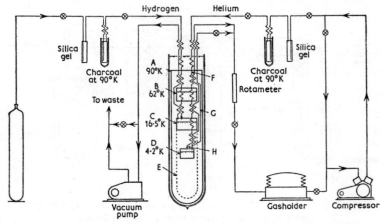

FIG. 25. A small-capacity hydrogen-helium liquefier (after Chester and Jones, 1953).

example (Chester and Jones, 1953) of which the circuit diagram is shown in Figure 25, uses isenthalpic cooling for both gases.

The Ashmead liquefier at the Mond Laboratory in Cambridge (Ashmead, 1950) is a combined liquefier on a larger scale, with a helium liquefaction rate of 4 l/hour and using 5 litres of liquid hydrogen (produced internally) per hour. The heat exchangers, and the three cans which contain liquid air, liquid hydrogen, and pumped liquid hydrogen respectively, are supported from the main top plate and are surrounded by the main vacuum jacket. Problems of vacuum maintenance have been reduced by brazing the slightly domed brass faces onto each can and soldering the cooling coils, which carry the compressed gas, onto the outside of these cans. Perhaps the only more successful way of avoiding trouble over years of operation is that of the Collins liquefier in which an atmosphere of the gas being circulated surrounds all the working parts and is reasonably free from

PLATE I

(a)

(b)

PLATE II

PLATE III

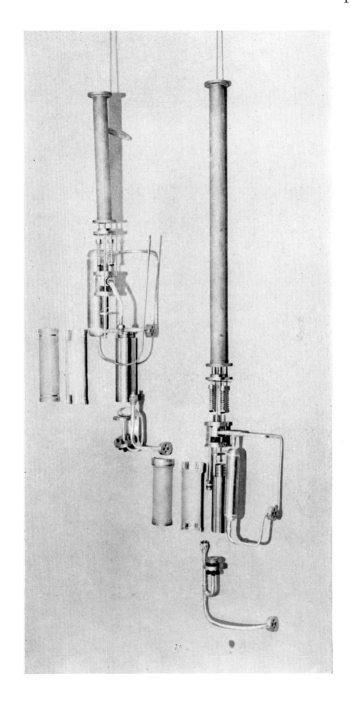

PLATE IV

convection; however, in a large liquefier this method does require a rather large surrounding dewar vessel to isolate the interior.

6. Gas purification

It is generally necessary that the gas stream entering a liquefier should be free of significant amounts of any impurity which may condense in the working parts of the liquefier. This is particularly important in a 'circulation liquefier' employing expansion engines, as very small quantities of any impurity which may condense as a solid in the engine chamber can cause the engine to seize. Likewise, blockage of the Joule–Thomson valve or of the heat exchanger is a considerable nuisance and may in fact be quite dangerous. In the Collins liquefier small vessels containing adsorbent charcoal are placed in the high-pressure circuit preceding the entry of gas to each of the two engines. However, as in other liquefiers, it is desirable to remove most of the impurities before the gas enters the precooling stage even in the Collins machine. In many small liquefiers this cleaning stage may be a liquid-nitrogen-cooled charcoal trap which also acts as a precoolant.

The major impurities likely to be present in a high-pressure helium stream may be divided into three groups: (i) oil vapour from the compressor, (ii) water vapour, (iii) gases such as oxygen, nitrogen, hydrogen. Those of group (iii) are most conveniently removed by a charcoal trap; water vapour may be removed by this if it is not present in such a quantity as to saturate the charcoal. If oil vapour is present in appreciable quantities this will rapidly saturate the charcoal and make it permanently ineffective as a gas adsorbent; compressors should be used which do not 'carry over' much oil vapour into the gas stream or an effective oil filter must be placed in the high-pressure exit line. Such a filter may be a vessel containing copper or steel wool and of sufficient dimensions that the velocity of the gas stream in it is not too great; this allows the oil particles to collect on the copper wool and then oil may be drained or blown out of the vessel at intervals through a drain-valve in the bottom.

In most small liquefiers the total amount of water vapour present in the gas being circulated is relatively small and may be removed together with air and other gases by the charcoal trap. However, in large installations or in a hydrogen liquefier using electrolytic hydrogen, it is usual to place a silica gel drying column in the gas stream or to use refrigeration drying (cf. N.B.S. liquefier in § 1.5). When circulating hydrogen it is also usual to remove oxygen by a separate purifier—a 'Deoxo' unit which is a palladium catalyst supported on silica gel; these 'Deoxo' purifiers are commercially available from Baker and Company, Inc. of New Jersey.

A common form of charcoal cleaner is shown in Figure 27 (§ 2.1) but a convenient small cleaning trap may be easily made from brass tubing. One end of the tube is sealed by a brass plate 'sweated' or silver-soldered to it and the entry and exit tubes for the gas stream are soldered through this plate; it is preferable to wrap fine metal gauze around the open ends of these two tubes to prevent charcoal dust being carried over by the gas. The main brass tube is then packed with coconut charcoal of adsorbent grade and the bottom end is sealed with a brass plate. The charcoal may then be activated by connecting the entry or exit tube to a mechanical pump and warming the unit with a gas flame or electrical heater to a temperature of 100°–200° C for a few minutes. It is placed in a convenient glass dewar which is kept filled with liquid nitrogen during the cleaning operation.

The amount of gas required to saturate activated charcoal at 77° K depends somewhat on the gas and varies with the type of charcoal used. Generally, charcoals have a specific surface in the range 100–1,000 m^2/g and will adsorb 0·2–0·25 cm^3 of gas (S.T.P.) per sq. metre of surface (J. A. Morrison, private communication). Activated coconut charcoals of adsorbent grade have specific surfaces approaching 1,000 m^2/g; for example, Brunauer (1943) in his book on physical adsorption quotes figures of 170–230 cm^3/g for the adsorption of N_2, A, O_2, CO_2, on coconut charcoal at about 90° K and gives values of 700–900 m^2/g for the surface areas of this charcoal.

Although some other adsorbent materials (see also discussion on metal dewars, § 2.1) may have a slightly higher adsorptivity than charcoal for certain gases, charcoal seems to be the most suitable adsorbing agent for the mixture of impurities that may be present in a helium gas stream.

It should also be emphasized that high-pressure cleaning is more effective than low-pressure cleaning, i.e. passing an impure gas at 100 atmospheres pressure through a cooled charcoal cleaner will yield a product with a lower percentage of impurity than by passing the same gas at 1 atmosphere over the charcoal. In either case the adsorption pressure of the impurity at the surface of the charcoal is a function of the temperature and of the volume of impurity already adsorbed, and not of the total gas pressure; hence increasing the total pressure by a factor of a hundred decreases the percentage of impurity that is retained by the gas stream by a like factor.

REFERENCES

AMONG the more general references from which the writer has drawn the material for this chapter are the following:

COLLINS, S. C. (1956). 'Helium liquefiers and carriers', *Handb. der Physik*, **14**, 112.

DAUNT, J. G. (1956). 'The production of low temperatures down to hydrogen temperature', ibid. **14**, 1.

DAVIES, M. (1949). *The Physical Principles of Gas Liquefaction and Low Temperature Rectification*, Longmans Green & Co.

JACKSON, L. C. (1934). *Low Temperature Physics*, Methuen, London.

KEESOM, W. H. (1942). *Helium*, Elsevier, Amsterdam.

RUHEMANN, M. and B. (1937). *Low Temperature Physics*, Cambridge University Press; this includes an historical account of the development of low-temperature physics and discusses the thermodynamic cycles involved in different methods of gas liquefaction.

VAN LAMMEREN, J. A. (1941). *Technik der tiefen Temperaturen*, Springer Verlag, Berlin.

OTHER REFERENCES

AHLBERG, J. E., ESTERMANN, I., and LUNDBERG, W. D. (1937). *Rev. Sci. Instrum.* **8**, 422.

ASHMEAD, J. (1950). *Proc. Phys. Soc.* B **63**, 504.

BREWER, D. F., and EDWARDS, D. O. (1956). *J. Sci. Instrum.* **33**, 148.

BRUNAUER, S. (1943). *The Adsorption of Gases and Vapours, Vol. 1, Physical Adsorption*, Princeton University Press.

CHESTER, P. F., and JONES, G. O. (1953). *Proc. Phys. Soc.* B **66**, 296.

CLUSIUS, K. (1953). *Z. Naturf.* **8a,** 479.

COLLINS, S. C. (1947). *Rev. Sci. Instrum.* **18,** 157.

COOKE, A. H., ROLLIN, B., and SIMON, F. E. (1939). Ibid. **10,** 251.

CROFT, A. J. (1952). *J. Sci. Instrum.* **29,** 388.

—— and SIMON, F. E. (1955). *Bull. Inst. int. Froid,* Annexe 1955–2, p. 81. Paris.

DASH, J. G., COOK, D. B., ZEMANSKY, M. W., and BOORSE, H. A. (1950). *Rev. Sci. Instrum.* **21,** 936.

DAUNT, J. G., and MENDELSSOHN, K. (1948). *J. Sci. Instrum.* **25,** 318.

—— and JOHNSTON, H. L. (1949). *Rev. Sci. Instrum.* **20,** 122.

DEBYE, P. (1926). *Ann. Physik,* **81,** 1154.

DESORBO, W., MILTON, R. M., and ANDREWS, D. H. (1946). *Chem. Rev.* **39,** 403.

FAIRBANK, H. A. (1946). *Rev. Sci. Instrum.* **17,** 473.

GIAUQUE, W. F. (1927). *J. Amer. Chem. Soc.* **49,** 1864.

—— and MACDOUGALL, D. P. (1933). *Phys. Rev.* **43,** 768.

DE HAAS, W. J., WIERSMA, E. C., and KRAMERS, H. A. (1933). *Physica,* **1,** 1.

HERCUS, G. R., and WHITE, G. K. (1951). *J. Sci. Instrum.* **28,** 4.

JOHNSON, V. J., and WILSON, W. A. (1955). *Proc. 1954 Cryogenic Engng. Conf.* N.B.S. Report No. 3517, p. 246.

JONES, G. O., LARSEN, A. H., and SIMON, F. E. (1948). *Research,* **1,** 420.

KAPITZA, P. (1934). *Proc. Roy. Soc.* A, **147,** 189.

KEESOM, W. H. (1933). *Leiden Comm. Suppl.* **76a.**

KEYES, F. G., GERRY, H. T., and HICKS, J. F. G. (1937). *J. Amer. Chem. Soc.* **59,** 1426.

KOHLER, J. W. L., and JONKERS, C. O. (1954). *Phillips Tech. Rev.* **16,** 69.

KURTI, N., and SIMON, F. E. (1935). *Proc. Roy. Soc.* A, **149,** 152.

LATHAM, A., and MCMAHON, H. O. (1949). *Refrig. Engng.* **57,** 549.

LONG, H. M., and SIMON, F. E. (1953). *Appl. Sci. Res.* A **4,** 237.

MEISSNER, W. (1928). *Phys. Z.* **29,** 610.

MENDELSSOHN, K. (1931). *Z. Phys.* **73,** 482.

PARKINSON, D. H. (1954). *J. Sci. Instrum.* **31,** 178.

PICKARD, G. L., and SIMON, F. E. (1948). *Proc. Phys. Soc.* **60,** 405.

ROLLIN, B. V. (1936). Ibid. **48,** 18.

RUHEMANN, M. (1930). *Z. Phys.* **65,** 67.

SCHALLAMACH, A. (1943). *J. Sci. Instrum.* **20,** 195.

SCOTT, R. B., and COOK, J. W. (1948). *Rev. Sci. Instrum.* **19,** 889.

SIMON, F. E. (1930). *Ergebn. exakt. Naturw.* **9,** 222.

—— (1932). *Z. ges. Kälteindustr.* **39,** 89.

—— (1956). 40th Guthrie lecture, *Phys. Soc. Lond. Yearb.,* p. 1.

SPOENDLIN, R. (1954). *J. Res. C.N.R.S.* **28,** 1.

STARR, C. (1941). *Rev. Sci. Instrum.* **12,** 193.

WOOLLEY, H. W., SCOTT, R. B., and BRICKWEDDE, F. G. (1948). *J. Res. Nat. Bur. Stand.* **41,** 379.

CHAPTER II

STORAGE AND TRANSFER OF LIQUEFIED GASES

1. Dewar vessels

Introduction

ALTHOUGH this section might be more appropriately termed 'containers for liquefied gases' than merely 'dewar vessels', Sir James Dewar's contribution to low-temperature research by the invention of the evacuated double-walled vessel can scarcely be over-emphasized.

The efficiency of storage of any liquefied gas is related to its latent heat of vaporization and normal boiling-point. The latter factor partially determines the extraneous heat inflow from the surroundings and the former governs the evaporation rate as a function of that inflow.

TABLE IV

Latent heat of vaporization and boiling-point at standard atmospheric pressure of some common gases

Gas	CO_2[†]	O_2	A	N_2	Ne	H_2	^4He
Latent heat (cal/gm) .	137	51·0	37·9	47·8	20·8	106·8	5·2
Latent heat (cal/cm³).	223	58·1	53·5	38·6	25	7·56	0·65
Boiling-point (° K) .	194·6	90·1	87·4	77·3	27·2	20·4	4·2

† Solid.

In designing a container the problem is that of reducing the heat inflow to a minimum, determined by difficulties of construction and the allowable loss of liquid per unit time. The chief sources of heat are radiation to the walls of the containers, radiation down the neck of the storage vessel, heat conduction down the neck or walls, convection in the vapour above the liquid surface, and heat conduction through the residual gas in the surrounding vacuum space. Most of these factors are discussed in detail in Chapter VI and in various papers on the design of liquid-helium containers; for example, Wexler (1951) (see also Wexler and Jacket, 1951) and Sydoriak and Sommers (1951) examined the problem of designing suitable containers for storing liquid helium in the laboratory; recently Scott (1957) has considered the thermal design of large storage vessels for liquid helium and liquid hydrogen.

Liquid-air dewars

Glass dewar flasks (Figures 26 *a* and 26 *b*), both silvered to reduce radiant heat inflow and unsilvered, are available commercially in a wide range of sizes. Usually of Pyrex, they can be

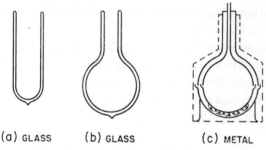

(a) GLASS   (b) GLASS   (c) METAL

Fig. 26. Common types of dewar flask.

made by any competent glass-blower with a suitable glass-blowing lathe. Frequently a special shape, length, or diameter of dewar is needed and this may have to be made. A description of the silvering and evacuation procedure has been given by Scott, Cook, and Brickwedde (1931). They found that after silvering by a modified Brashear process, the Pyrex dewar gave best results if slowly raised in temperature to 400° C, then baked for a short period at 550° C and later cooled to about 400° C before sealing. The resulting evaporation rates for liquid air and liquid hydrogen showed that the emissivity of the silver coating is about 0·03. Quite satisfactory dewars also result if the baking temperature is only carried up to about 450° C, and then the danger of distorting the glass walls, which will occur for Pyrex at temperatures slightly in excess of 550° C, is eliminated.

In the spun metal variety (Figure 26 c) the difficulty of complete outgassing makes it necessary to have an internal adsorbent trap. For this purpose a few ounces of adsorbent coconut charcoal† should be attached in a wire-gauze cage to the inner (cold) wall of the vacuum space, so that it is well exposed to the vacuum system. Such metal flasks, usually of spun copper, with clean polished surfaces facing the vacuum space, and with an inner neck of a low-conductivity alloy (monel, K-monel, inconel, etc.) can be 'home-made'. However, the difficulty and cost of having

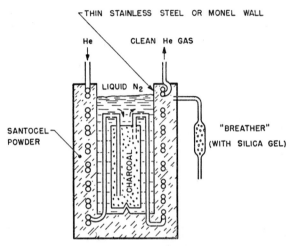

FIG. 27. A charcoal purifying trap cooled by liquid nitrogen.

patterns made for the spinning and of the spinning itself, usually make it advantageous to buy the commercial article. For example, Superior Air Products and Hofman Laboratories Inc. in the United States and Guest and Chrimes (England) make a range of dewar sizes; the loss per day of liquid nitrogen by evaporation from a Supairco 25-litre container is about 2·5 litres.

For construction of liquid-air containers, thermal insulators such as Santocel or Styrofoam can be of great use (Figures 27, 28). An example is a metal container surrounding a charcoal purifying trap shown in Figure 27. If the size and construction of the metal vessel do not allow evacuation, or if the vacuum that

† Recent research on liquid-air containers (Beher, 1957) suggests that some other adsorbents, e.g. Chabazite, Cullite, Sepiolite, may be equally or slightly more efficient than charcoal as adsorbers of residual gas; however, the difference is not great and these other adsorbents require rather higher activation temperatures than that of 150°–200° C which suffices for charcoal.

can be maintained is only of the order of a few millimetres of mercury, a powdered insulator such as Santocel (Monsanto Chemical Company) provides good insulation by reducing conduction, convection, and radiation across the space between the walls. Some data for heat inflow through Santocel (White, 1948; Reynolds *et al.*, 1955) are as follows: at an average temperature of about 180° K, i.e. for walls respectively at room temperature and liquid-nitrogen temperatures, the mean thermal conductivity is about 0·2 mW/cm °K at atmospheric pressure, 0·06 mW/cm °K at about 1 mm pressure, and 0·016 mW/cm °K at pressures below $\frac{1}{100}$ mm (further data in Chapter XI below).

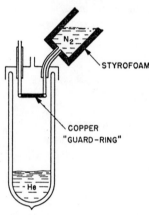

FIG. 28.   Use of a Styrofoam container for supplying liquid nitrogen to a thermal 'guard-ring'.

Small conveniently shaped liquid-nitrogen containers such as that shown in Figure 28 can be cut from an 'exploded' polystyrene plastic, e.g. Styrofoam (Dow Chemical Company). Cutting may be done with a 'cork-borer' type of cutter, hacksaw blade, hot wire, etc. Although such Styrofoam containers have been used for liquid oxygen, this is rather dangerous as the combination is very highly inflammable.

In the arrangement of Figure 28 used by the writer, the short double-walled supply pipe to the cooled 'guard ring' was a push-fit in the bottom of the Styrofoam container sealed by a coating of heavy grease. Marshall (1955) reports on the use of Styrofoam liquid-hydrogen containers and remarks that they may be conveniently glued with Araldite AN101 cement. Also Nelson (1956) found that a cement consisting of a polysulphide adhesive EC801 (Minnesota Mining and Manufacturing Co.) mixed with EC1063 as initiator was suitable for cementing tubes containing optical windows into Styrofoam liquid-nitrogen containers. As Styrofoam dissolves very rapidly in many organic solvents, the most suitable cements are those not containing such solvents but those which are either cold setting due to a chemical action, e.g. polymerization, or a water reaction as in plaster of Paris and Weldwood cement. The manufacturers of Styrofoam (Dow Chemical Company) give a large list of suitable cements and also give a value for thermal conductivity of about $0 \cdot 37$ mW/cm $^{\circ}$K at room temperature which decreases (Waite, 1955) to about $0 \cdot 16$ mW/cm $^{\circ}$K at 160° K.

Liquid-hydrogen containers

Apart from its inflammable nature and small latent heat, liquid hydrogen poses an additional problem when storage for any appreciable period of time is desired. Hydrogen contains molecules of two different kinds, ortho-hydrogen and para-hydrogen, in which the spins of the two protons are respectively parallel and antiparallel. Due to the different energies of the two states, the equilibrium concentration varies from 100 per cent para-hydrogen at or below 20° K to about 25 per cent para-hydrogen at room temperature. At liquid-nitrogen temperature the states are almost equally probable.

In the absence of a catalyst the rate of conversion is relatively slow with a time constant of the order of 50 hours, so that normal hydrogen gas cooled from room temperature, liquefied, and transferred to a storage container may contain nearly 75 per cent ortho-hydrogen when first stored. Over a period of days, ortho-para conversion occurs with a heat of transformation of 310 cal/mole (see Larsen, Simon, and Swenson, 1948, for determination of rate of conversion and evaporation) to be compared with a heat of vaporization of 216 cal/mole. After 2 days nearly 30 per cent of the liquid has been lost purely due to this internal process. Figure 29 illustrates the rate of loss for various initial equilibrium concentrations, e.g. where the liquid hydrogen stored had an initial ortho-hydrogen concentration corresponding to the equilibrium concentration at 300° K, 120° K, 90° K, etc.

As a result of this investigation by Larsen *et al.*, the ortho-para conversion stage was incorporated in the hydrogen liquefier at Oxford, mentioned in Chapter I; the charcoal cleaner at 75° K acts as a partial converter with the result that the same loss by evaporation due to the transformation, which would have occurred after one day of storage in the absence of any previous conversion occurs after about three days. More recently as a result of investigations on the large hydrogen liquefier at the National Bureau of Standards (Boulder), more efficient catalysts have been found, which promote ortho-para conversion in the

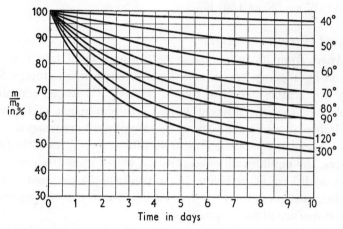

FIG. 29. Effect of ortho-para conversion: graphs show the mass of liquid hydrogen m remaining after days of storage, as a percentage of the initial mass m_0 (after Larsen, Simon, and Swenson, 1948).

liquid immediately after liquefaction and before transfer to storage vessels. In this method (Barrick *et al.*, 1955; Weitzel *et al.*, 1957) the overall liquefaction rate is reduced somewhat, but since the conversion to para-hydrogen occurs in the liquid (20° K) practically 100 per cent para-hydrogen is obtained and the loss in storage due to the transformation is reduced to zero. With ferric hydroxide gel as the catalyst, it is found that conversion occurs at a rate of 2·6 cm³ of liquid per cubic centimetre of catalyst per minute, so that about 1·5 litres of ferric hydroxide are sufficient to catalyse the 240 l/hour output of the Boulder liquefier.

This ortho-para conversion is important when considering the type of container in which liquid hydrogen is to be kept. If efficient storage with low evaporation loss is needed, conversion to the para state should be nearly complete and the liquid should be kept in a carefully designed liquid-nitrogen-protected dewar vessel (for example the helium-hydrogen containers of Superior Air Products) with evaporation loss rates of about 1 per cent per day. If, however, the liquid initially contains a large percentage of ortho-hydrogen, considerable evaporation loss is inevitable and storage in an ordinary unprotected dewar vessel—a metal liquid-air container—may be suitable. As the vapour pressure of air is negligible at liquid-hydrogen temperatures, liquid hydrogen creates a high vacuum when placed in the dewar vessel so that the major external heat inflows are radiation across the walls and heat coming down the neck of the dewar by radiation and conduction. Hence in the standard narrow-necked metal dewar, normally used for liquid air, radiation across the vacuum space is the major source of heat leak and this will be, at worst, comparable with that due to ortho-para conversion. However, it has been generally observed that metal dewars with liquid-nitrogen-cooled shields do have a rather larger heat leak when used with liquid hydrogen than with liquid helium, probably because of the slow release of dissolved hydrogen gas from the metal walls into the vacuum chamber (cf. Scott, 1957).

Liquid-helium dewars for research cryostats

The design of low-loss liquid-helium containers has received considerable attention in the past ten years, and has resulted in commercially available dewar flasks from which the evaporation is only about 1 per cent of their capacity in 24 hours. Till recently most liquid helium was kept in glass dewar vessels and these are still the most common for short-period storage, e.g. surrounding an experimental cryostat.

It was observed many years ago that helium gas diffuses through glass, the diffusion rate in the hard boro-silicate glasses being quite high (see Keesom, 1942, for references and data; also Rogers, Buritz, and Alpert, 1954). Whereas the diffusion rate at room temperature for soft glass and for Jena 16 III measured in cubic centimetres diffusing per second through 1 cm^2 of wall 1 mm thick with 1 atmosphere pressure difference is about $0 \cdot 4 \times 10^{-12}$, it amounts to $0 \cdot 5 \times 10^{-10}$ for Pyrex (Urry, 1932).

Thus in a Pyrex dewar in which 100 cm² of glass at room temperature are exposed to helium gas, the thickness of the glass being 2 mm and the volume of the vacuum space being 1 litre, the time required for the helium pressure to reach 10^{-5} mm Hg will be approximately 30 minutes.

Fortunately the diffusion rate decreases very rapidly with temperature and most of the inner wall of a helium dewar is well below room temperature, much of it at 4° K. It is found in practice that a figure of ~100 hours or 6–10 days of research operation are quite feasible with a Pyrex dewar before it becomes sufficiently 'soft' that the evaporation rate is markedly higher and therefore needs re-evacuation. The English Monax glass and its near equivalent in the United States, Kimball N51A glass, are both much less permeable, but are not always readily available in the sizes required for making experimental dewar vessels. The relative merits of these different glasses for dewar vessels have been discussed by Giauque (1947), Lane and Fairbank (1947), and Desirant and Horvath (1948) among others.

To illustrate the helium evaporation rates which may be encountered in experimental research, Figure 30 shows a rather typical glass helium dewar pumped to a high vacuum and surrounded by a dewar vessel filled with liquid nitrogen. The helium dewar is 60 cm in length and 7 cm internal diameter; it is approximately half-filled with liquid helium and is (a) silvered except for a 1-cm-wide viewing slit along its length, (b) as before but having a loose-fitting plug of Styrofoam, 2 in. thick, suspended about 12 cm from the top of the dewar, (c) silvered except for the slit but not surrounded by liquid nitrogen. Some approximate figures for evaporation rate in cubic centimetres of liquid helium per hour are shown on the figure.

To simplify the repeated re-evacuations necessary in Pyrex dewars, the writer has found the following arrangement satisfactory. A short glass side tube is provided near the top of the dewar, to which a small stop-cock is attached by Tygon (flexible plastic) tubing. The flexible connexion reduces the chance of breakage; the vacuum space is flushed with air and re-evacuated for a few minutes on a mechanical pump or a diffusion pump after every six to seven days of experimental use. In other cases an extended glass 'pip' may be put on the tail of the dewar for repumping but should be sufficiently extended that it can be broken and resealed without introducing strains into the bottom of the dewar. Unless the dewar is also to be used with liquid air, the degree of vacuum is not important as the liquid helium

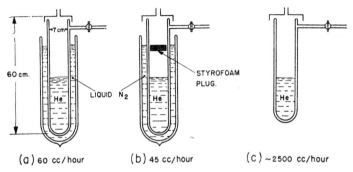

60 cm.   7 cm   LIQUID N₂   He   He   STYROFOAM PLUG.   He

(a) 60 cc/hour   (b) 45 cc/hour   (c) ~2500 cc/hour

Fig. 30. Rate of evaporation of liquid helium from a glass dewar.

rapidly freezes out any air left in the vacuum space. Indeed, it is often convenient to leave about 1 mm air pressure to assist precooling by the liquid air in the outer dewar. Such 'soft' dewars with a few millimetres pressure of air as exchange gas, have been used in the Mond Laboratory (see Allen, 1947) for many years.

An interesting commercial development in the field of helium dewars has been the construction of narrow-tail metal dewars suitable for experiments in high magnetic fields. Narrow-tailed glass dewars have been used in many laboratories but are necessarily wider in the tail than a metal dewar of the same internal diameter. As there are usually two dewars used in these experiments—an inner dewar to contain liquid helium and an outer dewar to contain liquid nitrogen—the total saving in width of tail and resultant possible narrowing of the magnet pole gap are considerable. Hofman Laboratories Inc. produce a 'Solenoid Dewar' of this double-container type in a variety of sizes; these are based on that originally developed by Dr. W. E. Henry of the Naval Research Laboratories.

Liquid-helium storage dewars

Obviously the relatively high evaporation rates make dewars of the type shown in Figure 30 unsuitable for long-term storage. Even when fully silvered and surrounded by liquid nitrogen, the large heat inflows down the neck of a cylindrical dewar produce evaporation rates which over a 24-hour period leave little liquid helium.

In 1951 at the Westinghouse Research Laboratories, Wexler and his collaborators analysed the problem of heat inflow; their analysis led to the design and construction of a spherical metal dewar of 12·5 litre capacity which when surrounded by liquid nitrogen gave an evaporation rate of only 100 cm³ of liquid helium per 24 hours (Wexler, 1951, Wexler and Jacket, 1951). This very low evaporation was obtained using a 20-cm length of ⅝ in. diameter inconel tube (0·010 in. wall) as the dewar neck, blackening the inner surface of the tube to prevent any 'funneled' radiation reaching the helium, and also inserting a metal test-tube down the neck as a further radiation trap. They showed that this residual evaporation was due principally to radiation from the liquid-nitrogen-cooled outer sphere to the inner highly polished copper sphere. Thermal conduction down the narrow inconel tube is quite small as fairly efficient heat exchange occurs between the evaporating cold helium gas and the tube wall.

These evaporation rates led Wexler to a figure of 0·0069 for the emissivity of the polished copper vessel at 4·2° K for 77° K black body radiation, a figure much higher than that calculated from the electrical resistance by classical theory but in fair agreement with the value based on the theory of the anomalous skin effect (see Ramanathan, 1952, for infra-red absorption data and Chapter VI below).

Shortly after this work by Wexler, the Hofman Laboratories Inc. produced a similar commercial liquid-helium vessel which in the 20-litre size has an evaporation rate of about 250 cm³ per 24 hours. This dewar is surrounded by a cylindrical liquid-nitrogen container, whose rather high liquid-nitrogen consumption of about 12 litres per 24 hours is a serious drawback. The later commercial container shown schematically in Figure 31 from Superior Air Products† has a much more satisfactory liquid-nitrogen loss rate of about 2 l/day. With a radiation shield in the neck of these dewars the liquid-helium loss ranges from 200 to 300 cm³ per 24 hours in the 25-, 50-, and 75-litre sizes. If no such shield is used but they are simply closed by a

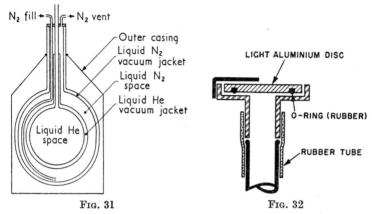

FIG. 31.   FIG. 32.

FIG. 31. A commercial metal dewar for the storage of liquid helium
or liquid hydrogen.

FIG. 32. Simple non-return valve to prevent air or water vapour condensing in the helium-storage dewar.

non-return valve (or open to the atmosphere) the average loss rate in the 25-litre size is 300–320 cm³ of liquid helium per 24 hours. Incidentally, Collins (1956) reported that at M.I.T. a standard metal liquid-air container of 25-litre capacity was filled with liquid helium and surrounded by an improvised liquid-nitrogen jacket and evaporated only 317 cm³ per 24 hours.

In Plate IV (facing p. 33) a 25-litre liquid-helium container is shown resting on a convenient fork-lift dolly which enables it to be raised by a hydraulic pump to various heights at which it is required for 'siphoning' liquid helium into experimental cryo-stats. A steel tube of ½-in. diameter for 'reaming' out any solid air in the neck of the dewar and a rubber diaphragm level-indicator (see § 2.3 below) are attached to the dolly. The dewar is normally closed by the non-return valve (Figure 32) which

† Hofman Laboratories now also produce a helium or hydrogen container
of this type in sizes ranging from 10 to 75 litres capacity.

prevents air or moisture condensing in the neck of the dewar and keeps the liquid under a very slight overpressure. Similarly, condensation in the liquid-nitrogen vents is prevented by the length of plastic tubing, which has a 2-in. slit in it to allow nitrogen gas to escape. The liquid-nitrogen space is refilled every one

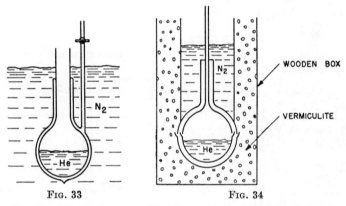

Fɪɢ. 33.

Fɪɢ. 34.

Fɪɢ. 33. A Pyrex dewar modified for storing liquid helium (Sydoriak and Sommers, 1951).

Fɪɢ. 34. A commercial copper (liquid-air) dewar modified for storing liquid helium (Gonzalez, White, and Johnston, 1951).

to two weeks; to avoid the necessity of recooling the inner helium container from 77° to 4° K (requiring several litres of liquid helium) it is desirable to leave a small quantity of liquid helium in the dewar. Of course this is no longer true when there is an interval of weeks between successive transfers of liquid helium.

Sydoriak and Sommers (1951), and also Gonzalez, White, and Johnston (1951), have described low-evaporation-loss containers which can be constructed by modifying standard liquid-air dewars.

That shown in Figure 33 is a 12-litre silvered glass dewar, made by extending the neck of a standard commercial dewar and surrounding it by a Santocel-insulated can filled with liquid air. The observed evaporation loss was about 23–32 cm³ of liquid helium per hour which contrasts with the loss of about 100 cm³/hour from a standard 4-litre spherical dewar immersed in liquid nitrogen and having no modification to the neck.

Gonzalez *et al.* modified a 10-litre copper dewar (from Linde Air Products) by attaching a monel cylinder (0·024 in. wall) to the outer copper sphere (Figure 34) and filling it with liquid nitrogen; they found that this arrangement gave an evaporation rate of about 240 cm³ per 24 hours, but an uneconomical liquid nitrogen consumption of 1·5 l/hour, necessitating frequent replenishment.

2. Transfer siphons

Introduction

In low-temperature physics, the term 'transfer siphon' has come to mean a tube suitable for transferring low-boiling-point liquids without serious loss by evaporation, although the actual transfer is usually initiated and sustained by a gas overpressure rather than by a siphoning action.

Apart from ease of construction and mechanical reliability, the design of a transfer tube is largely governed by loss considerations; the total heat of the inner wall of the transfer device and the total heat inflow to the stream of liquid during transfer should be small in comparison with the latent heat of vaporization of the liquid being transferred.

Liquid air

If liquid air, nitrogen, or oxygen is being transferred a distance of a few feet in a quantity of a litre in 10 or 15 seconds, then the tube can be simply a length of thick-walled rubber tube ($\frac{1}{4}$ in. inner diameter, $\frac{3}{4}$ in. outer diameter). The inner wall of such a rubber tube rapidly freezes hard so that the tube is rigid, but due to its poor heat conductivity the outer surface remains relatively warm and pliable during a brief period of transfer—say about one minute required to fill a 4-litre flask with an overpressure of $\frac{1}{4}$ to $\frac{1}{2}$ atmosphere on the storage container; thin-walled rubber tubing will freeze hard, become brittle, and may fracture. Alternatively, any metal tube which can be bent to the required shape is suitable for liquid-air transfer but if the transfer tube is to be left in the storage container over long periods of time, it is desirable that the tube in the neck of the container should be a low-heat-conductivity alloy—monel, German silver, cupro-nickel.

If the liquid-air transfer is to be rather slower and occupy many minutes, then a wrapping of glass wool, asbestos tape, etc., may be sufficient to make the losses negligible.

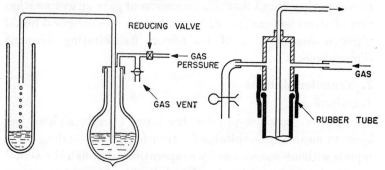

Fig. 35. The transfer of a liquefied gas; inset shows a simple brass coupling for use with a narrow-necked metal dewar.

When transfer is to be an almost continuous process and/or over a relatively large distance, a properly insulated transfer tube is needed, e.g. a double-wall metal vacuum siphon. Equally efficient for heat insulation is a metal tube surrounded by a layer of Styrofoam or Santocel, but this requires a greater diameter for the same degree of insulation.

Figure 36 shows the main features of a liquid-air siphon, modelled on that described by Jones and Larsen (1948). The dimensions are not critical but care must be taken in choosing materials and wall thickness so that the 'bends' can be made without crimping or splitting the tube. After attaching the spacers to the inner tube with a spot of solder and fitting this tube into the outer tube, the positions of the bends are marked, the internal metal surfaces are oiled and then heated and filled with Cerrobend (or Wood's metal); when cool the tubes are bent to shape and then reheated for the Cerrobend to be removed and the interior cleaned. Then the system should be carefully vacuum-tested before filling the 'cold' end with adsorbent charcoal. The tubes and charcoal should be well warmed with a flame to outgas them during evacuation and prior to sealing off. With the aid of petrol (or refrigeration) unions a number of such tubes, either straight or bent, can be joined together to carry liquid air from storage flasks to various points where it is required.

In the case of liquid air it is most common to use compressed gas from cylinders or supply lines, to force the liquid through the transfer siphons. If such transfers are fairly frequent, the process of pressurizing and depressurizing the container at each

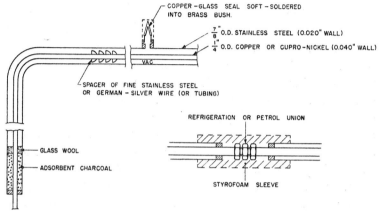

FIG. 36. Liquid-air siphon. A method of coupling two transfer tubes is shown in the inset.

transfer both wastes and frequently contaminates the liquid. In cases where cost and purity are important it is convenient to leave the container sealed by a spring-loaded blow-off valve—designed to blow-off at 3–4 lb/sq. in.; by means of a valve in the transfer tube, liquid can be drawn off under this pressure head when desired. A useful sealing device of this type has been described by Wexler and Corak (1950). Commercial firms, e.g. Hofman Laboratories Inc., produce liquid-discharge tubes fitted with either manually or electrically controlled valves.

Hydrogen and helium

In designing a transfer tube for liquid helium (or liquid hydrogen) the same considerations apply that have been discussed above, but the much lower latent heat of vaporization becomes an important factor. As an example, assume that the inner wall of a liquid-helium siphon is a metal of atomic weight 100, density 10 g/cm^3, Debye characteristic temperature $\theta_D \sim 300°\text{K}$, and is in the form of a tube of diameter 3 mm, wall thickness 0·5 mm, and length 100 cm. Then the enthalpy or total heat at room temperature of this inner tube is about 1,200 cal/g mol, so the enthalpy of the tube is $\dfrac{1,200 \times \text{density} \times \text{volume}}{\text{atomic weight}} \simeq 600$ cal. This indicates that if only the latent heat of liquid helium is used to precool the siphon, about 1 litre of liquid would be required (the latent heat of helium is about 0·65 cal/cm³ of liquid). Fortunately, however, the heat capacity of the evaporated gas also cools the tube wall; each cubic centimetre of liquid produces helium gas with a heat capacity at constant pressure of 0·15 cal deg⁻¹, representing an enthalpy at room temperature of about 40 cal/cm³ of liquid equivalent. If we can hope to use about half the cooling content of the evaporated gas, then only about 30 cm³ of liquid would be required to precool the siphon. In practice the wall thickness of the inner tube is usually rather less than suggested in this example so that the total heat content at room temperature of the inner tube of a typical helium siphon (e.g. see Figure 37 below) might be 500 calories and require about 50 cm³ or less of liquid helium for precooling.

Glass siphons are quite suitable for liquid helium or liquid hydrogen, and can be made quite quickly by a glass-blower who has the necessary experience to bend concentric glass tubes without allowing them to touch each other; for liquid hydrogen they can be used without silvering but are usually silvered for transferring liquid helium. However, they do require very careful handling so that the all-metal siphon usually has a much longer mechanical life. For transfer of liquid hydrogen or helium neither type requires a high degree of evacuation as the liquid acts as an efficient 'getter' for any air left in the space between the walls. The writer has found that the type of metal siphon shown in Figure 37 is very suitable, uses little liquid for initial cooling, and has a good mechanical life provided that the outer tube is sufficiently light that its weight does not cause bending or 'crimping' of the tubes at the joints 7 or 8. The numbers on the figure indicate the usual order in which the various joints—made with 'Easy-Flo' silver solder except where shown otherwise—are made. The most important joints are those marked 1 and 2, 5 and 6 which must be high-vacuum-tight to avoid a helium leak into the vacuum space. As in the case of a liquid-air siphon, frost on the outer wall indicates any cold spots where there is a serious contact between the two tubes; small

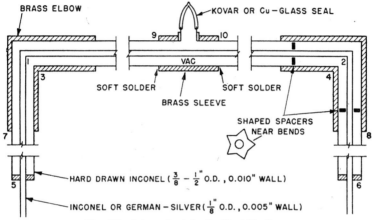

FIG. 37. A transfer tube for liquid helium.

Plexiglass stars or similar spacers near the elbows and near the middle of the long horizontal section avoid this trouble.

Provided that a liquid-helium transfer occupies a time of only a few minutes, the problem of radiation is not serious. If, as in the example above, we assume an inner tube of 3 mm diameter, 100 cm long, and further assume that its emissivity $\epsilon \sim 0.05$ and that it is exposed to room temperature radiation from a surrounding black body, then the heat inflow

$$\dot{Q} = \sigma A \epsilon (T_1^4 - T_2^4)$$
$$\simeq 5.7 \times 10^{-12} \times 100 \times 0.05(300)^4 \text{ J/sec}$$
$$= 0.23 \text{ J/sec}$$
$$\simeq 3 \text{ cal/min},$$

which is sufficient to evaporate about 5 cm³ of liquid helium per minute.

A method of transfer applicable to both liquid helium and liquid hydrogen is shown schematically in Figure 38 and in the photograph of Plate IV. Provision for collecting the evaporated gas is shown, but if this is unnecessary, the 'sealing' of the siphon into the cryostat—either through a rubber bung or a rubber sleeve—is dispensed with and the length of rubber by-pass tube is not required. Use of the rubber football bladder as a means of creating an overpressure in the storage flask has become a

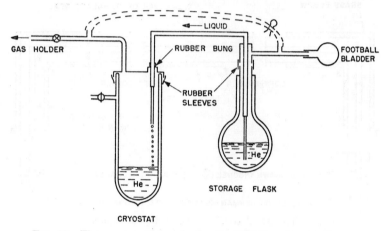

Fig. 38. The process of transferring liquid helium from a storage dewar into a cryostat.

fairly common practice and works quite well with helium and hydrogen; a fluctuating pressure applied with the fingers to the 'bladder' causes an oscillation of warm gas into the flask and maintains quite easily the pressure of about $\frac{1}{4}$ to $\frac{1}{2}$ p.s.i. required for transfer. In cases where a substantially higher overpressure is required, e.g. where the pressure in the gas holder (and therefore in the gas-return pipe and cryostat dewar) is relatively high, a gas cylinder with reducing valve can supply the overpressure required to force the liquid through the transfer tube.

It is sometimes desirable to have a junction in the transfer tube; for example, when it is more convenient to have sections of the siphon permanently attached to the respective dewars, from which and to which the liquid is being transferred. Figure 39 shows a sleeve coupling which can be sealed against leakage by a strip of cellulose tape or rubber tape.

The reader who may wish for further details of the construction of liquid transfer 'siphons', is referred to the papers by Stout (1954) and Jacobs and Richards (1957); these describe siphons which may be made fairly easily and are suitable for liquid

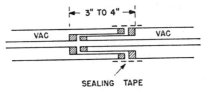

FIG. 39. A coupling for liquid helium (or hydrogen) transfer tubes.

helium as well as other low-boiling-point liquids. Mathewson (1955) has described a flexible transfer tube designed for use with liquid hydrogen; also Wexler (1954) and Fiske (1955) have reported on methods of making transfer tubes, tube couplings, and valves for use with liquid helium and liquid hydrogen.

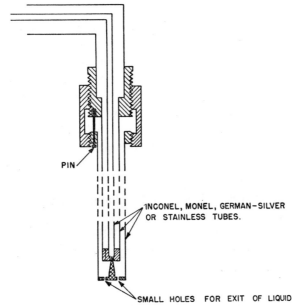

FIG. 40. A valve on a transfer tube.

Valves

A valve is sometimes required in a transfer siphon, for example when drawing off liquid helium from a liquefier. The example in

Figure 40 shows a stainless steel needle (total taper 10°–20°) seating in cylindrical bush of brass or some other metal softer than the stainless steel needle; this bush also seals the end of the double-walled vacuum siphon. The valve is actuated by a knurled brass piece which screws on to two brass sleeves, one soldered to the upper outside transfer tube and the other to the low conductivity metal tube which moves the valve needle; one of the threads is right hand and the other is left hand, and a metal pin prevents the lower sleeve from turning as the knurled head is turned. Descriptions of such needle valves and also ball valves used for the same purpose have been given by Croft and Jones (1950), Scott and Cook (1948), and in the manuals of the Arthur D. Little Corporation which describe their Collins liquefier.

3. Liquid-level indicators

Introduction

A number of devices for determining the level of a liquefied gas in a dewar have been described in the past few years; some of these have been suitable for only one or two liquids and others for most liquefied gases; some have been essentially discontinuous in nature, i.e. only registering when the liquid reaches a certain level, and others have been continuous recorders of level; some also have been used to actuate a transfer of liquid into the dewar. Many indicators are thermometric in principle, e.g. the change in vapour or gas pressure with temperature, or the change in electrical resistance or expansion of a bimetallic strip are used in level detectors which depend on the change in temperature at or near the liquid surface.

Rather than discuss the details of all these level indicators, let us consider some examples of the types which seem to satisfy most requirements.

Examples

In the hydrostatic pressure-head type of depth gauge, an oil-filled U-tube or some other form of differential manometer records the difference in pressure between the base of the column of liquid in the container and the pressure above the surface. These are universally applicable to liquids, but they are rather insensitive in the case of liquefied gases of very low density such as hydrogen.

A rather different type of indicator using a differential mano- meter was designed by Jones and Swenson (1948); see also Croft

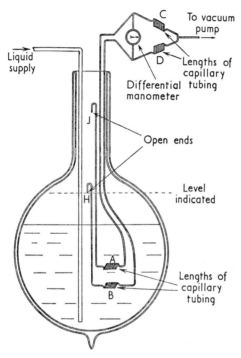

FIG. 41. An indicator for use with low-boiling-point liquids (after Jones and Swenson, 1948).

and Jones, 1950) to indicate when the liquid-hydrogen container in the Oxford hydrogen liquefier was filled to a certain point (Figure 41). The capillary tubes of 0·4 mm inner diameter copper, 10 cm long form a hydrodynamical 'Wheatstone' bridge so that when liquid reaches the level H, the bridge goes off balance quite sharply.

When there is no restriction on the vertical movement of the depth gauge so that the level can be found by searching with a 'probe' of some kind, there are very simple devices which can be made. By placing the ear above the end of an open tube (for example, $\frac{1}{4}$ in. diameter brass or German silver tube) and lowering it into a dewar, an unmistakable 'bubbling' noise can be heard when the liquid (helium, hydrogen, nitrogen, oxygen) level is first reached; however, this is rather unsatisfactory for detecting liquid helium or hydrogen levels in narrow-neck metal storage flasks. Another remarkably simple device, which uses the human finger as a sensing element and is very suitable for helium and can be used for hydrogen, is the rubber diaphragm level finder (Gaffney and Clement, 1955). It is very easily made with a small piece of thin rubber sheet cut from a rubber glove which seals the top of a small brass cup at the end of an open tube (0·1 in dia.). Spontaneous oscillations in the gas column in the narrow tube cause the rubber diaphragm to vibrate with a frequency which falls quite markedly when the lower end of the tube reaches the liquid level. The sensitivity may be increased considerably by using a stethoscope to detect the oscillations of the rubber diaphragm.† Alternatively, a wider brass cup or funnel extending above the diaphragm can serve to amplify the sound of the oscillations.

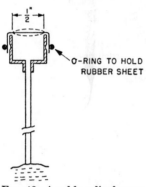

FIG. 42. A rubber diaphragm level finder for liquid helium (Gaffney and Clement, 1955).

Before the writer's attention was first drawn to this diaphragm type of level finder, he used a carbon resistor in a bridge circuit, activated by a small 30-V hearing-aid battery, which was very light and could be mounted on the top of the dipstick (inconel tube in Figure 43). With the aid of a small 100-μA meter the bridge is balanced when R is in liquid helium; a deflexion on the meter of about 30 per cent of full scale occurs once the resistor leaves the liquid. The operation of such devices (see also Mapother, 1954) depends on the more rapid dissipation of heat

† The writer is indebted to Messrs. F. W. Richardson and J. Broome for drawing his attention to these refinements.

from the resistor when in the liquid rather than in the vapour, and also on the high temperature coefficient of resistance of a carbon resistor (e.g. Allen-Bradley type resistors) at very low temperatures. An alternative to the carbon resistor is a fine filament of any pure metallic element, in which rapid heat dissipation is essential to maintain the fine wire at a low temperature and hence in a region of small electrical resistance. Fine platinum wires and Wollaston wires have been used successfully and detailed analyses of the performance of such level finders has been given by Wexler and Corak (1951; also Maimoni, 1956).

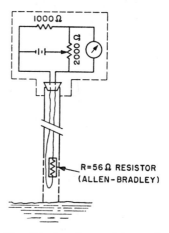

Fig. 43. A carbon resistor used as a liquid-helium level finder.

Float gauges are another means of indicating the level of a liquefied gas; these are particularly suitable in closed vessels such as the stages of a liquefier when an indication of level of liquids in the various dewars is required. In the Oxford hydrogen liquefier (Jones, Larsen, and Simon, 1948), sealed 'bulbs' of thin-walled German silver float in each of the three liquid-air dewars; light German silver tubes are attached to the 'bulbs' and these indicate the level by their height in glass viewing tubes at the top of the liquefier.

Styrofoam also makes a very suitable float as it has a density even less than that of liquid hydrogen; Babiskin (1950) mentions its use in liquid-helium dewars, the Styrofoam having a light balsa wood stick attached above it as an indicator. Kitts and Harler (1954) describe a convenient optical dip-stick for determining liquid levels in a metal dewar; attached to the bottom of their dip-stick is a small cylinder of Styrofoam which is pivoted away from its centre and is illuminated by a tiny lamp.

The superconducting depth gauge (Feldmeier and Serin, 1948) is suitable for liquid helium and gives a continuous record of liquid height as registered by the resistance of a tantalum wire. Tantalum is superconducting below 4·3° K, so that if not completely immersed in liquid a comparatively small heat inflow will raise it sufficiently above the normal boiling temperature (4·2° K) of liquid helium to restore its electrical resistance. Rasor (1954) in his article on 'Equipment and technique for a small cryogenics laboratory', describes a simple tantalum wire depth gauge in which the 0·005 in. diameter tantalum wire is wound on a threaded bakelite tube and the ends of the wire are attached to an ohm meter, calibrated to read directly in litres of liquid helium.

Some other level finders suitable for low-boiling-point liquids are the electronic capacitance detector of Dash and Boorse (1951; also Williams and Maxwell, 1954) and the 'optical' dipstick made from a lucite rod (Geake, 1954).

4. Liquid-level controllers

A type of level indicator which can also activate a transfer of liquid is very useful in many low-temperature laboratories. The problem of keeping liquid-air traps filled by some automatic process is often important, e.g. in charcoal purifiers, precooling dewars, etc. Two simple devices for doing this are shown in Figures 44, 45, below. In the first (based on that of Lounsbury, 1951) a commercial bimetallic strip thermostat activates a microswitch relay; this in turn operates a solenoid valve allowing compressed air into a storage container, forcing the liquid across into the dewar. When the liquid reaches the bimetallic strip, the relay opens, the solenoid valve closes and the overpressure in the container is slowly released through a 'bleed' valve (e.g. needle valve which is slightly open) or by means of a second solenoid valve, and then the transfer stops.

An alternative to the bimetallic strip is the vapour-pressure controller (Figure 45 after Davies and Kronberger, 1952). Davies and Kronberger fill a small bulb (2) with a pressure of about 2 atmospheres of the gas, the level of whose liquid phase is being controlled; by having a relatively large dead volume (4) at room temperature they ensure that the operation of the

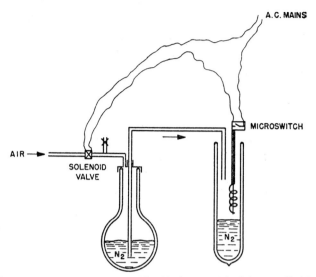

FIG. 44. Automatic transfer of liquid nitrogen (air, O_2) controlled by bimetallic strip.

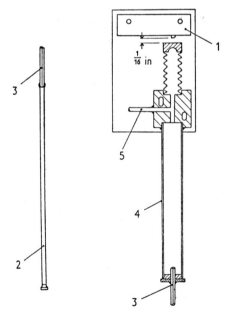

FIG. 45. A liquid-nitrogen level controller (after Davies and Kronberger, 1952).

microswitch does not depend too critically on the temperature of the vapour above the liquid surface. Jones (1948) developed a rather similar device and used the expansion or contraction of a bellows to operate the liquid-air inlet valve by a direct mechanical linkage.

Similar in principle to these latter devices and particularly simple is a small glass level controller (after Sherwood, 1952) in which a platinum-mercury switch is used to control electric power to a heater in a liquid-air container. This heating produces an overpressure in the container sufficient to transfer liquid air to another dewar; when the dewar is nearly filled, the relay opens, heating ceases, and the overpressure is released slowly through a 'bleed' valve. A simple level controller which uses a float-indicator to operate a microswitch relay and thereby activate a heater in the storage flask has been described recently by Henshaw (1957).

REFERENCES

ALLEN, J. (1947). *Rep. Int. Conf. Cambridge*, 1946, **2**, 87. The Physical Society, London.

BABISKIN, J. (1950). *Rev. Sci. Instrum.* **21**, 941.

BARRICK, P. L., WEITZEL, D. H., and CONNOLLY, T. W. (1955). *Proc. 1954 Cryogenic Engng. Conf.* N.B.S. Report No. 3517, p. 210.

BEHER, J. T. (1957). *Proc. 1956 Cryogenic Engng. Conf.* N.B.S., Boulder, Colorado, p. 182.

COLLINS, S. C. (1956). *Handb. der Physik*, **14**, 112.

CROFT, A. J., and JONES, G. O. (1950). *Brit. J. Appl. Phys.* **1**, 137.

DASH, J. G., and BOORSE, H. A. (1951). *Phys. Rev.* **82**, 851.

DAVIES, M. G., and KRONBERGER, H. (1952). *J. Sci. Instrum.* **29**, 335.

DESIRANT, M. C., and HORVATH, W. J. (1948). *Rev. Sci. Instrum.* **19**, 718.

FELDMEIER, J. R., and SERIN, B. (1948). Ibid. 916.

FISKE, M. D. (1955). Ibid. **26**, 90.

GAFFNEY, J., and CLEMENT, J. R. (1955). Ibid. 620.

GEAKE, J. E. (1954). *J. Sci. Instrum.* **31**, 260.

GIAUQUE, W. F. (1947). *Rev. Sci. Instrum.* **18**, 852.

GONZALEZ, O. D., WHITE, D., and JOHNSTON, H. L. (1951). Ibid. **22**, 702.

HENSHAW, D. E. (1957). *J. Sci. Instrum.* **34**, 207.

JACOBS, R. B., and RICHARDS, R. J. (1957). *Rev. Sci. Instrum.* **28**, 291.

JONES, G. O. (1948). *J. Sci. Instrum.* **25**, 239.

JONES, G. O., and LARSEN, A. H. (1948). *J. Sci. Instrum.* **25**, 375.
—— and SWENSON, C. A. (1948). Ibid. **72**.
—— LARSEN, A. H., and SIMON, F. E. (1948). *Research*, **1**, 420.
KEESOM, W. H. (1942). *Helium*, p. 131, Elsevier, Amsterdam.
KITTS, W. T., and HARLER, F. L. (1954). *Rev. Sci. Instrum.* **25**, 926.
LANE, C. T., and FAIRBANK, H. A. (1947). Ibid. **18**, 522.
LARSEN, A. H., SIMON, F. E., and SWENSON, C. A. (1948). Ibid. **19**, 266.
LOUNSBURY, M. (1951). Ibid. **22**, 533.
MAIMONI, A. (1956). Ibid. **27**, 1024.
MAPOTHER, D. (1954). *Cold Facts*, August 1950. Arthur D. Little Corporation.
MARSHALL, L. (1955). *Rev. Sci. Instrum.* **26**, 614.
MATHEWSON, R. C. (1955). Ibid. **616**.
NELSON, L. S. (1956). Ibid. **27**, 655.
RAMANATHAN, K. G. (1952). *Proc. Phys. Soc.* A **65**, 532.
RASOR, N. S. (1954). *Rev. Sci. Instrum.* **25**, 311.
REYNOLDS, M. M., BROWN, J. D., FULK, M. M., PARK, O. E., and CURTIS, G. W. (1955). *Proc. 1954 Cryogenic Engng. Conf.* N.B.S. Report No. 3517, p. 142.
ROGERS, W. A., BURITZ, R. S., and ALPERT, D. (1954). *J. Appl. Phys.* **25**, 868.
SCOTT, R. B., COOK, J. W., and BRICKWEDDE, F. G. (1931). *J. Res. Nat. Bur. Stand.* **7**, 935.
—— —— (1948). *Rev. Sci. Instrum.* **19**, 889.
—— (1957). *J. Res. Nat. Bur. Stand.* **58**, 317.
SHERWOOD, J. E. (1952). *Rev. Sci. Instrum.* **23**, 446.
STOUT, J. W. (1954). Ibid. **25**, 929.
SYDORIAK, S. G., and SOMMERS, H. S. (1951). Ibid. **22**, 915.
URRY, W. D. (1932). *J. Amer. Chem. Soc.* **54**, 3887.
WAITE, M. J. (1955). *Proc. 1954 Cryogenic Engng. Conf.* N.B.S. Report No. 3517, p. 158.
WEITZEL, D. H., DRAPER, J. W., PARK, O. E., TIMMERHAUS, K. D., and VAN VALIN, C. C. (1957). *Proc. 1956 Cryogenic Engng. Conf.* N.B.S., Boulder, Colorado, p. 12.
WEXLER, A. (1951). *J. Appl. Phys.* **22**, 1463.
—— and CORAK, W. S. (1950). *Rev. Sci. Instrum.* **21**, 583.
—— —— (1951). Ibid. **22**, 941.
—— and JACKET, H. S. (1951). Ibid. **282**.
—— (1954). Ibid. **25**, 442.
WHITE, J. F. (1948). *Chem. Engng. Progr.* **44**, 647.
WILLIAMS, W. E., and MAXWELL, E. (1954). *Rev. Sci. Instrum.* **25**, 111.

CHAPTER III

HEAT EXCHANGERS

1. Introduction

WHILE the topic of 'heat exchangers' is a very general one, the use of the word in low-temperature physics is usually confined to systems in which heat is transferred from an entering warm gas stream to a returning cold gas stream; the mathematical formulae developed for dealing with these systems can also treat cases where heat is transferred from a gas stream to a cold liquid bath. The problem of calculating desirable dimensions for countercurrent heat exchangers and for cooling coils is common to both the design of gas liquefiers and such associated equipment as purifying traps.

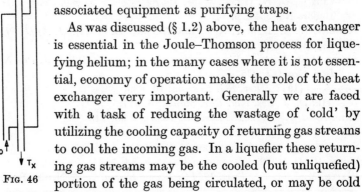

FIG. 46

As was discussed (§ 1.2) above, the heat exchanger is essential in the Joule–Thomson process for liquefying helium; in the many cases where it is not essential, economy of operation makes the role of the heat exchanger very important. Generally we are faced with a task of reducing the wastage of 'cold' by utilizing the cooling capacity of returning gas streams to cool the incoming gas. In a liquefier these returning gas streams may be the cooled (but unliquefied) portion of the gas being circulated, or may be cold gas evaporated from a liquid refrigerant used in the cooling or purifying stages. For maximum efficiency in the interchange process a maximum amount of heat should be transferred from the incoming gas stream to the outgoing streams, so that the temperature of the outgoing gas at its exit approaches closely the temperature of the incoming gas at its entry point into the system. In Figure 46, a warm gas enters at temperature T_1 and leaves at T_x, exchanging heat with a cold gas entering at T_0 and leaving at T_2.

In the limit of maximum efficiency $T_2 \to T_1$ and temperature $T_0 < T_x < T_1$, but the value of T_x can only be found if the relative heat capacities of the two gas streams are known, i.e. the mass flow per second in each stream and the specific heat of the gas in each stream. Of course, in the case where the returning stream has a greater heat capacity than the down-flowing stream, then $T_x \to T_0$, and T_2 may be appreciably less than T_1, but this is an artificial condition which is scarcely likely to arise in the cases with which we are concerned.

Associated with the calculation of efficiency of heat transfer is the calculation of the pressure drop for the gas flowing through the exchanger. It is generally necessary that the pressure drop be small in comparison with the total entry or exit pressure of the gas.

2. Calculation of pressure gradient and heat transfer
Pressure drop

Consider a gas flowing in a circular pipe of diameter D cm and length L cm, a total mass m g passing any section per second. Then if the density of the gas be ρ g cm^{-3} and viscosity η c.g.s. units (poises), classical hydrodynamics and dimensional analysis (see, for example, Jakob, 1949; McAdams, 1954) indicate that the pressure drop Δp in dyn cm^{-2} is given by

$$\Delta p = \frac{1}{2}\psi \frac{LG^2}{D\rho} \text{ where } G = \frac{4m}{\pi D^2} \text{ g cm}^{-2} \text{ sec}^{-1}, \tag{1}$$

and ψ is a dimensionless factor which is given by

$$\psi = 64\left(\frac{\eta}{GD}\right) \tag{2}$$

for laminar flow (Poiseuille flow) or

$$\psi = 0{\cdot}316\left(\frac{GD}{\eta}\right)^{-0{\cdot}25} \tag{3}$$

for turbulent flow (see Figure 47).

The dimensionless factor (GD/η) is usually called the Reynolds number, denoted by Re. In the case of a straight pipe of circular section, the condition for turbulence is that Re > 2300, but this critical Reynolds number varies considerably for different shapes of the carrying tube. In most applications to low temperature equipment, Re $\gg 2300$ and the flow will be turbulent, a fact that is assumed in the calculation of heat transfer coefficients given below.

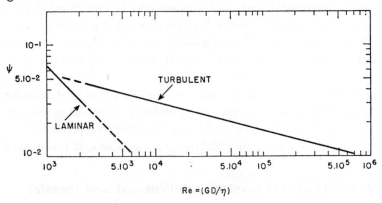

Fig. 47. The dimensionless factor ψ as a function of the Reynolds number.

For generality the equation for Δp may be extended to the case of non-circular section tubes, by defining a hydrodynamic diameter D_h given by

$$D_h = 4 \times \frac{\text{cross-sectional area of tube considered } (A)}{\text{total perimeter of surfaces in contact with gas stream } (P)} \quad ; (4)$$

then G is the mass flow per cm²/sec, i.e. $G = m/A$, and

$$\Delta p = \psi L G^2 / 2 \rho D_h. \qquad (5)$$

Heat transfer coefficient

If the gas flowing through the tube is at a temperature different by an amount ΔT from the temperature of the tube wall, heat will be transferred at a rate

$$\dot{Q} = h\Delta T,$$

where the coefficient h is the 'heat transfer coefficient'. For turbulent flow, the temperature is sensibly constant across the section of the tube and the major temperature difference occurs across the thin layer of gas at the tube surface. By dimensional arguments Nusselt (1909) related the heat transfer coefficient h to the thermal conductivity λ of the gas, the effective diameter

D_e, the dimensions of the tube, viscosity of the gas η, and its heat capacity C_p. The effective diameter D_e is now defined by

$$D_e = 4 \times \frac{\text{cross-sectional area of tube considered}}{\text{perimeter of surface to which the gas stream transfers heat}} \tag{6}$$

so that in some cases D_e may be quite different from D_h. For example, in the simple countercurrent exchanger of two concentric tubes (in Figure 48), the gas stream flowing in the annular space 1 will suffer a viscous drag due to surfaces of perimeter $= \pi D_1 + \pi D_2$; for our purposes the gas transfers heat only to the inner tube of perimeter πD_2.

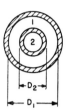

FIG. 48

Therefore to calculate Δp, we use

$$D_h = 4\,\frac{(\pi D_1^2/4 - \pi D_2^2/4)}{\pi D_1 + \pi D_2} = (D_1 - D_2),$$

and to calculate h_1, we use

$$D_e = 4\,\frac{(\pi D_1^2/4 - \pi D_2^2/4)}{\pi D_2} = \frac{(D_1^2 - D_2^2)}{D_2}.$$

Nusselt's equation for h in the dimensionless form is

$$\text{Nu} = \text{const. } (\text{Re})^x(\text{Pr})^y(D_e/L)^z,$$

where   Nusselt's number $\text{Nu} = hD_e/\lambda$,

Reynolds number $\text{Re} = GD_h/\eta$,

and   Prandtl's number $\text{Pr} = \eta C_p/\lambda$. $\tag{7}$

Experimental values for the constant and for the indices x, y, z have been obtained under various conditions. z is found to be extremely small so that $(D_e/L)^z \simeq 1$; it is also found that $x = 0.8$, $y \simeq 0.4$, and the constant has a value of about 0.02.

In the form given by McAdams (1954) for turbulent flow $hD_e/\lambda = 0.023(D_e G/\eta)^{0.8}(C_p \eta/\lambda)^{0.4}$. This can be reduced to the more useful dimensional form

$$h = \frac{0.023}{(\text{Pr})^{0.6}}\,C_p\,\frac{G^{0.8}\eta^{0.2}}{D_e^{0.2}}, \tag{8}$$

where h is in cal/cm^2 sec $^\circ$K if λ is in cal/sec cm $^\circ$K, and C_p in cal/g $^\circ$K.

General equations for heat interchange

By applying considerations of conservation of energy to a section of the exchanger shown in Figure 49, an equation relating the heat transfer coefficients h_1 and h_2 of the two gas streams and their heat capacities $m_1 c_1$, $m_2 c_2$ to the dimensions and temperature distribution may be obtained.

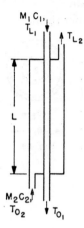

FIG. 49

Here c_1 and c_2 are the specific heats of the gases in cal/g °K, T_{L_1} is the entry temperature of gas stream no. 1 and T_{0_1} its exit temperature; similarly T_{0_2} and T_{L_2} are the entry and exit temperatures respectively of the second gas stream (upflowing stream). If this countercurrent exchanger consists of two concentric tubes, and the inner tube has an internal diameter D_1 and external diameter D_2 then (Mandl, 1948)

$$L = \frac{\alpha}{\gamma} \ln \frac{T_{L_1} + \beta/\gamma}{T_{0_1} + \beta/\gamma}, \qquad (9)$$

where

$$\alpha = m_1 c_1 \left\{ \frac{1}{h_1 S_1} + \frac{\Lambda}{\lambda' S'} + \frac{1}{h_2 S_2} \right\}, \qquad (10)$$

$$\beta = \left\{ \frac{m_1 c_1}{m_2 c_2} T_{0_1} - T_{0_2} \right\}, \qquad (11)$$

$$\gamma = 1 - m_1 c_1 / m_2 c_2, \qquad (12)$$

the heat-transfer perimeters

$$S_1 = \pi D_1,$$
$$S_2 = \pi D_2,$$
$$S' = \pi (D_2 - D_1) / \ln(D_2/D_1),$$

and the thickness of the wall of the inner tube is

$$\Lambda = (D_1 - D_2)/2;$$

$\lambda' =$ thermal conductivity of material of the inner tube.

An important and common case is when $m_1 c_1 = m_2 c_2$, i.e. when the same quantity of the same gas flows in each stream, then (9) reduces in the limit as $m_1 c_1 \to m_2 c_2$, to

$$L = \frac{\alpha}{\beta} (T_{L_1} - T_{0_1}). \qquad (13)$$

In a more general case where the down-flowing stream flows in n identical parallel tubes (each of inner and outer diameter D_1 and D_2 respectively) and each carries m_1/n g/sec of gas, (9) and (13) are modified, to become

$$L = \frac{\alpha}{\gamma n} \ln \frac{T_{L_1} + \beta/\gamma}{T_{0_1} + \beta/\gamma} \qquad (14)$$

and
$$L = \frac{\alpha}{\beta n} [T_L - T_0]. \qquad (15)$$

Physical data for gases and some approximate formulae

Before summarizing the formulae and discussing examples of construction and calculation of heat exchangers, it is interesting to see what simplification can be made to the above formulae without seriously affecting their accuracy.

When designing a heat exchanger, the approximate temperature ranges are fixed so that the density ρ and viscosity η are not affected by altering the dimensions or the flow rate. We may note then that the pressure drop

$$\Delta p \propto \frac{G^{1.75}}{D_h^{1.25}} \propto \frac{m^{1.75}}{A^{1.75} D_h^{1.25}}, \qquad (16)$$

where A is the cross-sectional area of the tube; for a circular cross-section $\Delta p \propto m^{1.75}/D^{4.25}$, so that the pressure drop decreases very rapidly with increase in tube diameter, and increases somewhat less rapidly with increase in the mass flow of gas.

The accompanying Figures 50 and 51 give some representative data on the viscosity and thermal conductivity of air, N_2, O_2, H_2, and He; the data are taken from Keesom (1942) for He, and from the Landolt–Bornstein tables for the other gases.

At pressures below about 200 atmospheres, these properties are not very sensitive to change in pressure so that in most heat exchanger problems any change with pressure may be neglected, particularly as the pressure drop Δp and the heat transfer coefficients h are rather insensitive to changes in η or λ. Similarly, the specific heat data (shown in Table V together with normal densities) may be used fairly generally without considering the effect of pressure or temperature.

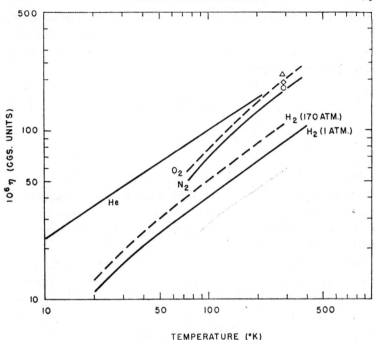

TEMPERATURE (°K)

FIG. 50. Viscosity of some gases as a function of temperature; the experimental points represent values for air at 20° C and 160 atmospheres (△), 80 atmospheres (◇), and 1 atmosphere (○).

TABLE V

	Air	N₂	O₂	H₂	He
C_p (cal/g °K) at 0° C . .	0·240	0·248	0·219	3·40	1·25
ρ (g/l at S.T.P.) . . .	1·292	1·250	1·428	0·090	0·179

In Table VI are given some values for Prandtl's number ($\mathrm{Pr} = C_p\, \eta/\lambda$) calculated for He, H_2, and air at different temperatures† from the data in Figures 50, 51, and Table V. The relative constancy of Pr and more particularly of $(\mathrm{Pr})^{0·6}$ suggests that a simpler form for calculating h can be used in practice.

† A very useful source of reference for data on the transport properties of the gases air, argon, N_2, O_2, H_2, CO_2, are the *Tables of Thermal Properties of Gases* published as N.B.S. Circular 564 (1955) by the U.S. Government Printing Office, Washington, D.C. These include tabulated values of viscosity, specific heat, thermal conductivity, and Prandtl's number.

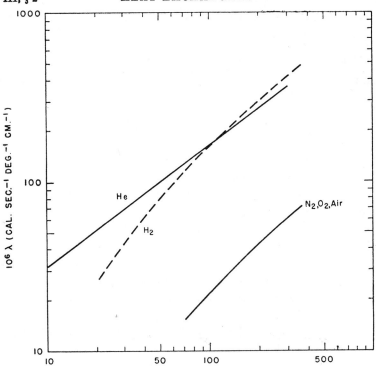

FIG. 51. Variation of thermal conductivity of gases with temperature.

TABLE VI

	T, °K	Pr	$(\mathrm{Pr})^{0\cdot6}$	$(\eta)^{0\cdot2}$
He .	10	0·93	0·96	0·12
	50	0·81	0·88	0·146
	100	0·76	0·85	0·15₉
	180	0·72	0·82	0·17₂
H₂ .	50	0·72	0·82	0·12
	180	0·72	0·82	0·143
Air	180	0·75	0·82	0·16₇

Thus, assuming $(\mathrm{Pr})^{0\cdot6} \simeq 0\cdot85$, equation (8) reduces to

$$h \simeq 0\cdot027 C_p\, G^{0\cdot8} \eta^{0\cdot2}/D_e^{0\cdot2}.$$

Also, since η and D_e appear in the form $\eta^{0\cdot2}$ and $D_e^{0\cdot2}$ a further rough approximation that may be used is to assume that

$\eta^{0 \cdot 2} \simeq 0 \cdot 15$ (see Table VI) and that $D_e^{0 \cdot 2} \simeq 1$ since $D_e \sim 1$ cm in many instances.

Hence $\qquad\qquad h \simeq 0 \cdot 004 C_p\, G^{0 \cdot 8},$ \hfill (17)

and we have $\qquad h \propto G^{0 \cdot 8} = (m/A)^{0 \cdot 8},$ \hfill (18)

which for a circular tube becomes $h \propto m^{0 \cdot 8}/D^{1 \cdot 6}$.

Equations (16) and (18) are useful when considering the suitability of varying the tube diameter or mass flow of gas through a heat exchanger. Obviously, for a maximum value of $h/\Delta p$, the hydrodynamic diameter D_h and cross-sectional area A should be large, but must eventually be limited by the requirement of turbulence, and by difficulties of construction.

As shown by equations (13) and (14) the length L required to give any particular temperature distribution is proportional to α, which in turn depends (from (10)) on the sum of the reciprocals of the effective heat transfers. The second term in (10) involving the heat conducted across the wall of the exchanger tube is given by $\Lambda/\lambda' S'$. For a circular pipe, this term reduces to $2t/\lambda'\pi(D_1 + D_2)$ provided that D_2/D_1 approaches 1, i.e. provided that the wall thickness t is small in comparison with the diameter;

then $\qquad\qquad \alpha = m_1 c_1 \left\{ \dfrac{1}{h_1 S_1} + \dfrac{t}{\lambda' \pi \overline{D}} + \dfrac{1}{h_2 S_2} \right\}.$ \hfill (19)

Also, the thermal conductivity of the metal wall is usually much greater than the coefficients h for heat transfer from the gas stream to the wall so that this term $t/\lambda'\pi\overline{D} = t/\lambda' S'$ is negligible in comparison with

$$\frac{1}{h_1 S_1} + \frac{1}{h_2 S_2}.$$

Summary of formulae

$$\Delta p = \psi L G^2 / 2\rho D_h, \qquad\qquad [(5)]$$

where $\qquad\qquad \psi = 64/\mathrm{Re}$ (laminar flow) \hfill [(2)]

or $\qquad\qquad \psi = 0 \cdot 316(\mathrm{Re})^{-0 \cdot 25}$ (turbulent flow). \hfill [(3)]

$$h = \frac{0 \cdot 023}{(\mathrm{Pr})^{0 \cdot 6}} C_p \frac{G^{0 \cdot 8} \eta^{0 \cdot 2}}{D_e^{0 \cdot 2}} \quad (\mathrm{Pr} = C_p\, \eta/\lambda) \qquad [(8)]$$

$$\simeq 0 \cdot 004 C_p\, G^{0 \cdot 8}. \qquad\qquad [(17)]$$

$$L = \frac{\alpha}{\gamma n} \ln \frac{T_{L_1} + \beta/\gamma}{T_{0_1} + \beta/\gamma} \quad (m_1 c_1 \neq m_2 c_2) \qquad [(14)]$$

$$L = \frac{\alpha}{n\beta} (T_{L_1} - T_{0_1}) \quad (m_1 c_1 = m_2 c_2), \qquad [(15)]$$

where
$$\beta = \frac{m_1 c_1}{m_2 c_2} T_{0_1} - T_{0_2}, \qquad [(11)]$$

$$\gamma = 1 - m_1 c_1 / m_2 c_2, \qquad [(12)]$$

and
$$\alpha = m_1 c_1 \left\{ \frac{1}{h_1 S_1} + \frac{\Lambda}{\lambda' S'} + \frac{1}{h_2 S_2} \right\}, \qquad [(10)]$$

$$\simeq m_1 c_1 \left\{ \frac{1}{h_1 S_1} + \frac{1}{h_2 S_2} \right\}, \qquad (20)$$

where $S_1 = \pi D_1$, $S_2 = \pi D_2$.

Cooling of a gas stream by a liquid bath

The cooling of a gas by passing it through a coil immersed in a cold liquid is common; equations [(14)] and [(11)] are easily simplified to give the cooling efficiency as a function of length. It is assumed that heat transfer both from the wall to the liquid and across the tube wall are very good in comparison with that from the gas stream to the wall of the carrying tube; then the second and third terms in the bracket on the right-hand side of (10) can be neglected. If the bath temperature be T' and a stream of m g/sec of gas of specific heat c cal/g °K enters a tube at temperature T_L and leaves the tube (of length L cm) at temperature T_0, then

$$L = \frac{mc}{hS} \ln \left\{ \frac{T_L - T'}{T_0 - T'} \right\}, \qquad (21)$$

where h is defined by equation [(8)] and S is the inner perimeter of the tube. For a given efficiency, that is for given values of $(T_L - T')/(T_0 - T')$, the required length L is proportional to m/hS; so that, for a circular tube of diameter D,

$$L \propto m/hD \propto m/G^{0.8}D \propto D^{0.6}m^{0.2}.$$

As the diameter is increased, the pressure drop in the gas stream decreases very rapidly (as $D^{-4.25}$) and the required length increases slowly with diameter (as $D^{0.6}$).

3. Methods of construction

Introduction

Many types of heat exchanger have been made but most appear to be derivatives of the two basic patterns mentioned in Chapter I—those of Linde and Hampson. In considering their relative merits, a number of factors must be borne in mind: (i) the relative difficulties of construction, (ii) the difficulty of mathematical analysis, (iii) the efficiency of heat transfer that can be obtained while keeping the pressure drop within reasonable bounds, (iv) the total mass and hence total heat capacity of the assembly. As far as factor (ii) is concerned, the Linde pattern lends itself to mathematical treatment, while in the Hampson pattern it is usually extremely difficult to make any theoretical estimate of the pressure drop or heat transfer in the low-pressure gas stream; thus in the latter case a combination of experience and experimental trial are needed to produce an efficient exchanger. The factor (iv) concerning heat capacity is particularly important in most laboratory liquefiers where a fairly short cooling-down time is desired; the time required to reach the equilibrium temperature distribution increases with the mass of the heat exchanger.

The Linde type of exchanger

Some examples of Linde-pattern exchangers are shown in Figure 52 (see also Plate II between pp. 17 and 18). In (*a*), (*b*), and (*c*) the tubes are concentric and the outer wall contributes seriously to the pressure drop in the gas stream occupying the outer annular space, but assists very little in raising the heat transfer coefficient, since there is merely a touch contact between the inner tube and the outer tube. Frequently the central tube(s) is used for the high-pressure stream, and the low-pressure stream occupies the annular space between the tubes; however, there are often advantages in a construction such as (*c*) where a large inner tube may be used for the low-pressure stream to minimize $\Delta p/h$ and the high-pressure flow is through a narrow gap between the tubes.

Those shown in (*d*) and (*e*) are solder-bonded parallel-tube exchangers which are also amenable to mathematical analysis and are efficient, provided that the solder-bonding between the tubes is adequate. These are most simply made by tying the tubes together at intervals of a few inches with a twist of wire and then drawing the long bundle of tubes slowly through a

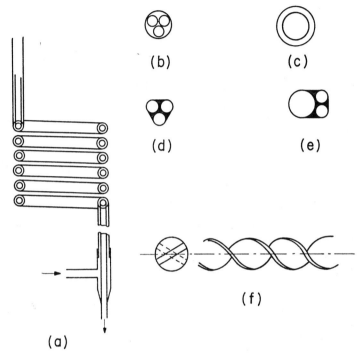

FIG. 52. Some heat exchangers of the Linde pattern.

molten bath of soft solder. The solder bath may be contained in a length of channel iron supported above bunsen burners; care should be taken to clean the tube surfaces of dirt or grease and to wet them thoroughly with soldering flux before they enter the solder bath.

The Figure 52 (*f*) shows a section of a twisted-tube exchanger in which the inner tube is flattened and twisted into a 'corkscrew' shape before insertion into the outer jacket tube. This twisted tube exchanger was devised by Nelson about 45 years ago and first described by Bichowsky (1922).

In concentric tube exchangers, heat transfer in the outer space can be improved by winding a copper wire helically around the inner tube, and bonding it with soft solder. This increases the heat transfer surface and the turbulence, but also increases the pressure gradient slightly.

Hampson exchangers

The Linde exchanger is at its greatest disadvantage when one gas stream is at low pressure—allowing only a small pressure gradient—and the flow rate is large. The Hampson-type exchanger largely avoids this by shortening the low-pressure return path of the gas stream. As mentioned before it is much more difficult to treat mathematically with any degree of accuracy and also must be constructed accurately with uniform spacing between the tubes that build up the spiral pancake pattern. The main heat exchanger used by Collins (1947) in his helium liquefier (see Chapter I and Plates I a and I b) is a particularly efficient type of Hampson exchanger in which the high-pressure tubing ($\frac{1}{4}$-in. diameter cupro-nickel) is 'finned' with copper ribbon and wound in a helix in the annular space between two co-axial cylinders of low thermal conductivity metal. The copper ribbon 0·010 in. by 0·040 in. is edgewound and solder-bonded to the high-pressure tubing, and with the aid of the cotton cord interwinding produces a good heat transfer between the low-pressure returning helium stream and the high-pressure tube.

In another variation of the Hampson spiral described by Nicol, Smith, Heer, and Daunt (1953), the high-pressure tube of $\frac{1}{4}$ in. outer diameter, 0·030 in. wall copper is effectively finned by threading the copper tube in a die, mounted in a lathe. The threads, 28 per inch, are cut 0·015 in. deep and the tube is then annealed and wound in layers on a central tube; cotton cords are interwound with the tubing to guide the low-pressure gas stream into close contact with the finning.

Condensation of impurities

An obvious feature of these various countercurrent heat interchangers is the necessity of avoiding condensation of impurities in the tubing. So that blocking by impurities in the incoming gas stream shall not occur, the gas must be of fairly high purity or be pre-cleaned to remove any large quantities of water, oil, or other gases before entering the exchanger (see § 1.6). To avoid this necessity Collins (1946) developed a reversing interchanger for use with low-pressure air liquefiers. In this, impurities from the incoming stream (no. 1) may collect in the tube A of the exchanger for a period of about 3 minutes, after which the exchanger is 'reversed' so that the outgoing clean gas stream (no. 2) flows up through A, blowing out the impurities, while stream 1 is now flowing down through tube B, previously cleaned out by stream no. 2. Such a system allows the use of ordinary atmospheric air without any previous purification.

Some general remarks

The material used for heat exchanger tubing is largely dictated by the availability of tube of the required dimensions and by the fact that it must be bent, for most low-temperature equipment, into a helix or a spiral without splitting or crimping. Both copper and copper-nickel (annealed) bend easily and if a trial bend shows there is a danger of their crimping they may be filled with Cerrobend or Wood's metal. A somewhat less robust but very simple method of filling tubes before bending, is to fill them with water and freeze the water by immersion in liquid air; the bending round a wood or metal mandril must then be done rapidly before the ice melts.

Copper may be an undesirable material in some instances because of its high heat conductivity. The heat flow along the exchanger due to thermal conduction should be negligible in comparison with the heat content of the gas stream. The formulae and the analyses which we indicated in § 2 are only valid if the exchange of thermal energy between the heat exchanger and the surroundings is very much smaller than the energy exchanged between the gas streams; this also implies that the exchanger should be in an evacuated chamber or in a stagnant gas atmosphere within a dewar vessel.

In the Linde type of heat exchanger, a rough calculation will often show that copper is quite acceptable as a tube material due to the long length of path which the heat must travel; in a Hampson exchanger the major heat conduction will occur along the walls of the two cylinders which enclose the annular space, and this usually necessitates the use of stainless steel, monel, or inconel for these walls.

4. Examples of heat-exchanger analysis

(a) Cooling of hydrogen gas by liquid nitrogen

Consider cooling a stream of compressed hydrogen gas in a bath of liquid nitrogen; the gas enters at a temperature of 120° K, a pressure of 100 atmospheres, and at a rate equivalent to 300 l. (S.T.P.)/min. The temperature of the pumped liquid nitrogen is 64° K. The problem is to find suitable dimensions for the immersed cooling coil such that the hydrogen gas will be cooled to within 1° K of the bath temperature.

$$T_L = 120° \text{ K}, \quad T' = 64° \text{ K}, \quad \text{and} \quad T_0 \simeq 65° \text{ K}.$$

Therefore average temperature of gas $\overline{T} = 92 \cdot 5°$ K.

Hence we obtain the viscosity $\eta \simeq 43 \times 10^{-6}$ c.g.s. units,

$$\lambda \simeq 150 \times 10^{-6} \text{ cal/cm sec } °\text{K},$$

and the density
$$\rho = 0 \cdot 090 \times 10^{-3} \times 100 \times \frac{273}{92 \cdot 5}$$

$$= 0 \cdot 0266 \text{ g/cm}^3.$$

The mass flow
$$m = \frac{300 \times 0 \cdot 090}{60} = 0 \cdot 45 \text{ g/sec.}$$

Assume, as a trial, a coil of copper tubing of internal diameter 0·4 cm, and length L cm, then the Reynolds number

$$\text{Re} = GD/\eta$$

$$= \frac{0 \cdot 45 \times 0 \cdot 4}{\pi (0 \cdot 2)^2 \times 43 \times 10^{-6}} \quad (G = 3 \cdot 57 \text{ g/sec cm}^2)$$

$$= 33,200.$$

Therefore the flow will be turbulent as required.

Pressure drop

$$\Delta p = \psi LG^2/2\rho D$$
$$= \psi \times L \times 12 \cdot 7/(0 \cdot 4 \times 0 \cdot 0266 \times 2),$$

and obtaining

$$\psi = 0 \cdot 026 \text{ from Figure 47,}$$
$$\Delta p = 15 \times L \text{ dynes/cm}^2/\text{cm} \simeq 1 \cdot 5 \times 10^{-3} \text{ atm/m,}$$

From equation [(8)], heat transfer coefficient

$$h = \frac{0 \cdot 023}{(\text{Pr})^{0 \cdot 6}} C_p \frac{G^{0 \cdot 8} \eta^{0 \cdot 2}}{D_e^{0 \cdot 2}}.$$

Now $C_p \eta/\lambda = 3 \cdot 4 \times 43 \times 10^{-6}/150 \times 10^{-6} = 0 \cdot 97$

$$(C_p = 3 \cdot 4 \text{ cal/g } ^\circ \text{K}),$$

therefore $(\text{Pr})^{0 \cdot 6} = 0 \cdot 98.$

Hence

$$h = \frac{0 \cdot 023}{0 \cdot 98} \times 3 \cdot 4 \times \frac{2 \cdot 8 \times 0 \cdot 14}{0 \cdot 833}$$

$$= 0 \cdot 0376 \text{ cal/cm}^2 \text{ sec } ^\circ \text{K}.$$

From equation (21), desirable length

$$L = \frac{mc}{hS} \ln \left[\frac{T_L - T'}{T_0 - T'} \right]$$

$$= \frac{0 \cdot 45 \times 3 \cdot 4}{0 \cdot 038 \times 1 \cdot 26} \ln \left[\frac{120 - T'}{T_0 - 64} \right]$$

$$= 73 \log \left[\frac{120 - T'}{T_0 - 64} \right]$$

$$\simeq 73 \log \frac{56}{\Delta T} \text{ cm,} \qquad\qquad (22)$$

where $T_0 = 64 + \Delta T.$

Thus as $\Delta T \to 0$, the efficiency $\to 100$ per cent, and for $\Delta T = 1^\circ$ K, i.e. about 98 per cent efficiency, we require $L = 128$ cm, to which corresponds a pressure gradient $\Delta p = 0 \cdot 002$ atm. Figure 53 shows a graphical solution of (22) above. It is apparent from the low value of Δp that a much smaller diameter tube could be used without making Δp excessive. For example, reducing the tube diameter to one-half of its assumed value would increase Δp about thirty times, but would increase h nearly four times and decrease the required length (for the same efficiency) by a factor of nearly two.

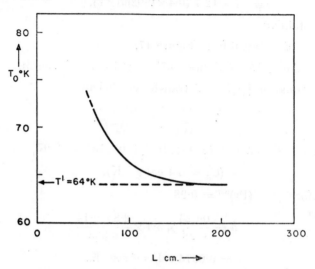

Fig. 53. Exit temperature of hydrogen gas as a function of the length of the cooling coil.

In Chapter I the efficiency of a heat exchanger was defined as the heat transferred divided by the heat available for transfer. In the example just given this is seen to be equivalent to a first approximation to

$$\text{efficiency} = \frac{T_L - T_0}{T_L - T'} = 1 - \frac{\Delta T}{(T_L - T')}.$$

(b) *Helium heat exchanger operating between liquid oxygen and liquid hydrogen temperatures*

In this example from a Linde liquefier illustrated by Figure 54, helium at 20 atmospheres pressure enters the heat exchanger at temperature $T_{L_1} = 90°$ K, flowing at 8 m³/hour. The returning gas stream at a pressure of 1 atmosphere enters the exchanger at temperature $T_{0_2} = 15°$ K, the flow rate being 7 m³ (at S.T.P)/hour (assuming a liquefaction efficiency $\mathcal{E}$ of 0·14). At the average temperature $\overline{T} = 52·5°$ K, viscosity $\eta = 70 \times 10^{-6}$ c.g.s. units,

$\lambda = 110 \times 10^{-6}$ cal/cm sec °K, $C_p = 1.25$ cal/g °K, ρ (S.T.P.)
$= 0.179 \times 10^{-3}$ g/cm³.

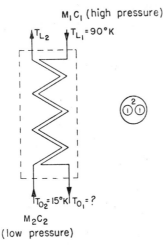

$M_1 C_1$ (high pressure)

T_{L_2}　　$T_{L_1} = 90°K$

$T_{O_2} = 15°K$　$T_{O_1} = ?$

$M_2 C_2$
(low pressure)

Fig. 54

Hence　　　$m_1 = 0.4$ g/sec,　　　$\rho_1 = 1.8 \times 10^{-2}$ g/cm³;

　　　　　　$m_2 = 0.35$ g/sec,　　　$\rho_2 = 0.9 \times 10^{-3}$ g/cm³.

High-pressure circuit

Assume the compressed gas flows through two inner tubes
($n = 2$) of copper, 0.15 cm inner diameter in parallel.

Since　　　$D_h = 0.15$ cm,　　$G_1 = 11$ g/cm² sec,

therefore　　　　　　Re $= 2.4 \times 10^4$ (turbulent flow),

　　　　　　　　　$\psi = 2.5 \times 10^{-2}$,

and so, from (5),　　$\Delta p = 0.056$ atm/m length.

Also Prandtl's number　　Pr $= 0.80$

and　　　　　　　　　　$D_e = 0.15$ cm.

Therefore, from (8), the heat transfer coefficient

　　　　　$h_1 = 4.8 \times 10^{-2}$ cal/cm² sec °K.

Low-pressure circuit

The jacket tube of 0.5 cm inner diameter cupro-nickel encloses the two copper tubes (0.24 cm outer diameter, 0.15 cm

inner diameter), so that the low-pressure stream flows through an annular gap of area $= \frac{1}{4}\pi[(0\cdot5^2)-2\times(0\cdot24^2)]$, and the total perimeter is given by $P = \pi(2\times0\cdot24+0\cdot5)$.

Then $\qquad\qquad D_h = 4A/P = 0\cdot138 \text{ cm},$

and proceeding as before,

$$\Delta p = 0\cdot15 \text{ atm/m.}$$

In the case of heat transfer, the effective perimeter is simply the circumference of the two inner tubes, i.e. the outer jacket is neglected.

Then $\qquad\qquad D_e = 0\cdot28 \text{ cm},$

and we obtain $\qquad h_2 = 1\cdot64\times10^{-2} \text{ cal/cm}^2 \text{ sec } °\text{K.}$

Length L as a function of T_{0_1}

Assuming $\qquad\qquad \mathscr{E} = 0\cdot14,$

so that $\qquad m_1 c_1/m_2 c_2 \simeq 1\cdot14,$

then from [(11)], [(12)], and [(10)]

$$\beta = 1\cdot14 T_{0_1}-15,$$
$$\gamma = -0\cdot14,$$

and $\qquad \alpha = 0\cdot4\times1\cdot25\left[\dfrac{100}{4\cdot8\times0\cdot47}+\dfrac{100}{1\cdot64\times0\cdot75}\right]$

(using $S_1 = 0\cdot47$ cm, $S_2 = 0\cdot75$ cm).

Note that the second term in equation (10), $t/\lambda'\pi\overline{D}$, has a value of about $0\cdot08$ (assuming $\lambda' \simeq 1$ cal/cm sec $°$K for copper), which is negligible in comparison with those terms involving h_1 and h_2.

Thence

$$L = \frac{\alpha}{\gamma n}\ln\left\{\frac{T_{L_1}+\beta/\gamma}{T_{0_1}+\beta/\gamma}\right\}$$
$$= -514\log_{10}\frac{1\cdot14 T_{0_1}-27\cdot6}{T_{0_1}-15},$$

which for $\qquad T_{0_1} = 25°$ K gives $L = 537$ cm,

$$\qquad\qquad\qquad 26° \text{ K } \quad ,, \quad ,, \quad 380 \text{ cm,}$$
$$\qquad\qquad\qquad 28° \text{ K } \quad ,, \quad ,, \quad 247 \text{ cm,}$$
$$\qquad\qquad\qquad 30° \text{ K } \quad ,, \quad ,, \quad 183 \text{ cm,}$$
$$\qquad\qquad\qquad 35° \text{ K } \quad ,, \quad ,, \quad 109 \text{ cm.}$$

If we require exchanger efficiency η of $0 \cdot 96$,

$$\eta = 0 \cdot 96 = 1 - \frac{T'_{0_1} - 24 \cdot 2}{90 - 24 \cdot 2},$$

therefore $T'_{0_1} = 26 \cdot 8° \, \mathrm{K}$, requiring $L \simeq 300$ cm.

For $L = 300$ cm, Δp (high pressure) $= 0 \cdot 17$ atm,

$$\Delta p \text{ (low pressure)} = 0 \cdot 45 \text{ atm.}$$

REFERENCES

In this chapter the author has made extensive use of the mathematical treatment of heat exchangers by Mandl (1948), but detailed discussion of the problem has been given in many more accessible texts such as Jakob (1949) and McAdams (1954). A recent review article by Daunt (1956) has a useful section dealing with heat exchangers. Also Starr (1941) treated the problem with particular reference to small hydrogen liquefiers. An article by Jacobs and Collins (1940) described some results of experimental investigations of the efficiencies of various types of exchanger. Other useful general references are Bosworth (1952) and Hausen (1950).

BICHOWSKY, F. R. (1922). *J. Industr. Engng. Chem.* **14**, 62.

BOSWORTH, R. C. L. (1952). *Heat Transfer Phenomena*, Wiley & Sons, N.Y.

COLLINS, S. C. (1946). *Chem. Engng.* **53**, Dec., 106.

—— (1947). *Rev. Sci. Instrum.* **18**, 157.

DAUNT, J. G. (1956). *Handb. der Physik*, **14**, 1.

HAUSEN, H. (1950). *Wärmeübertragung im Gegenstrom, Gleichstrom und Kreuzstrom*, Springer, Berlin.

JACOBS, R. B., and COLLINS, S. C. (1940). *J. Appl. Phys.* **11**, 491.

JAKOB, M. (1949). *Heat Transfer*, vol. i, Wiley & Sons, N.Y.

KEESOM, W. H. (1942). *Helium*, Elsevier, Amsterdam.

McADAMS, W. H. (1954). *Heat Transmission*, 3rd edn., McGraw-Hill, N.Y.

MANDL, F. (1948). Thesis. Oxford.

NICOL, J., SMITH, J. S., HEER, C. V., and DAUNT, J. G. (1953). *Rev. Sci. Instrum.* **24**, 16.

NUSSELT, W. (1909). *Z. ver. dtsch. Ing.* **53**, 1750.

STARR, C. (1941). *Rev. Sci. Instrum.* **12**, 193.

CHAPTER IV

TEMPERATURE MEASUREMENT

1. Introduction

ACCORDING to the zeroth law of thermodynamics any two bodies which are in thermal equilibrium with a third body are in thermal equilibrium between themselves; that is, when placed in thermal contact there is no transfer of heat from one to the other. Such bodies are said to be at the same temperature. A temperature scale may then be defined in terms of any of a number of thermometric properties of the system, and the scale and the size of particular temperature intervals (or degrees) may be fixed by reference to such common physical phenomena as boiling-points, melting-points, phase changes, etc. Thus the thermal expansion of a solid, liquid, or gas, the electrical resistance or thermoelectric power of a metal, and the magnetic susceptibility are all physical parameters which in the case of a particular chosen substance could be used to define a temperature scale, with the scale in degrees being a linear (or other chosen function) of the particular parameter for that substance. However, even if the same numbers on each of these scales were used to represent the temperatures of two or more chosen fixed points, there is no obvious reason why the different scales should agree at other temperatures or why any one of them should have a particular fundamental significance. Such a multitude of scales would be obviously rather unsatisfactory and very unsatisfying.

However, useful temperature scales can be based on the physical properties of particular systems and one particularly important scale depends on the properties of gases as determined experimentally: it has been found that at sufficiently low pressures the isotherms of gases are described by Boyle's law, i.e. the product of pressure and volume, pV, is constant. The 'perfect' or 'absolute' gas scale of temperature assigns numerical values to the temperature θ on the basis of the relation $\theta = a(pV)$ in the limit as $p \to 0$.

If it is then agreed that there shall be 100° between the ice point and steam point, the constant a is fixed so that

$$a = \frac{100}{\lim(pV)_s - \lim(pV)_i}$$

and the ice-point temperature,

$$\theta_i = 100 \frac{\lim(pV)_i}{\lim(pV)_s - \lim(pV)_i}.$$

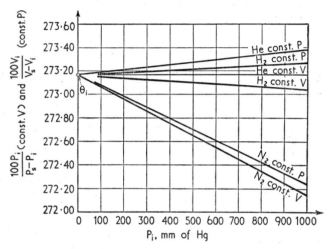

FIG. 55. The absolute ice point determined by graphical extrapolation (from *Heat and Thermodynamics*, 2nd edn., by M. W. Zemansky. Copyright, 1943, McGraw-Hill Book Co.).

For such a centigrade absolute gas scale, it has been found experimentally for a number of gases (see Figure 55 from Zemansky, 1943) that in the low-pressure limit, θ_i has a value of 273·15°.

The real significance of this scale goes beyond this apparent wide applicability to various gases. The second law of thermodynamics may be stated in the form 'that no heat engine operating in a closed cycle, can transfer heat from a reservoir at a lower temperature to a reservoir at a higher temperature'. From this follows an alternative statement that no engine can be more efficient than an ideal Carnot engine, which operating between two reservoirs has an efficiency depending only on the temperatures of these reservoirs.

Such a Carnot engine, taking in heat Q_1 at a temperature θ_1 in a reversible isothermal process and rejecting heat Q_2 at temperature θ_2, has an efficiency

$$\eta = 1 - \frac{Q_2}{Q_1} = f(\theta_1, \theta_2).$$

In such a Carnot cycle the two portions of the isotherms (Figure 56) are bounded by a pair of adiabatic lines. It may be shown generally that

$$Q_1:Q_2:Q_3:Q_4:\ldots = f(\theta_1):f(\theta_2):f(\theta_3):f(\theta_4):\ldots.$$

By identifying this ratio $f(\theta_1):f(\theta_2):f(\theta_3):\ldots$ etc., directly with the ratio $T_1:T_2:T_3:\ldots$ etc., a temperature scale independent of the system or of the working substance can be defined. This scale is called the Kelvin scale or absolute thermodynamic scale.

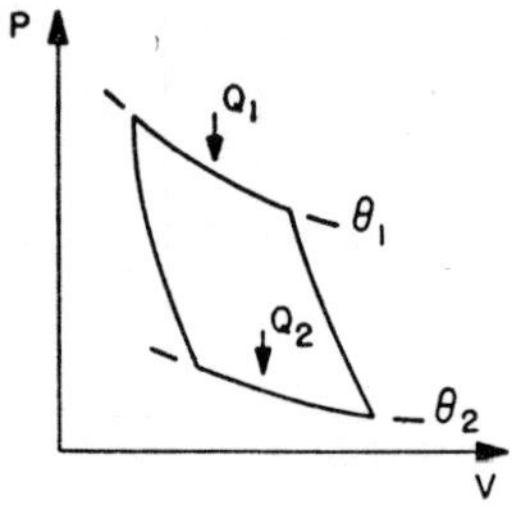

For a perfect gas, or for a real gas in the limit of low pressures, pV is a function of temperature only and hence the internal energy is only a function of temperature so that such a gas could be used as the working substance in a Carnot cycle. It can be shown that

FIG. 56. A Carnot cycle.

$$\frac{T_1}{T_2} = \frac{\theta_1}{\theta_2}.$$

If, as in the case of the gas scale, we fix numerical values for the temperature T on the thermodynamic scale by assuming $T_{\text{steam}} - T_{\text{ice}} = 100°$, the two scales will coincide.

On the thermodynamic or Kelvin scale there is a temperature at which the heat Q_1 taken in is zero and this corresponds to a temperature $T_1 = 0$, called the absolute zero of temperature. That such a temperature exists follows from the second law; that such a temperature is unattainable in a finite number of steps follows from the third law, as we discussed at the beginning of Chapter I.

2. Relation of thermodynamic and gas scales to the international scale

So we have a thermodynamic scale of temperature, which in principle at least can be realized by the absolute gas scale; in practice with real gases it can be realized with a degree of accuracy which depends on the accuracy of the gas thermometry and the accuracy of the corrections which are applied to the real gas to account for its non-ideality. However, accurate gas thermometry over a wide temperature range is exceedingly difficult; the necessity of a scale which could be more easily realized and reproduced in practice was met in 1927 when the Seventh General Conference on Weights and Measures adopted the International Temperature Scale. This scale was based on the same fundamental fixed points: ice point and steam point, taking the ice point as 0° Celsius (0° C) and the steam point as 100° Celsius (100° C). The instruments for its realization are the electrical resistance of platinum as a thermometer and at high temperatures ($>$ 600° C) the thermocouple and radiation pyrometers.

To quote from Hall (1956):

the original aim of the international scale was to provide a practical scale of temperature reproducible to very high accuracy and as nearly as possible identical with the thermodynamic Celsius scale. That is to say, it should be identical with the thermodynamic Celsius scale to within the limits of measurement with the gas thermometer, but it should offer the higher reproducibility obtainable with such instruments as the platinum resistance thermometer, not in themselves capable of defining an absolute scale.

A further development in the international Celsius scale has been the replacement in 1948 of the ice point (melting-point of ice under one atmosphere pressure) by the triple point of ice, so that although the ice point is still 0° C (Int. 1948), it is defined as being 0·0100° C below the triple point of ice. Thus the two fundamental points used in fixing the international scale experimentally were the triple point at 0·0100° C and the steam point at 100° C.

As far as fixing the Kelvin or thermodynamic scale is concerned it would seem an unnecessary constraint to use two fixed points (ice and steam) as there is already a fixed point at the absolute zero. Kelvin pointed this out in 1854 and Giauque returned to the attack in 1938, proposing that the then best known value of the ice point on the absolute gas scale should be adopted permanently to define the scale. Finally in 1954 after examination of the values for θ_i or T_i obtained by precision gas thermometry in Germany (involving recalculation of the earlier results from the Physikalisch-Technische Reichsanstalt), Japan, Holland, and the United States, a value of 273·15° K was adopted by the Tenth General Conference of Weights and Measures. They recommended that the thermodynamic scale should henceforth be defined by one fundamental fixed point, the triple point of water, and that the best value for the temperature of this point is 273·16° K on the thermodynamic scale in use up to the present.

So now we have two scales, one defined at the ice (or triple) point and steam point, and the other at the absolute zero and the ice (or triple) point. Since each of these may be expressed in degrees Celsius or degrees Kelvin we have the situation depicted below (after Hall, 1955, 1956):

International Scale

International Temperature	*International Kelvin Temperature*
t	$T_{\text{Int}} = t + 273 \cdot 15$
°C (Int. 1948)	°K (Int. 1948)

Thermodynamic Scale

Thermodynamic Celsius Temperature	*Thermodynamic Temperature*
$t_{\text{Th}} = T - 273 \cdot 15$	T
°C (therm)	°K

3. Fixed points

In Table VII below are the fundamental and primary fixed points of the international temperature scale. With the exception of the point at 0° C they are stated with a degree of accuracy rather better than that which has been so far realized on the gas scale and therefore have no thermodynamic justification. However, this is an accuracy which the particular thermometric instruments used for realizing the international scale approach in their reproducibility.

TABLE VII

Fixed point (under pressure of 1,013,250 dynes/cm²)			Value adopted 1948
Boiling-point of oxygen (Primary fixed)	.	.	$-182 \cdot 970°$ C
Melting-point of ice (Fundamental†)	.	.	0
Boiling-point of water (Primary fixed)	.	.	100·000
Boiling-point of sulphur (Primary fixed)	.	.	444·600
Freezing-point of silver (Primary fixed)	.	.	960·8
Freezing-point of gold (Primary fixed)	.	.	1,063·0

† In fact, the melting-point of ice is no longer a fundamental point but is fixed by reference to the triple point of ice at 0·0100° C. It may be better regarded as a primary fixed point at 0·0100° C below the triple point (the fundamental point). The writer is very grateful to Dr. H. Preston-Thomas for discussion and elucidation of the present position with regard to these scales of temperature.

For purposes of interpolation and for extrapolation above the gold point the international scale is divided into three regions:

(a) $-182 \cdot 97°$–$630 \cdot 5°$ C. The scale is defined here by the platinum resistance thermometer of which the physical and chemical purity are such that $R_{100}/R_0 \geqslant 1 \cdot 391$. In the region above 0° C, the resistance is then represented by the Callendar equation

$$t = 100 \frac{R_t - R_0}{R_{100} - R_0} + \delta \frac{t}{100}\left(\frac{t}{100} - 1\right)$$

and the three constants are to be determined by measurement at the ice (or at the triple point), steam, and sulphur points.

For temperatures below 0° C, a four-constant equation is employed of which the Callendar–Van Dusen form is

$$t = 100 \frac{R_t - R_0}{R_{100} - R_0} + \delta \frac{t}{100}\left\{\frac{t}{100} - 1\right\} + \beta \left\{\frac{t}{100}\right\}^3 \left\{\frac{t}{100} - 1\right\},$$

and the additional constant β is ascertained by a measurement at the oxygen point.

(b) $630 \cdot 5°$–$1,063°$ C. Here the platinum + 10 per cent rhodium against pure platinum thermocouple defines the scale, using the equation
$$E = a + bt + ct^2.$$

a, b, c are determined by measuring the thermoelectric force E

at the freezing-points of silver, gold, and antimony; this latter antimony point of 630·5° C is to be checked against a platinum resistance thermometer in the case of a particular antimony sample or the thermocouple may be checked directly against a resistance thermometer in the vicinity of 630·5° C.

(c) Above 1,063° C. A standard optical pyrometer is used to compare the intensity of radiation from a luminous black body of unknown temperature with that from a black body at the freezing-point of gold. This range of temperature is of much less concern to the low-temperature physicist.

It is of interest that these are the only fixed points subject to international agreement, and that therefore the 'fixed' points of more immediate concern to the low-temperature physicist, viz. those below 90° K (Table VIII), are always liable to fluctuation in consideration of further available experimental evidence. However, they are probably known in terms of thermodynamic temperature to an accuracy as great as those points set out in the previous table. An illustration of the magnitude of this fluctuation is seen in Figure 57 (after Scott, 1955) which shows a comparison of the temperature scales from four major centres of thermometric research.

TABLE VIII

'Fixed' points below 90° *K*†

Point	T, ° K
Boiling-point of oxygen. . . .	$90 \cdot 18$ $(-182 \cdot 970°$ C$)$
Triple point of oxygen . . .	$54 \cdot 36_3$
Boiling-point of normal hydrogen	$20 \cdot 39_0$
Boiling-point of equilibrium hydrogen	$20 \cdot 27_3$
Triple point of normal hydrogen .	$13 \cdot 95_7$
Triple point of equilibrium hydrogen	$13 \cdot 81_3$
Boiling-point of helium . . .	$4 \cdot 214_3$
λ-point of helium . . .	$2 \cdot 173_5$

† These values are intended to be consistent with the tempera-ture-vapour pressure data given below in § 5 (Table XI). See however, the discussion of the thermodynamic scale below 90° K by Moessen, Aston, and Ascah (1954).

Other useful secondary points are the boiling-point of nitrogen at about 77·36° K and the normal sublimation temperature of carbon dioxide at −78·51° C (Int.).

It is well to note that there are considerable experimental difficulties associated with the accurate realization of many of these fixed points. In the case of the low-temperature points involving CO_2, O_2, N_2, and H_2, there are not only the problems of purity to be considered but also those of supercooling or superheating. Detailed references to these and other fixed points,

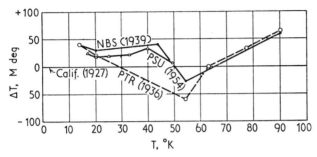

Fig. 57. A comparison of temperature scales: Calif., University of California; NBS, National Bureau of Standards; PSU, Pennsylvania State University; PTR, Physikalisch-Technische Reichsanstalt (after Scott, 1955).

and also the problems of their determination have been given by Hoge (1941) and Scott (1941) (cf. also Kannuluik and Law, 1946, on the realization of the CO_2 fixed point).

4. Gas thermometry

Introduction

Of all forms of precision thermometry, high-precision gas thermometry would seem the most demanding and has therefore remained the province of a mere handful of laboratories. Apart from the difficulties of correcting for the non-ideality of the gas used and at low pressures for the thermo-molecular pressure difference—both of which are discussed briefly at the end of this section—there are many other corrections and difficulties to be overcome; some details of the Leiden and Berlin gas thermometers are given by Keesom (1942), and recently Beattie (1955) has described the M.I.T. precision gas thermometer. In the proceedings of the 1939 Conference on *Temperature Its Measurements and Control in Science and Industry* (Reinhold

Publishing Corp. N.Y., 1941) various authors have discussed the salient features of gas thermometry at both low and high temperatures.

Neither the scope of this book nor the author make it appropriate to deal in detail with such precision gas thermometry, but some details of the less accurate but more common types of gas thermometer used in everyday low-temperature research are of considerable interest. Gas thermometry in its simpler form not only gives results directly in terms of absolute temperature and has a sensitivity which can be increased by using higher filling pressures at lower temperatures but is unaffected by magnetic fields and is easily adapted to differential thermometry, i.e. measurement of small temperature differences.

Simon's gas thermometer

Figure 58 shows the particularly simple form due to Simon (see Ruhemann, 1937) in which the thermometer, usually helium gas-filled, is essentially constant volume due to the very small change in volume of the Bourdon spiral in the pressure gauge B. The bulb A which is at the low temperature to be measured, has volume V and is connected by a fine capillary to the gauge of volume v. This is simply a vacuum dial gauge which for more accurate results can be a calibrated standard gauge, capable of reproducing its readings to $\frac{1}{10}$ per cent of full-scale deflexion.

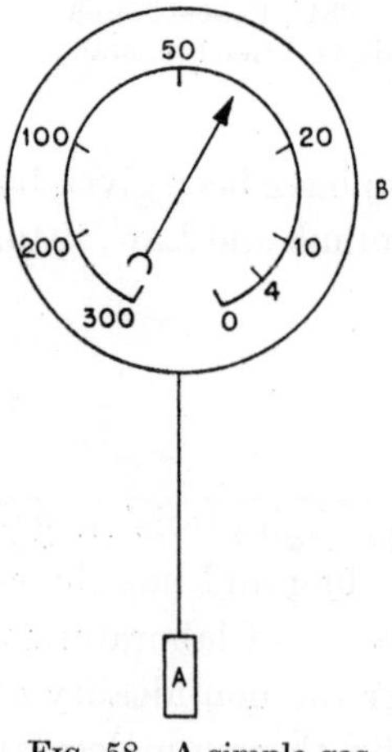

FIG. 58. A simple gas thermometer.

If we assume the thermometric gas is 'perfect' within the required limits of accuracy, then for a constant mass of gas,

$$\frac{pV}{T} = \text{constant.}$$

The system may be filled to a pressure p_0 at room temperature T_0; then, neglecting the capillary volume, the pressure p at a temperature T is given by

$$\frac{pv}{T_0}+\frac{pV}{T} = \frac{p_0 v}{T_0}+\frac{p_0 V}{T_0},$$

whence

$$p = p_0\frac{(v+V)T}{VT_0+vT} \tag{23}$$

or

$$\frac{1}{T}(VT_0)+v = \frac{1}{p}(p_0 v+p_0 V). \tag{24}$$

If one or if neither of the volumes v and V are known, they can be found by calibrating the system using two or three known temperatures. Then (23) can be used to determine the unknown temperature T from the pressure reading p. Alternatively, from (24) a graph of $1/T$ against $1/p$ can be drawn using two (or three as a check) experimental values of T, p obtained by immersing the bulb A in liquids of known temperature, e.g. liquid helium, liquid nitrogen, and liquid oxygen.

As discussed by Woodcock (1938), the sensitivity of this type of thermometer can be increased considerably at low temperatures by making v large in comparison with V. Then only at low temperatures will the majority of the gas be in the bulb A, so that at high temperatures it is very insensitive to change in T (but unfortunately sensitive to changes in room temperature T_0). Therefore the scale on the gauge in Figure 58 can be expanded at the low-temperature end as much as desired by making v/V sufficiently large. In such cases the thermometer is of little use at higher temperatures, although it may be capable of an accuracy of $\pm\frac{1}{20}°$ K at temperatures below 30° K.

Note that if a linear dependence of p on T is required, so that the sensitivity is more or less independent of the temperature, then V must be large in comparison with v; this means physically that the major part of the helium gas is in the variable temperature bulb A at all temperatures and therefore to a first approximation p is proportional to T.

Oil or mercury manometer

A more accurate variant of this latter situation (where $V \gg v$) is shown in Figure 59; a thermometer bulb (volume V, temperature T) is connected by 0·5 mm outer diameter (0·3 mm inner diameter) German-silver capillary tubing to a glass mano-meter. This constant volume manometer is filled with mercury or butyl phthalate and the liquid is adjusted to the fiducial mark 'O' in the right-hand arm by means of the liquid reservoir below. Butyl phthalate, which has a density of about 1·04 g/cm³, is very suitable and allows the use of a brass sylphon bellows for the reservoir and capillary tubing (say, 1·5 mm bore) in the mano-meter. Due to the effects of surface tension in these capillary tubes, it is advisable to use precision bore tubing (e.g. 'Veridia' from Chance Bros. (England) or precision bore Pyrex from H. S. Martin, Illinois, or Wilmad Glass Company, New Jersey) particu-larly for differential thermometry when a second short manometer arm is added to the system. Mercury has certain advantages as a manometer fluid as it is easily outgassed of air and does not absorb helium, but it requires a wider bore manometer tubing (at least 10 mm inner diameter) and a slightly

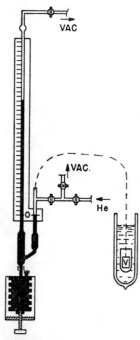

FIG. 59. A constant-volume gas thermometer.

different form of adjustable reservoir, e.g. a stainless steel piston sealed with an O-ring, moving in a stainless steel cylinder.

We may generalize the formulae given above to include the case where the dead volume v is at room temperature t, and the system is filled to a pressure p_0 at a fixed point T_0 other than room temperature; then $T(p)$ is given by

$$\frac{T}{p} = \frac{T_0}{p_0}\left(\frac{1+vT/Vt}{1+vT_0/Vt}\right) = \frac{T_0}{P_0}\frac{(1+\Delta)}{(1+\Delta_0)}. \qquad (25)$$

In the cryostat used by the writer, the copper bulb of volume V is limited by the experimental conditions to about 5 cm³ capacity and then v is made small, usually 0.5–1.0 cm^3. The value of V is found by volume measurement or from the construction, and v is found from (25) by filling at $T_0 = 273°\,$K or $T_0 = 295°\,$K and then cooling to $90°$ or $77°$ K. Having found v, and assuming that t always remains $295°$ K (an air-conditioned room), a convenient table of $(1+\Delta)/(1+\Delta_0)$ is drawn up for various temperatures, e.g. for $T_0 = 295°$ K, $T_0 = 77.3°$ K, $T_0 = 4.2°$ K. Finally the pressure p is read by means of a reflecting glass scale marked from 0 to 100 cm with lines 1 mm apart; such scales are commercially available.

Used in this way, the thermometer gives readings which appear to be correct to $\pm\frac{1}{20}°$ K in the range $90°$–$55°$ K over which it can be checked against the vapour pressure of liquid oxygen. Again, from $4.2°$ to $1.8°$ K it is correct to $\frac{1}{100}°$ K. By checking with a calibrated platinum resistance thermometer, the scale is correct within the limit of reading from $90°$ up to about $140°$ K and from $4°$ up to about $20°$ K.

However, if the thermometer bulb is near, say, $40°$ K and (Figure 59) part of the connecting capillary is in liquid helium, then with small bulbs a substantial fraction of the gas is in the capillary (even if it is only 0.3 mm inner diameter); corrections should be applied if the temperature is to be known to an accuracy of 2 per cent or better. This, of course, depends on the relative dimensions of the bulb and capillary; the use of larger thermometer bulbs reduces such corrections. Between room temperature and about $100°$ K it is advisable to correct for the contraction of the thermometer bulb as the total change in bulb volume amounts to about 1 per cent in cooling from room temperature to $100°$ K.

A differential manometer

For measurement of thermoelectric power or thermal conductivity, small temperature differences are measured and a gas thermometer of the type just discussed is easily adapted (see Figure 60). For this, the absolute temperature T_A and T_B of two thermometer bulbs A and B are read as before by measuring the height h in centimetres of oil with respect to the fiducial mark 'O'. Then

$$\frac{T}{p_{(\text{cm oil})}} = \frac{T_0}{p_{0(\text{cm oil})}} \frac{1+\Delta}{1+\Delta_0}.$$

If the cross-sectional area of the bore of the capillary tube is
A cm², it is easily shown that

$$\frac{\delta T}{\delta p} = \frac{T}{p}\left(1+\frac{vT}{Vt}\right) + \frac{AT^2}{Vt} \quad \text{where } \delta T = T_A - T_B \text{ and } \delta p = \delta h_{\text{cm oil}},$$

whence
$$\frac{\delta T}{\delta p} = \frac{T_0(1+\Delta)^2}{P_0(1+\Delta_0)} + \frac{AT^2}{Vt}. \tag{26}$$

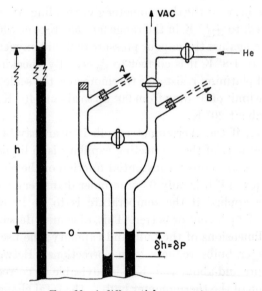

FIG. 60. A differential manometer.

By tabulating $(1+\Delta)^2/(1+\Delta_0)$ for the different values of T_0
normally used and also tabulating AT^2/Vt, $\delta T/\delta p$ can be quickly
read off the table and the conversion from δh to δT made. The
small difference δp is usually read with a cathetometer although
we have found that where $\delta h \leqslant \frac{1}{2}$ in. a geodetic survey level, e.g.
Wild N3 level, can be used more speedily and gives δh to $\pm\frac{1}{100}$ mm
with less trouble in levelling.

Butyl phthalate manometers similar to the type shown in
Figure 60 were described by Hulm (1950). Note that such gas

TABLE IX

Example of table for use with gas thermometer

(Dead volume $v = 1\cdot29$ cm³, $V = 4\cdot46$ cm³, $t = 295°$ K, and $1\cdot5$ mm
inner diameter glass capillary is used in manometer)

For $T_0 = 77\cdot3°$ K				For $T_0 = 4\cdot2°$ K			
T	$\dfrac{1+\Delta}{1+\Delta_0}$	$\dfrac{(1+\Delta)^2}{(1+\Delta_0)}$	$\dfrac{AT^2}{Vt}$	T	$\dfrac{1+\Delta}{1+\Delta_0}$	$\dfrac{(1+\Delta)^2}{(1+\Delta_0)}$	$\dfrac{AT^2}{Vt}$
50	0·979	1·022	0·034	2	0·998	1·000	..
60	0·984	1·042	0·048	5	1·001	1·006	..
70	0·993	1·061	0·066	10	1·006	1·016	0·001
80	1·001	1·079	0·086	15	1·011	1·026	0·003
90	1·011	1·099	0·109	20	1·016	1·036	0·005
100	1·020	1·119	0·135				

thermometers have the merit that by refilling to a suitable pressure at $4\cdot2°$ K they can be used with a high sensitivity in the liquid-helium temperature range as well as at higher temperatures. Their sensitivity as a differential thermometer may be increased by using mercury for the total pressure measurement (h) and oil for the difference measurement (δh). A variant of this was described by Mendelssohn and Pontius (1937) in which the mercury manometer and differential oil manometer are separate. In either case, the use of mercury allows a total pressure to be used which is about ten times larger than is possible with an oil column of the same height, but the lower density liquid, oil, is still used for measuring small differences in temperature.

Summarizing the precautions to be observed in this form of practical gas thermometry, we note:

(i) Correction for dead volume v, included in the formulae above.

(ii) Requirement that the temperature of the manometer (usually room temperature) be kept fairly constant, particularly when vT is comparable with Vt; at very low temperatures $Vt \gg vT$ and the problem is not significant.

(iii) Necessity for uniform bore tubing to avoid capillarity corrections.

(iv) Contraction of thermometer bulb which may be important at temperatures above that of liquid nitrogen.

(v) Correction for volume of gas in the connecting capillaries which may be in a temperature gradient. This is a more difficult correction to make and is largely avoided by making V very large in comparison with the volume of the capillary. In cases where the capillary is partially at $4 \cdot 2°$ K and the thermometer bulbs are at a much higher temperature, this can cause a substantial error.

However, temperatures can be measured with an inaccuracy of a few parts per thousand over a quite wide temperature range by these methods without any arduous precautions and purely by reference to two or three easily available fixed points.

Corrections for a non-perfect gas and for thermo-molecular pressure difference

Before leaving the subject of gas thermometry it is pertinent to illustrate the magnitude of the corrections that may arise from non-ideality of the gas and from thermo-molecular pressure differences.

If the equation of state of a gas is expressed as

$$pv = A(1 + Bp + \text{terms in } p^2, \text{ etc.}),$$

the virial coefficients B, etc., can be found experimentally and can be used to correct the real gas scale to the true thermodynamic scale. Whereas the third and fourth virial coefficients are very small, the second virial coefficient B has values (see Table X after Keesom, 1942) which even for helium can produce a significant correction to the gas scale, particularly at high pressures and low temperatures.

TABLE X

$T°K$	2·6	4·0	14·0	22·0	50	100	300
$10^3 B$	−5·30	−3·61	−0·549	−0·101	+0·338	+0·492	+0·508

The deviations of the standard constant-volume helium gas scale (using $p_0 = 1$ m Hg at $0°$ C) from the thermodynamic scale are shown in Figure 61 below (after Hoge, 1941).

The other correction due to thermomolecular pressure difference arises when the mean free path of the gas molecules is sufficiently large to be comparable with the width of the capillary connecting the thermometer bulb to the manometer; that is, at very low pressures there is a difference in pressure between the ends of the capillary tube when a temperature difference exists between the bulb and the manometer. Our knowledge of the magnitude of this effect is largely a result of experimental

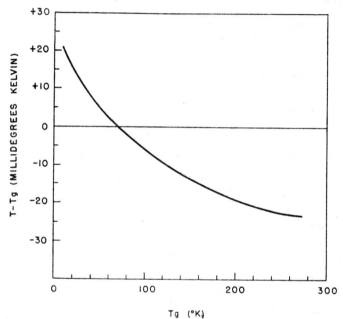

FIG. 61. Deviations of the helium-gas scale (T_g) from the thermo-dynamic scale (T) for $p_0 = 1$ m Hg.

work done at Leiden (see Keesom 1942, for summary and references). This work indicates that for helium in the hydro-dynamic region, i.e. when the diameter of the capillary $2R$ is greater than the mean free path, the thermomolecular pressure difference Δp is given by

$$\frac{\Delta p}{p} = 724 \cdot 2 \frac{1}{(Rp)^2} \left\{ 1 - \left(\frac{T_2}{273 \cdot 1} \right)^{2 \cdot 294} \right\}. \qquad (27)$$

This assumes that the temperature at the hot (manometer) end is 273·1° K, T_2 is the temperature at the cold end, R is in centimetres and p in microbars. Thus, if $T_2 = 4 \cdot 2° \text{K}$, $R = 1$ mm, and $p \simeq 1$ cm Hg ($\simeq 13{,}000 \ \mu\text{b}$), then $\Delta p/p \sim 4 \times 10^{-4}$.

In most thermometry applications this correction is negligible, but in some vapour-pressure measurements where the total pressure p is of the order of $\frac{1}{10}$ mm Hg or less, the mean free path for helium atoms may be comparable with the tube width. At $\frac{1}{10}$ mm pressure, the mean free path in helium is about $\frac{1}{100}$ mm at $4°$ K, $\frac{3}{10}$ mm at $80°$ K, and ~ 1 mm at room temperature; in some of these cases the correction Δp becomes considerable and the 'hydrodynamic region' formula above is no longer applicable (see Keesom, 1942). For further data on the 'intermediate' region—between the hydrodynamic and the Knudsen regions—the reader is referred to Keesom (1942) or Roberts and Sydoriak (1956). These latter authors at the Los Alamos Scientific Laboratory have measured thermomolecular pressure ratios for He^3 and also calculated a series of values for He^4 from the Weber–Schmidt equation; they have circulated some of these data privately in a very convenient graphical form.

5. Vapour pressure thermometry

Introduction

The vapour pressure of a liquefied gas is a rapidly varying function of the temperature and therefore forms a convenient secondary thermometer. Fortunately the vapour pressures of the commonly used liquids have been measured and tabulated as a function of the absolute thermodynamic temperature so that they form a reliable series of 'primary' scales of temperature for many low-temperature physicists. Thus over the respective temperature ranges from $1°$ to $4 \cdot 2°$ K, $14°$ to $20°$ K, $55°$ to $90°$ K, $63°$ to $77°$ K, the vapour pressures of liquid helium, hydrogen, oxygen, and nitrogen can be used to calibrate resistance or thermoelectric thermometers and to check the accuracy of gas thermometers.

Theoretically the vapour pressure of a liquid may be obtained by integration of the Clausius–Clapeyron relation

$$\frac{dP}{dT} = \frac{\Delta S}{\Delta V} = \frac{L}{T \Delta V},$$

where ΔV is the change in volume at vaporization and L is the latent heat.

If L is constant, $$\log P = \frac{A}{T} + B,$$

and more generally, if L is a linear function of temperature,

$$L = L_0 + aT;$$

therefore $$\log P = \frac{A}{T} + B \log T + c. \qquad (28)$$

Although equations of this type can be fitted quite closely to the experimental values of vapour pressure, it is usually convenient to tabulate P as a function of T and use such a table to find $T(P)$ from experimental values of the vapour pressure.

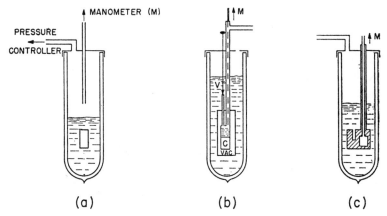

Fig. 62. Vapour-pressure measurement.

Some typical experimental situations in which vapour pressure is measured are sketched schematically above (Figure 62). In (a) a liquid is boiling under atmospheric or some controlled pressure and the vapour pressure above the surface is measured by a tube which leads to a pressure gauge. In such an instance temperature inhomogeneities in the liquid may make the recorded vapour pressure a rather poor indication of the true temperature at points within the liquid.

The second case (b) shows a fairly common type of cryostat in which the inner space C has a small chamber attached which can be filled with liquid from the dewar through the valve V. A tube connected to the pressure gauge at one end is taken down to a point close to the surface of the liquid in the small chamber. This liquid may be boiling under atmospheric or under reduced pressure. If this chamber is of a good heat-conducting metal (e.g. copper), and there are no points along the sampling tube which are colder than the liquid in the chamber, then the vapour pressure will form a good indication of the liquid temperature. However, in either of these cases (a) or (b) a trace of impurity in the liquid will affect the result markedly, e.g. a trace of oxygen in nitrogen or vice versa alters considerably the vapour pressure of the liquid at a given temperature. For accurate calibration of other thermometric instruments, the type of cryostat shown in Figure 62 (c) is commonly used. Here a copper block is immersed in the liquefied gas and a small hole or capsule in the copper block forms a vapour-pressure bulb into which pure gas is condensed. The tube which transmits the vapour pressure to an external manometer is prevented from touching the outer liquid bath, which may have 'cold' spots or regions at a lower temperature than the condensed phase in the bulb; this tube can be wound with an electrical heater if it appears likely that the surrounding liquid is appreciably colder than the pure liquid in the inner chamber. Additional holes in the copper block allow insertion of resistance thermometers, gas thermometers, thermocouples, etc., which may be under test.

As may be realized from the discussion of ortho-para conversion in Chapter II, liquid hydrogen presents a special problem in so far as normal H_2 (75 per cent ortho, 25 per cent para) boils under standard pressure at $20 \cdot 39°$ K, while equilibrium-H_2 (practically pure para-hydrogen in thermodynamic equilibrium at its boiling-point) boils at $20 \cdot 27°$ K. However, for most purposes, if pure hydrogen gas taken from a room-temperature reservoir is condensed into the bulb, its boiling-point will remain quite close to $20 \cdot 39°$ K for some hours. If a very precise determination is required, then a small quantity of a suitable catalyst such as of neodymium oxide, ferric hydroxide gel, or chromic anhydride (see Chapter II and Los and Morrison, 1951) may be placed in the bulb; then by allowing an hour or so to elapse before measurement, it may be assumed that the liquid present is equilibrium-H_2.

For purposes of pressure measurement, a mercury column or accurate dial gauge (e.g. Budenberg standard vacuum gauge or a Wallace and Teirnan gauge) may be used at normal pressures, and an oil manometer, McLeod gauge, or hot-wire gauge for lower pressures.

As was mentioned in the previous section, the effect of the thermo-molecular pressure difference must be taken into account when the pressure to be measured is sufficiently low that the mean free path of the gas molecules becomes comparable with the diameter of the connecting tubes. As a guide to when this condition is liable to arise, it may be noted that at room temperature, the mean free path l for most gases is of the order of 100 cm at 10^{-4} mm Hg; hence, being inversely proportional to pressure, $l \sim 1$ cm at 10^{-2} mm Hg, 1 mm at 10^{-1} mm Hg, and $\frac{1}{10}$ mm at 1 mm Hg pressure; l decreases with temperature as T^m where the exponent m has values of 1·1–1·3 for most gases.

By using tubes $\frac{1}{2}$ cm or more in diameter, the corrections are made negligible unless measurements of vapour pressure are extended to the range well below 1 mm Hg. A detailed discussion of these corrections in the hydrodynamic, intermediate, and molecular (or Knudsen) regions have been given by Keesom (1942) in the case of helium.

Data

Table XI below contains data for the vapour pressure of liquid helium, hydrogen, nitrogen, and oxygen.

A very useful compilation of vapour-pressure data including that for neon has been given by Linder (1950). However, his data for helium are from the 1948 scale, i.e. from the vapour-pressure-temperature data for liquid helium agreed upon by representatives of various cryogenic laboratories in 1948, based on earlier work in Leiden and measurements below 1·6° K by Bleaney and Simon at Oxford. Since that time there has been an experimental re-examination and major revision of the

TABLE XI. *Vapour pressure*

p (mm Hg)	⁴He (20°C mm Hg) Scale T_{55E} Clement, Logan, & Gaffney (1955)	Equilibrium-H₂ (0°C mm Hg) Woolley, Scott, & Brickwedde (1948)	Normal-H₂ (0°C mm Hg) Woolley, Scott, & Brickwedde (1948)	N₂ (0°C mm Hg) Armstrong (1954) ($T > 63.2°K$) Keesom & Bijl (1937) ($T < 63.2°K$)	O₂ (0°C mm Hg) Hoge (1950a)
800	4.265_2° K	20.44° K	20.56° K	..	90.69
780	4.238_1	20.37	20.48	77.58° K	90.43
760	4.210_5	20.27_3	20.39_0	77.36_4	90.18
740	4.182_4	20.18	20.30	77.14	89.93
720	4.153_8	20.09	20.21	76.91	89.67
700	4.124_6	20.00	20.11	76.67	89.41
680	4.094_8	19.90	20.02	76.43	89.14
660	4.064_5	19.80	19.92	76.18	88.86
640	4.033_5	19.70	19.82_5	76.93	88.58
620	4.001_8	19.60	19.72	75.68	88.29
600	3.969_4	19.50	19.62	75.41	87.99
580	3.936_3	19.40	19.52	75.13	87.69
560	3.902_4	19.30	19.41	74.85	87.38
540	3.867_6	19.18_5	19.30	74.56	87.06
520	3.832_0	19.06_5	19.18_5	74.27	86.72
500	3.795_4	18.94	19.06	73.97	86.37
480	3.757_8	18.82	18.94_5	73.66	86.01
460	3.719_1	18.69	18.82	73.34	85.65
440	3.679_2	18.57	18.69	73.00	85.29
420	3.638_2	18.43_5	18.55	72.66	84.89
400	3.595_7	18.29	18.40_5	72.30	84.48
380	3.551_9	18.15	18.26	71.92	84.06
360	3.506_4	18.00	18.11	71.54	83.62
340	3.459_1	17.83_5	17.96	71.13	83.16
320	3.410_0	17.67	17.79	70.70	82.68
300	3.358_7	17.50	17.62	70.25	82.18
290	3.332_2	17.41_5	17.53	70.01	81.92
280	3.305_1	17.32_5	17.43_5	69.77	81.65
270	3.277_3	17.22	17.34	69.53	81.36
260	3.248_8	17.13	17.25	69.28	81.07
250	3.219_6	17.03	17.15	69.02	80.78
240	3.189_5	16.93	17.05	68.75	80.48
230	3.158_6	16.82_5	16.94	68.48	80.16
220	3.126_6	16.71_5	16.83_5	68.18	79.83
210	3.094_0	16.61	16.71_5	67.88	79.49
200	3.060_1	16.49	16.60	67.57	79.14
190	3.025_1	16.36	16.48_5	67.25	78.77
180	2.988_8	16.23_5	16.36_5	66.91	78.39
170	2.951_2	16.10	16.23	66.56	77.98
160	2.911_9	15.97	16.10	66.20	77.57
150	2.871_0	15.83	15.95	65.81	77.13
140	2.828_2	15.68	15.80	65.42	76.65
130	2.783_3	15.52	15.64	64.98	76.16
120	2.735_9	15.35	15.47	65.52	75.64
110	2.685_9	15.18	15.29	64.03	75.08
100	2.632_6	15.00	15.10	63.50†	74.47

† Triple point at 63.15° K (94.0 mm Hg) from Keesom and Bijl (1937).

TABLE XI (cont.)

p (mm Hg)	^{4}He (20°C mm Hg) Scale T_{55E} Clement, Logan, & Gaffney (1955)	Equilibrium-H$_2$ (0°C mm Hg) Woolley, Scott, & Brickwedde (1948)	Normal-H$_2$ (0°C mm Hg) Woolley, Scott, & Brickwedde (1948)	N$_2$ (0°C mm Hg) Armstrong (1954) ($T > 63.2°K$) Keesom & Bijl (1937) ($T < 63.2°K$)	O$_2$ (0° C mm Hg) Hoge (1950a)
90	$2.575_5°$ K	$14.77°$ K	$14.89°$ K	$62.94°$ K	73.80
80	2.514_0	14.56	14.68	62.39	73.09
70	2.447_0	14.30	14.42	61.77	72.29
60	2.373_0	14.04	14.15	61.06	71.39
50	2.290_0	13.73†	13.83‡	60.24	70.39
45	2.244_1	13.57_5	13.67	..	69.81
40	2.194_5§	13.40	13.51	59.28	69.15
35	2.140_6	13.21	13.30	..	68.46
30	2.081_9	12.99	13.09	58.08	67.67
25	2.016_7	12.74	12.85	..	66.74
20	1.942_2	12.46	12.57	56.48	65.67
18	1.908_8	12.32	12.43	..	65.17
16	1.872_7	12.17_5	12.28	55.65	64.59
14	1.833_3	12.02	12.11_5	..	64.00
12	1.789_4	11.83	11.92	..	63.32
10	1.739_9	11.62	11.72	..	62.50
9	1.712_4	11.50	11.59	..	62.07
8	1.682_5	11.36	11.47	..	61.58
7	1.649_6	11.23	11.34	..	61.01
6	1.613_0	11.08	11.17	..	60.39
5	1.571_4	10.88	10.98	..	59.68
4	1.522_9	10.65	10.76	..	58.80
3.5	1.495_1	10.53	10.64	..	58.29
3.0	1.464_1	10.38	10.50	..	57.73
2.5	1.428_7	10.23	10.32	..	57.06
2.0	1.387_3	10.02	10.12	..	56.28
1.5	1.336_8	..	..	..	55.28‖
1.0	1.270_9				
0.9	1.254_6				
0.8	1.236_8				
0.7	1.217_2				
0.6	1.195_2				
0.5	1.170_0				
0.4	1.140_4				
0.3	1.104_2				
0.2	1.056_3				
0.1	0.982_4				
0.08	0.960_4				
0.06	0.933_4				
0.04	0.897_6				
0.02	0.841_6				
0.01	0.791_5				

† Triple point at $13.81_3°$ K (52.8 mm Hg).
‡ Triple point at $13.95_7°$ K (54.0 mm Hg).
§ λ-point at $2.173_5°$ K (38.002 mm Hg 20° C).
‖ Triple point at 54.36° K (1.14 mm Hg).

helium scale, undertaken both in Leiden and in the United States. As a result of this work (summarized by Hudson, 1955, and critically analysed recently by Keller, 1956) two scales have been produced by Clement, Logan, and Gaffney (1955) and Van Dijk and Durieux (1955), respectively denoted as scales T'_{55_E} and $T_{L_{55}}$; these scales differ from the 1948 scale by as much as a hundredth of a degree near the λ-point and again by two-hundredths at about 5° K, the differences at intermediate temperatures and temperatures below 2° K being generally $\leqslant 0 \cdot 005°$ K. The Clement scale T_{55_E} has been calculated from an analytic relation based on available experimental evidence while that of Van Dijk is a thermodynamic relation, in which experimental values for the thermodynamic constants have been used. The two scales differ by not more than 3 milli-degrees up to 4·5° K but the Van Dijk scale $T_{L_{55}}$ appears to be at variance with the Berman and Swenson (1954) vapour-pressure data in the region close to the critical temperature of 5·19° K. At the Paris Low Temperature Conference in 1955 (see, for example, Brickwedde, 1955; and also Keller, 1956) no general agreement on the adoption of one scale or the other was reached, but instead it was recommended that both scales were of considerable value and should be used as desired by the individual research worker, until such future time as further data and examination of existing data might permit the adoption of a single scale.

Copies of these two scales have been circulated by Clement (U.S. Naval Research Laboratory, Washington) and Van Dijk (Kamerlingh Onnes Laboratory, Leiden) and the scale reproduced here in Table XI is an abbreviated form of Clement's T'_{55_E}.

Gravity and temperature corrections

Readings of vapour pressure recorded from a 'liquid column' pressure gauge are subject to gravity and temperature corrections. Therefore for precise measurements in cases where the value of the acceleration due to gravity g, is substantially different from that at sea-level at latitude 45°, or where the temperature of the mercury column is substantially different from that used in the table, correction is necessary. Those values given in Table XI for helium are in terms of 20° C mm Hg, and the values for N_2, O_2, and H_2 are expressed as a function of standard millimetres of Hg (0° C).

Gravity corrections, which are usually extremely small, are given in various physical tables (e.g. *Smithsonian Physical Tables*, 9th revised edition (1954), p. 608) and are simply proportional to the difference between the acceleration due to gravity g, at the place considered and standard gravity, 980·665 cm sec^{-2}.† Hence the correction to barometric height h is

$$\Delta h = +\frac{(g-980\cdot665)}{980\cdot665} \times h. \qquad (29)$$

Similarly, the correction Δh due to a difference in temperature ΔT between the barometric column in question and the standard column referred to in the tabulation, is proportional to ΔT, i.e.

$$\Delta h = -\alpha\Delta T . h. \qquad (30)$$

For a mercury column and glass scale, this correction constant $\alpha = 0\cdot000172$ per ° C and for a mercury column and brass scale $\alpha = 0\cdot000163$ per ° C (see, for example, *Smithsonian Physical Tables*, 9th revised edition (1954), p. 607).

6. Electrical resistance of metallic elements

Introduction

In a metal, the free electrons responsible for electrical conduction are scattered by imperfections in the crystal lattice and by the thermal vibrations of the lattice. These processes limit the conductivity and so determine the electrical resistivity ρ. This resistivity is a function of the number of free electrons per atom n, the velocity of the electrons v, the electronic charge e, and the effective mean free path. The mean free path l, being partly limited by thermal vibrations whose amplitude is temperature-dependent, is itself therefore a temperature-dependent quantity. The charge e is a constant and n and v are practically independent of temperature so that this effective mean free path is the

† The figure of 980·665 is the standard value adopted in 1901 for use in barometer reductions and is quite close to the value for normal gravity at sea-level at latitude 45°.

principal factor in determining the temperature variation of electrical resistance.

We may define a resistivity ρ_r due to the static imperfections—either chemical impurities or physical impurities—and a resistivity ρ_i caused by thermal vibrations. Due to the static character of the impurities, ρ_i is the quantity which we expect

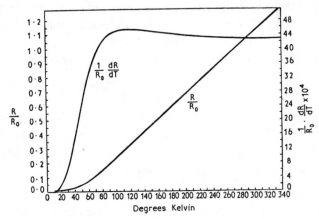

FIG. 63. Variation of resistance ratio and the temperature coefficient of resistance with temperature for a copper resistance thermometer (after Dauphinee and Preston-Thomas, 1954).

to change with temperature and the total resistivity may be written, assuming the validity of Matthiessen's rule,

$$\rho = \rho_r + \rho_i. \tag{31}$$

The thermometric property with which we are concerned is therefore ρ_i and $d\rho_i/dT$ determines the sensitivity of the electrical resistance thermometer. ρ_i for most metallic elements is approximately proportional to temperature down to temperatures in the vicinity of $\theta_D/3$; θ_D is the Debye characteristic temperature. Below this ρ_i decreases more rapidly with temperature and between about $\theta_D/10$ and $\theta_D/50$ (the lower limit of reliable investigation) $\rho_i \propto T^n$, where $3 < n < 5$. Therefore at very low temperature, the sensitivity of electrical resistance as a thermometric element decreases rapidly (Figure 63 after Dauphinee and Preston-Thomas, 1954), and even in the case of metallic elements of the highest available purity $\rho_i \ll \rho_r$ at temperatures in the vicinity of $\theta_D/100$. This enables us to determine ρ_r, which experimentally appears to be constant at the very low-temperature end of the scale.†

It is fairly obvious that the ideal metallic element for use as a resistance thermometer should have the following properties:

(i) A resistivity ρ_i which has a variation with T at higher temperatures which is as close to linear as possible; this simplifies the task of interpolation considerably.

(ii) For low-temperature use, the θ_D should be as low as possible so as to preserve a high sensitivity to a low temperature.

(iii) The element should be obtainable in a state of high purity so that ρ_r will be insignificant over a wide temperature range.

(iv) It should be a metal which is chemically inert and should have a high stability of resistance, so that its calibration is retained over long periods of time and not affected by thermal cycling.

(v) It must be capable of being mechanically worked, i.e. drawn into wire and wound into required forms.

The noble metal platinum fulfils most of these requirements quite adequately although from the low-temperature viewpoint its range of usefulness would be much greater if its Debye temperature were lower. However, metals like lead, bismuth, or gallium which have a low characteristic temperature ($\theta_D \simeq 100°$ K, cf. for Pt, $\theta_D \simeq 225°$ K) are rather unsuitable for other reasons.

Platinum thermometers

In § 4.3 we mentioned the use of the platinum resistance thermometer for realizing the international temperature scale between $-182\cdot97°$ and $630°$ C, using the formulae

$$t = \frac{1}{\alpha} \frac{R_t - R_0}{R_0} + \delta \frac{t}{100}\left(\frac{t}{100} - 1\right) + \beta\left(\frac{t}{100}\right)^3\left(\frac{t}{100} - 1\right) \qquad (32)$$

$$\text{for } -182\cdot97 < t < 0° \text{ C}$$

† Some metallic elements become superconducting, i.e. their total electrical resistance falls sharply to zero at a critical temperature, and this may prevent an accurate estimate of ρ_r.

and
$$t = \frac{1}{\alpha}\frac{R_t - R_0}{R_0} + \delta\frac{t}{100}\left(\frac{t}{100} - 1\right) \tag{33}$$

for $t > 0°$ C.

For a precision thermometer used to realize the international temperature scale, $\alpha = \{(R_{100}/R_0) - 1\}/100$ must have a value greater than 0·00391, a figure which corresponds approximately to a ratio of $\rho_r/\rho_{0°\text{C}}$ less than about 4×10^{-3}. The constants δ and β representing the departure of R_t from a linear dependence on temperature are determined by measuring R at the sulphur and oxygen points respectively. These and other requirements have been discussed in detail by Mueller (1941), Hall (1955), and Stimson (1955).

Alternatives to the Callendar forms of the resistance equations are the following:
$$R_t = R_0(1 + At + Bt^2); \quad t > 0°\text{ C} \tag{34}$$
$$R_t = R_0[1 + At + Bt^2 + C(t - 100)t^3]; \quad t < 0°\text{ C.} \tag{35}$$
These forms have certain advantages particularly when the '100° C' calibration point is significantly different from 100·000° C. The constants may be related to those in the Callendar equations:

$$A = \alpha(1 + \delta/100) \quad \text{and} \quad \alpha = A + 100B$$
$$B = -\alpha\delta/100^2 \qquad \qquad \delta = -100^2 B/(A + 100B)$$
$$C = -\alpha\beta/100^4 \qquad \qquad \beta = -100^4 C/(A + 100B).$$

A convenient method of calculating temperature t from R_t has been given by Schwab and Smith (1945). They suggest that a graph of R_t versus t be drawn from which a trial value of $t = t_1$ may be obtained. By substituting for t_1 in the equation
$$t_2 = \frac{(R_t/R_0) - 1}{A + Bt_1 + C(t_1 - 100)t_1^2} \qquad t < 0°\text{ C}$$
a much better value $t = t_2$ is obtained; if t_1 is correct to within 1° C, t_2 will be correct to 0·003° C down to $-25°$ C and to 0·057° C at $-190°$ C. Using a rather more complicated form
$$t_2 = \frac{(R_t/R_0) - 1 + Bt_1^2 + C(3t_1 - 200)t_1^3}{A + 2Bt_1 + C(4t_1 - 300)t_1^2}$$

a value for t_2 correct to $0\cdot001°$ C may be calculated if t_1 is correct to 2° C. Schwab and Smith give a table of values of $(3t_1-200)t_1^3$, $(4t_1-300)t_1^2$, etc., as a function of the trial temperature t_1, which assists considerably in calculating t_2.

An alternative and somewhat simpler method of converting from R_t to t is due to Werner and Frazer (1952). They have tabulated at 1° intervals from $-190°$ to 600° C, calculated values of R/R_0 for a thermometer having $\alpha = 0\cdot0040$, $\delta = 1\cdot493$, $\beta = 0\cdot1090$. By using their table and knowing the real α value a simple computation converts experimental values of R/R_0 into values of temperatures; small corrections due to differences in δ or β are made with the aid of subsidiary tables given by these authors.

The methods of construction which have been found to give a high degree of reproducibility are those in which annealed platinum wire is supported in a protective capsule in a condition of least mechanical constraint and is then re-annealed. In three particularly successful types of thermometers, fine platinum wire $0\cdot005-0\cdot01$ in. diameter of total resistance about 25 ohms at room temperature, is wound into a fine helix and then either (i) freely suspended in a Pyrex U-tube (Barber, 1950, 1955), (ii) supported in a bifilar fashion on opposite sides of a twisted silica ribbon (Russian method described by Stimson, 1955), or (iii) bifilar wound in a second larger helix which is loosely supported on a notched mica cross (Meyers, 1932). With four leads attached the thermometer is then sealed off in a silica, Pyrex, or platinum capsule under a small pressure of oxygen. For low-temperature use, some helium gas must be mixed with the oxygen to ensure good heat dissipation at low temperatures.

More recently Meyers has used straight platinum wire bifilar wound on a closely notched mica cross and a limited number of thermometers have been commercially available.† The American Instrument Company (Maryland) now produce $25\cdot5$-ohm platinum resistance thermometers of this later Meyers type, with a ratio $R_{100}/R_0 \geqslant 1\cdot392$ and encased in glass or in a platinum capsule. Coiled coil platinum thermometers are made by the

† Mr. C. H. Meyers, 6316 Brookside Drive, Rte. 3, Alexandria, Virginia.

Leeds and Northrup Company and recently 100-ohm platinum resistance thermometers of the capsule type have become available from the West German firm of Hartmann & Braun, A. G.; this last thermometer is much less expensive but appears to have a somewhat higher residual resistance ($R_4/R_{273} \simeq 10^{-2}$) in some samples tested. Despite this, it appears to be sufficiently accurate and reproducible for use in routine low-temperature research down to about 20° K.

Procedure at low temperatures

There is as yet no international scale below the oxygen point and no standard procedure defined for measuring such temperatures. Some years ago at the National Bureau of Standards, a series of platinum resistance thermometers of the Meyers type were carefully calibrated against a gas thermometer (Hoge and Brickwedde, 1939) from 14° K to the oxygen point. These thermometers have served as a very useful calibrating medium since that time. However, for those who wish to construct or buy resistance thermometers, and use them at low temperatures without recourse to a N.B.S. or other accurate calibration, the writer suggests the following procedure.

For many measurements, an accuracy of $\pm 0 \cdot 05°$ K suffices. Consider a thermometer (bought or home-made) of high-purity platinum wire: First ensure that it is well annealed and therefore not subject to marked hysteresis on thermal cycling, and measure its ice-point resistance, R_0. If it is to be used in the region from 90° K to room temperature, the constant α should be determined either by measuring R_{100} at the steam point or more simply by checking its resistance R_t in a well-stirred hot-water bath against an accurate sub-standard or standard mercury-in-glass thermometer; then assuming a value of about $1 \cdot 492$ for δ, the appropriate α may be calculated from (33). For subsequent use below the ice point a value for β can be assumed; β usually lies in the range $0 \cdot 109$–$0 \cdot 112$, so that a trial value of $0 \cdot 111$ should meet the demands of required accuracy. Whether in fact these demands are met by the assumed values of β, can be tested by measuring R at the oxygen point and in the intermediate region at the carbon dioxide sublimation point (see Scott, 1941, for methods of using O_2- and CO_2-point baths).

An alternative method, particularly suitable for measurements extending down to lower temperatures where no such equation as that of Callendar and Van Dusen is suitable, is to measure the ice-point and helium-point resistances† (R_{273} and $R_{4\cdot2}$) and then compare $(R_T - R_{4\cdot2})/(R_{273} - R_{4\cdot2})$ with a tabulated function for some standard thermometer. If Matthiessen's additivity rule were strictly valid, i.e. if the electrical resistance were simply the sum of a temperature-independent 'impurity' resistance and a 'thermal' resistance unaffected by the presence of impurities, then a function of the type

$$Z = (R_{T_1} - R_{T_2})/(R_{T_0} - R_{T_2})$$

should be identical for any of a series of thermometers of the same metallic element. The use of such a function was proposed originally by Cragoe and tested at the National Bureau of Standards. In cases where the range $T_0 > T_1 > T_2$ was not too great, say $54\cdot30°$–$90\cdot18°$ K, it appeared very successful. In other cases in which $T_0 = 90\cdot19°$ K and $T_2 = 20\cdot27°$ K, deviations of up to $0\cdot05°$ were found and suggestions were made by Hoge (1950 b) and Van Dijk (1952) for the use of somewhat more complicated functions, e.g. linear combinations of such Z-functions. However, Los and Morrison tested a number of high-purity platinum resistance thermometers between hydrogen and oxygen temperatures and found that the deviations in these, using

$$Z = \frac{R_T - R_{20\cdot273}}{R_{90\cdot190} - R_{20\cdot273}},$$

amounted to less than $\frac{1}{100}°$ K. Therefore, it would appear that such a method of tabulation and measurement can be extremely useful and sufficiently accurate to meet most needs. Since liquid helium is found reposing in storage flasks in most laboratories today, more commonly than is liquid hydrogen, the writer has

† Henceforth the subscript temperatures appearing in the text with R or ρ will be in °K as the discussion concerns low-temperature thermometry, rather than the standard thermometry from $-183°$ to $630°$ C. Also, R_{273} will be used to denote the ice-point resistance which is more strictly $R_{273\cdot15}$ or in the standard thermometrist's usage $-R_0$.

measured the resistance, $R_{4\cdot2}$, of one of the thermometers ($T4$) used by Los and Morrison (1951) and retabulated (Table XII) $Z = (R_T - R_{4\cdot2})/(R_{273} - R_{4\cdot2})$ as a function of the absolute temperature, T. This thermometer $T4$, having an α of $0\cdot0039255$ (and $R_{4\cdot2}/R_{273} = 4\cdot53 \times 10^{-4}$) was calibrated by Morrison (unpublished) against a N.B.S. calibrated thermometer over the temperature range $11°$–$170°$ K, and the tabulated Z-function has simply been recalculated from Morrison's values of R_T/R_{273}.

Thus by taking a suitable thermometer (for which $R_{4\cdot2}/R_{273} \leqslant 3 \times 10^{-3}$), measuring $R_{4\cdot2}$, R_{273}, and then at an unknown temperature T measuring R_T, the factor

$$Z = (R_T - R_{4\cdot2})/(R_{273} - R_{4\cdot2}) \qquad (36)$$

is found which may be checked against the table to yield a value for T; this value should not be in error by more than $0\cdot05°$ K.

Another very useful form of resistance thermometer is that in which an insulated strain-free wire of a suitable metallic element (necessarily isotropic in its thermal expansion) is wound onto a former of the same element, so that differential contraction on cooling is small. Dauphinee and Preston-Thomas (1954) described the use as a thermometer of commercial enamelled copper wire (46 B. & S. gauge), wound and held by baked Formel varnish on a copper calorimeter. They reported a high degree of reproducibility and found that for a number of different thermometers made from the same commercial wire, the deviation from one another in terms of $(R_T - R_{4\cdot2})/(R_{273} - R_{4\cdot2})$ represented considerably less than $0\cdot1°$ K.

In Table XII are tabulated values of the Z-function for copper from their data, and these might be expected to give a useful scale for other thermometers, accurate to $\frac{1}{10}°$ K, provided that the copper wire used is not seriously strained in winding and has a resistance ratio $R_{4\cdot2}/R_{273}$ comparable with $0\cdot01$.

General remarks on metallic elements as thermometers

Before concluding this treatment of the electrical resistance of metallic elements as thermometers, it is perhaps pertinent to consider the possible future development of such thermometers for use in the low-temperature range, particularly from $20°$ K

TABLE XII

$$Z = (R_T - R_{4\cdot2})/(R_{273} - R_{4\cdot2})$$

T, °K	Copper		Platinum	
	Z	$\Delta T/\Delta Z$	Z	$\Delta T/\Delta Z$
295	1·09467	230·8	..	..
273·15	1·00000	236·6	1·00000	..
260	0·94295	229·7	..	..
240	0·85589	228·5	..	..
220	0·76839	227·0	..	..
200	0·68030	225·1	..	..
180	0·59146	223·0	..	..
170	0·54662	221·5	0·581609	241·1
160	0·50148	221·1	0·540114	239·8
150	0·45626	219·2	0·498400	238·5
140	0·41064	218·2	0·456456	237·1
130	0·36482	217·7	0·414269	235·7
120	0·31888	217·6	0·371819	234·1
110	0·27292	218·6	0·329090	232·6
100	0·22718	222·9	0·286063	231·2
90	0·18231	227·8	0·242719	229·8
85	0·16036	233·1	0·220947	230·2
80	0·13891	245·0	0·199215	231·4
75	0·11850	253·0	0·177599	233·2
70	0·09874	269·8	0·156140	235·8
65	0·08021	292·4	0·134928	240·7
60	0·06311	328·1	0·114147	249·2
55	0·04787	379·1	0·094083	261·9
50	0·03468	432·0	0·074982	274·6
48	0·03005	472·8	0·067694	284·1
46	0·02582	497·5	0·060651	295·6
44	0·02180	570·0	0·053881	309·4
42	0·01829	647·2	0·047414	326·2
40	0·01520	743	0·041280	346·6
38	0·01251	816	0·035508	372·3
36	0·01006	943	0·030132	404·4
34	0·00793$_9$	1123	0·025183	445·1
32	0·00615$_9$	1371	0·020688	497·5
30	0·004700	1668	0·016666	565·6
28	0·003501	2045	0·013129	656·2
26	0·002523	2618	0·010079	779·4
24	0·001759	3484	0·007512	951·5
22	0·001185	4556	0·005409	1203
20	0·000746	..	0·003745	1472
19	..	..	0·003066	1705
18	..	..	0·002479	2000
17	..	..	0·001979	2381
16	..	..	0·001558	2862
15	..	..	0·001208	3495
14	..	..	0·000922	4357
13	..	..	0·000692	5447
12	..	..	0·000509	..

down to liquid-helium temperatures. Elements such as platinum, or to a slightly lesser extent copper, gold, silver, and palladium, have the virtue of relatively low Debye temperatures (200°–300° K), high ductility, reproducibility due to their elemental nature and their crystal structure, chemical inactivity (in varying degrees), and they can be obtained in high states of purity, i.e. $\rho_r \simeq \rho_{4\cdot2} \ll \rho_{273}$. However, unless their purity can be increased considerably by zone refining or other techniques so as to reduce chemical impurities to one part per million or less and physical impurities likewise so that ρ_r/ρ_{273} becomes comparable with 10^{-5}, their suitability as thermometers in the range below 10° or 12° K will be limited. As has been shown theoretically by Sondheimer and also experimentally, Matthiessen's rule is not strictly valid in the region where ρ_r and ρ_i are comparable. Hence at temperatures sufficiently low that $\rho_i \leqslant \rho_r$, the validity of using a simple tabulated universal function for $\rho_i = \rho - \rho_r$ appears both questionable and unlikely.

If, on the other hand, metallic elements with a $\theta_D \sim 100°$ K are suitable on other grounds, their resistance will be an approximately linear function of temperature down to about 30° K and their sensitivity as thermometers should be tolerably good down to 4° or 5° K. Unfortunately most elements in this category are unsuitable for some reason or other. The alkali metals—of which rubidium, caesium, and potassium have the lowest characteristic temperatures—are chemically very active and must generally be cast in glass capillaries, due to difficulties in handling them; therefore, although ρ_i may be relatively large at 5° or 6° K, it is not highly reproducible, due partly to the mechanical constraint imposed on the element.

Thallium has $\theta_D \simeq 90°$ K and can be obtained in a pure state, but is oxidized very quickly and is difficult to handle; gallium melts at room temperature and is highly anisotropic so might not be reproducible on thermal cycling. Two of the best possibilities are perhaps bismuth and indium, of which certainly the latter can be obtained in a very pure state with $\rho_r/\rho_{273} \simeq 10^{-4}$. Although both are difficult to buy in the form of fine wires, indium wire is easily extruded and preliminary measurements (White and Woods, 1957) suggest that it behaves reproducibly as a thermometer despite a slight anisotropy in its crystal structure.

7. Metallic alloys as resistance thermometers

Introduction

In an alloy we have the extreme case of an impure metallic element, in which the reverse situation holds to that considered desirable in our discussion of the previous section: that is, the major part of the electrical resistance at all temperatures is due to scattering by fixed impurities, so that the electron mean free paths are essentially constant and the total resistivity $\rho \simeq \rho_r$. In most alloys, the total resistivity is considerably greater than the intrinsic resistivity of the individual constituent elements and is rather insensitive to temperature. This insensitivity is not unexpected since the scattering effect of the thermal vibrations is insignificant compared with the scattering effect of the random arrangement of atoms of differing atomic radius on the lattice sites. Alloys might all be expected to be extremely insensitive thermometric systems.

Although this is generally true there are notable exceptions (see also discussion by Daunt, 1955) which fall into three main categories:

(i) 'anomalous' alloys such as manganin and constantan;
(ii) dilute alloys exhibiting a resistance minimum at low temperatures;
(iii) alloys with a superconducting component or inclusion.

'Anomalous' alloys

In class (i) manganin and constantan and perhaps a number of other alloys as yet neglected, exhibit an electrical resistance which is almost completely temperature insensitive at room temperature, but which begins to decrease quite markedly below about 200° K. Kamerlingh Onnes and Holst (1914) observed the temperature dependence shown in Figure 64. As a result constantan in particular has been used as a low-temperature resistance thermometer; Parkinson (see, for example, Simon, Parkinson, and Spedding, 1951) used it in the range below 20° K, for temperature measurement on a calorimeter.

For some years, the writer used a manganin resistor as a temperature-sensitive element to actuate an electronic temperature controller, in which the manganin resistance in close thermal contact with the experimental chamber of a cryostat (White, 1953) formed one arm of an a.c. Wheatstone bridge; in this case

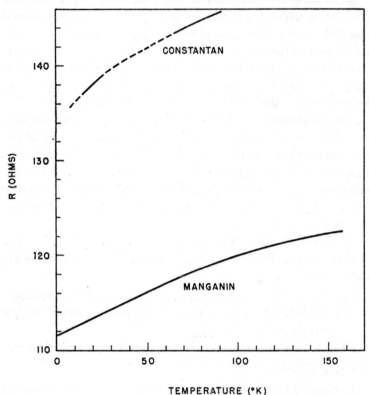

FIG. 64. Variation of resistance with temperature for manganin and constantan.

the manganin served adequately over the range from 5° to 150° K to control temperature to a few thousandths of a degree. Thermometers of this type generally seem to show some degree of hysteresis when the temperature is changed to a marked extent and then returned to its earlier value. This is probably not an intrinsic property of the alloy, so that annealed wires of manganin or constantan supported in a way which causes no mechanical strain when heated or cooled, rather than in the more common manner of having them wound on a solid former of some dissimilar material, may be quite reproducible in behaviour.

No explanation of the decrease in resistance which occurs for manganin or constantan below ∼ 150° K seems to have been given.

Electrical resistance minimum

Another mystery is the property (class (ii)) of the minimum in electrical resistance which appears in a large number of dilute alloys at temperatures from 25° K down (see review by Mac-Donald, 1956). In Leiden this minimum was first observed in samples of gold of quite high purity (de Haas, de Boer, and Van den Berg, 1933–4) and later in magnesium, aluminium, copper, silver, etc. It is now generally believed to be due to traces of certain impurity elements present; for example, the detailed work of MacDonald and Pearson on copper (MacDonald and Pearson, 1955; cf. Gerritsen and Linde, 1951, 1952) has shown that the presence of a few atoms per million of certain multivalent elements, e.g. iron, tin, germanium, gallium, arsenic, will produce a marked minimum in the electrical resistance at about 15°–25° K; the exact temperature of the minimum depends on the particular impurity element present and its relative proportion.

The rise in resistance with decreasing temperature, which occurs for $T < T_{min}$, makes these dilute alloys a possible temperature indicator. In many cases they are unsuitable due to (a) the increase being too small to give sufficient sensitivity, or (b) the temperature T_{min} being too low. One useful alloy is the dilute copper-iron alloy, and the temperature dependence of resistance of a Cu+0·056 atomic per cent Fe alloy is shown in Figure 65 (after Dugdale, 1957, private communication). Most of the copper alloys showing a resistance minimum have a T_{min} which is sufficiently high for them to be used in the region from 20° or 15° down, but below about 2° K the resistance again becomes relatively constant.

In the temperature range below 2° K, and in particular below

1° K (discussed more fully in Chapter VIII), samples of gold containing very small traces of impurity, e.g. iron, serve as useful thermometers. Figure 65 also illustrates the resistance–temperature relation for a very dilute gold-iron alloy (Au+about

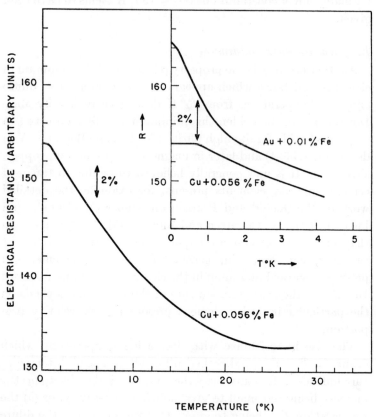

FIG. 65. Electrical resistance of dilute alloys at low temperatures.

0·01 atomic per cent Fe) calibrated by Dugdale and MacDonald (1957) against the helium vapour-pressure scale above 1° K and against the susceptibility of a paramagnetic salt below 1° K. The degree of reproducibility of such thermometers seems a little uncertain as many have been reported to show slight hysteresis but have been in situations where they were subject to mechanical strain when the temperature was changed. Since the impurity producing the minimum is generally present in very small amount and therefore is presumed to be in a homogeneous solid solution, they might be expected to be reproducible if strains are not present.

Superconducting inclusions in alloys

The third class (iii) mentioned above are those alloys which contain a superconducting element in relatively small proportion, and which at temperatures below 10° K exhibit a marked decrease in resistance which may extend over 5° or 6° K. Keesom and Van den Ende (1930), and later Babbitt and Mendelssohn (1935), found that in some samples of phosphor-bronze (92·7% Cu, 7% Sn, 0·2% P+traces of Pb, Be, Se, Ca, Mg) the resistance fell nearly linearly with temperature from about 7° K downward (Figure 66).

It seems that in the samples of phosphor-bronze which had this satisfactory thermometric behaviour, a trace of lead (0·1%) was present and that segregated inclusions of lead in the form of fine needles become superconducting below 8° K. Van Dijk (1951) and Daunt (1955) have also prepared leaded phosphor-bronze wires which behaved in this manner.

Babbitt and Mendelssohn (1935) also found that a silver-lead alloy containing 5 per cent lead had a very broad superconducting transition making it suitable as a resistance thermometer for the range 3·5°–7° K.

The use of leaded-brass for measuring temperatures in the region below 7° K was first suggested by Mendelssohn. Recently samples containing 62% Cu, 36% Zn, 0·08% Ni, and 1·73% Pb were tested by Parkinson and Quarrington (1954) who found that if suitably annealed the electrical resistance decreased very markedly over a temperature range of 2° or 3° K. Parkinson and Roberts (1955) later reported that by annealing these wires in a temperature gradient, a thermometer with an almost linear response over the range 1·5°–4° K was obtained.

The unfortunate features of this class (iii) of low-temperature thermometers, apart from their narrow range of usefulness, are the slight dependence of resistance on measuring current, their sensitivity to a magnetic field, and the critical nature of the method of preparation. By the very nature of their mode of action these features are to be expected.

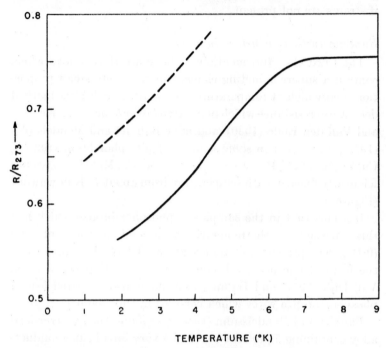

TEMPERATURE (°K)

FIG. 66. Electrical resistance of phosphor-bronze (leaded) at liquid-helium temperatures.

– – – Keesom and Van den Ende (1930).
——— Babbitt and Mendelssohn (1935).

8. Semi-conducting resistance thermometers

Introduction

The role of semi-conductors as thermometers was reviewed by Friedberg (1955) at the 1954 Washington symposium on 'Temperature', so that we will restrict ourselves to consideration of two particular aspects: the now well-established use of carbon resistance thermometers and the interesting possible development of elemental semi-conductors such as germanium, silicon, and tellurium as thermometers. This latter field, pioneered very recently at the Carnegie Institute of Technology by Friedberg and Estermann and at the Bell Telephone Laboratories by Geballe and his collaborators, is still in its infancy. Carbon thermometers, on the other hand, have been used for many years in the form of carbon-black films, 'Aquadag' films, etc. (see, for example, Giauque, Stout, and Clark, 1938), and since the investigations of Brown, Zemansky, and Boorse (1951) and Clement and Quinnell (1950) on commercial carbon resistors, they have become widely used.

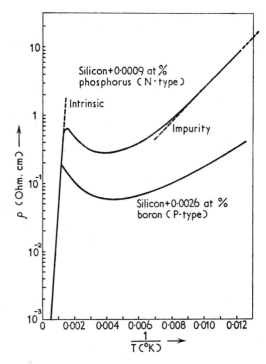

Fig. 67. Electrical resistance of elemental semi-conductors (after Friedberg, 1955).

Elemental semi-conductors

The typical behaviour of the elemental semi-conductor may be seen in Figure 67 (Friedberg, 1955). At high temperatures the conductivity is intrinsic, i.e. due to excitation of electrons from the valency band (otherwise full) to the conduction band (otherwise empty). The conductivity is a function of the number of

charge carriers and their mobility, and in the intrinsic region it
may be shown that

$$\rho \simeq A \exp(\Delta E/2kT),$$

where A is almost temperature independent. E is the energy
gap between the valence and conduction bands, having values
of 0·72 eV for Ge, 1·12 eV for Si, and 0·34 eV for Te.

At low temperatures, where $kT \ll \Delta E$, the conductivity is
due to the presence of impurities which contribute electrons
which may be excited across a gap of energy ΔE_D to the conduction band, or accept electrons from the valence band across a
gap ΔE_A leaving conduction holes in the valence band. Thus,
depending on the dominant type of impurity, the conduction at
low temperatures is N-type (due to electron carriers) or P-type
(due to hole carriers). In the respective cases, ρ is given approximately by $B \exp(\Delta E_D/2kT)$ or $B \exp(\Delta E_A/2kT)$, where B
depends on impurity concentration and varies slowly with
temperature. For the two 'doped' silicon specimens in Figure 67,
the two regions where $\log \rho \simeq \text{constant}/T$ are clearly shown.
In the intermediate temperature range, ρ may decrease with
decreasing temperature over a short interval; in this region,
intrinsic resistance is high and also the impurities—donors or
acceptors—are fully ionized so that the conductivity is approximately proportional to the mobility of the charge carriers. It is
apparent that by suitable selection of the semi-conductor and
addition of a specific impurity, a resistance element in which the
electrical resistance changes rapidly with temperature over a
quite wide temperature interval can be obtained.

Geballe, Morin, and Maita (1955) gave some figures for the
resistivity of arsenic-doped germanium crystals, which have a
room temperature resistivity of 0·018 ohm cm. Table XIII gives
typical resistance and sensitivity figures.

TABLE XIII

T, °K	R, ohms	$d \log R/d \log T$
50	2	1·1
20	9	1·1
4	155	2·5
2	1,600	3·0

In their tests, the germanium thermometers were mounted in a helium-filled capsule in a strain-free manner, and appeared to be reproducible to within $0 \cdot 0001°$ K at the boiling-point of helium after thermal cycling between room temperature and $4 \cdot 2°$ K. Further details of these investigations on germanium resistance thermometers have been given by Kunzler, Geballe, and Hull (1957).

Without the facilities of a well-equipped semi-conductor laboratory, the making of such resistance elements is obviously difficult, but if they become commercially available with a high reproducibility they should be extremely useful over the ranges of temperature from $100°$ K down to $1°$ or $2°$ K. Due to their rapid temperature variation of resistance it may be necessary to use more than one thermometer, i.e. samples differently doped or made from different semi-conductors, to cover this range or a wider range of temperature. One apparent restriction on their applicability is the need for calibration against a primary thermometer, since no simple mathematical expression appears to fit the data exactly over an extended temperature range. Thus we are still unable to buy or to make a semi-conducting thermometer of this type, measure its resistance at one or two fixed points, and then have a ready-made calibration by reference to a standard function or numerical table of values. That is not to say, however, that this may not be possible in a few years' time.

Carbon thermometers

Most carbon thermometers have a resistance which increases with decreasing temperature, and in many the relation $\log \rho \propto 1/T$ is tolerably well obeyed. However, it appears unlikely that carbon is a semi-conductor in the strict sense. Crystalline graphite is highly anisotropic, the resistivity in a natural crystal flake (Dutta, 1953) along the basal plane (usually denoted by $\rho_\perp$ as this is perpendicular to the hexagonal axis) being about 1×10^{-4} ohm cm at room temperature and perpendicular to the basal plane $\rho_\parallel$ being approximately 1 ohm cm. Whereas $\rho_\perp$ decreases with decrease in temperature, $\rho_\parallel$ increases as the temperature is decreased. This behaviour appears consistent with the model which emerges from recent calculations of band structure (Horton and Tauber, private communication, 1956); these suggest that in the direction parallel to the basal plane, there is a very small band overlap (cf. bismuth) but in the direction normal to the plane there is a narrow band gap; hence a single crystal should behave as a poor metallic conductor in one direction and a semi-conductor in the other.

No good agreement with this can be expected in carbon resistors as these are polycrystalline aggregates of microscopic graphite particles, in which not only the polycrystallinity but also impurities and the nature of the contact between particles affect the resistance.

The early use in California (Giauque, Stout, and Clark, 1938) of colloidal carbon films was followed in the ensuing twenty years by many applications of dry carbon blacks or colloidal suspensions of graphite ('Aquadag', India ink, etc.) for very low-temperature thermometry. An interesting example is that used by Mendelssohn and Renton (1955) in making measurements of the thermal conductivity of superconductors below $1°$ K:

Three close turns of 32 SWG enamelled copper wire were wound around the specimen [see Figure 68] and the ends were twisted so as to

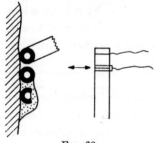

FIG. 68

tighten the wire down onto the rod. One end of the wire was cut above the twist and the other end used as a lead. Then the enamel on the outside of one of the turns was removed, and a colloidal suspension of graphite in alcohol was painted onto the wire and underlying specimen. After being dried the carbon layer acted as a thermometric substance between the wire and the specimen, the last two acting as end-contacts....

These thermometers have the virtue of high sensitivity at sufficiently low temperature, small heat capacity, and intimate thermal contact with the specimen whose temperature is to be measured. They do, however, show hysteresis effects when warmed up to room temperature and cooled again, and therefore must be recalibrated at each low-temperature experiment.

A further development in 1947 was the application of com-

mercially prepared carbon resistances by Fairbank and Lane
(1947). They cut out resistors from the I.R.C. carbon-coated
plastic card resistances and used them as second sound detectors,
i.e. to detect the temperature waves propagated in liquid helium
II; they found that the resistance $R \propto 1/T$ for these thermometers.

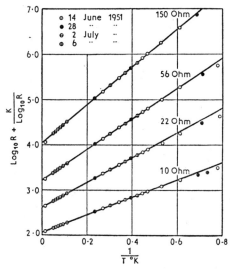

FIG. 69. Graphical test of equation (37) for four carbon resistors (after
Clement and Quinnell, 1952).

Shortly after this Clement and Quinnell (see, for example,
Clement and Quinnell, 1950, and the more complete discussion in
Clement and Quinnell, 1952) first reported on the successful
results of their search for a commercial carbon thermometer of
the normal cylindrical type, which has a high sensitivity and
reproducibility at low temperatures. They found that the
radio-type resistors manufactured by the Allen–Bradley
Company exhibit a resistance which varies rapidly with temperature, particularly below about 20° K (see Figure 69) and may
be expressed to within ±0·5 per cent by the semi-empirical
expression

$$\log R + K/\log R = A + B/T. \qquad (37)$$

As may be seen from Figure 69 (for the 1-W size) such resistors as the 22- or 56-ohm are particularly suitable for use from about 20° down to nearly 1° K.

More recently Clement *et al.* (1953) reported on the use of 2·7 and 10-ohm Allen–Bradley resistors in the region below 1° K, finding them suitable down to about 0·3° K (see Figure 70).

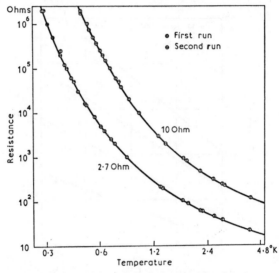

FIG. 70. Resistance of two carbon thermometers at low temperatures
(Clement *et al.*, 1953).

Pearce, Markham, and Dillinger (1956) also examined the response of the 10-ohm resistor in the region 2·0°–0·3° K and found that reproducible results were obtainable, although the constants in the equation were changed slightly if the resistor was warmed to room temperature and cooled again. They found that using the equation†

$$T = \frac{A \log_{10} R}{(\log_{10} R - B)^2} \tag{38}$$

(proposed by Clement in a paper read at the Ninth Annual Calorimetry Conference, Schenectady, 1954, and also by

† Markham *et al.* (1957) have pointed out that (38) is a special case of (37), expanded in the form $B \log R/T = (\log R)^2 - A \log R + K$, but is only applicable if the right-hand side of this latter equation is a perfect square; for some 2·7-ohm resistors they found this was not the case and the three-constant equation (37) was required.

Clement, Logan, and Gaffney, 1955), A and B had values of approximately 1·6 and 1·0 respectively for the 10-ohm resistor, so that $R \simeq 0\cdot1$ MΩ at 0·5° K, and $R \simeq 4\cdot0$ MΩ at 0·35° K.

In 1951 findings rather similar to those of Clement and Quinnell were reported by Brown, Zemansky, and Boorse (1951) for ½-W Allen–Bradley resistors although the authors proposed the use of a rather more complicated four-constant equation to express R as a function of T.

Two useful features of these carbon resistors are their comparative insensitivity to magnetic fields (see Clement and Quinnell, 1952) and almost complete insensitivity to the value of the measuring current, apart from considerations of self-heating. The relation between the dependence of the temperature rise in the thermometer with power input, dP/dT, and its thermal conductivity were investigated by Berman (1954); he established that in the 100-ohm (½-W) Allen–Bradley resistor,

$$dP/dT = 3\cdot9 \times 10^{-5}T^{1\cdot6} \text{ W/deg},$$

so that using 1 μA current heating is negligible at 4° K; at 1·59° K the mean temperature rise is 7×10^{-4} °K, and at 1·2° K the rise is $1\cdot3 \times 10^{-2}$ °K. In the 20-ohm size he found dP/dT to be about half as great as for the 100-ohm size.

Apart from their use below 1° K, these commercial carbon resistors have had considerable application in calorimetry measurements below 20° K, where they provide a very sensitive thermometer suitable for measuring small temperature changes. In these situations they are normally calibrated by determining the constants in (37) or (38) by reference to the vapour pressure of liquid helium or liquid hydrogen. Where subsequent interpolation is not considered sufficiently accurate, i.e. between 4·2° and 14° K, $R(T)$ may be checked against a gas thermometer and an error function showing the difference $\Delta T = T(R)_{Eq} - T_g$ can be obtained. Morrison, Patterson, and Dugdale (1955) have given a clear account of such a calibration procedure for a 10-ohm (½-W) Allen–Bradley resistor used in an adiabatic calorimeter. They employed the three-constant equation (37) and found an error function which has a normal maximum amplitude of about 0·02° K in the range between 20° and 3° K. When the cryostat was warmed to temperatures above that of liquid nitrogen, they found small changes in the constants (notably in A) and in the error function; however, the sensitivity dR/dT seems completely reproducible within the limits of error of measurement.

Rayne (1956) has also described a rather similar calibration procedure for a 10-ohm ($\frac{1}{2}$-W) resistor in his calorimeter; working over the range 4·2°–1·2° K, he used the two-constant equation and found

$$[(\log_{10} R)/T]^{\frac{1}{2}} \simeq a + b \log_{10} R,$$

where $$a = -0·746, \ b = 0·770.$$

Over a rather wider temperature range, this two-constant formula may prove too inaccurate unless a deviation curve is obtained. Keesom and Pearlman (1956) have given a good method of obtaining this: plot $(\log R/T)^{\frac{1}{2}}$ against $\log R$ to find the best estimate of the constant b, and then use this fixed value of b to calculate a from the equation as a function of T. The smoothed $a(T)$ curve is then used in interpolation.

Finally, it may be pointed out that some less temperature-sensitive brands of radio-resistor such as the I.R.C. or Erie resistors appear to be useful for measurements in the very low-temperature range.† Dugdale and MacDonald (private communication, 1956) have obtained values for the resistance of an I.R.C. (nominal 82-ohm at room temperature) resistor as a function of temperature down to about 0·1° K. They observed that $R \simeq 125$ ohm at 4·2° K, $R \simeq 138$ ohm at 2° K, $R \simeq 153$ ohm at 1° K, $R \simeq 185$ ohm at 0·3° K, but for $T < 0·3°$ K, R appeared to approach a constant value; however, they were uncertain from their data whether the resistor was in thermal equilibrium with the paramagnetic salt below 0·3° K. From 4·2°–0·3° K the resistance could be quite well expressed by a

---

† Recently (Nicol and Soller, 1957) a number of different commercial types of resistor have been tested as thermometers below 1° K; the results (kindly supplied by Dr. J. Nicol, now at the A. D. Little Corporation, Massachusetts) suggest that most are unsuitable because of insensitivity and/or instability except the Allen–Bradley resistors and certain resistors produced by the Speer Resistor Company of Bradford, Pennsylvania.

relation of the type $R = R_{4·2}+a/T+\Delta$, where a, Δ are constants. It does appear that the hysteresis effects on thermal cycling are more serious in the I.R.C. resistor than in the Allen–Bradley type.

Individual carbon resistance thermometers are generally used with a potentiometer acting as the d.c. resistance-measuring device. However, in thermal conductivity determinations, pairs of 'matched' carbon resistors have been used very successfully for measuring small temperature differences, both in a d.c. bridge (Mendelssohn and Renton, 1955) and in an a.c. bridge (Fairbank and Wilks, 1955).

9. Thermocouple thermometers

Introduction

In any metal in which there exists a temperature gradient we should expect to find a variation of the electron energy distribu-

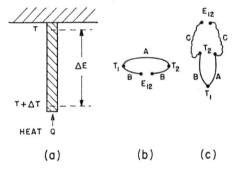

Fig. 71. Thermoelectric force.

tion function with temperature. At normal or low temperatures a small fraction of the electrons have energies in a narrow region of width kT at the top of the Fermi-Dirac distribution. As the temperature is raised, this narrow region expands, resulting in slightly more electrons having higher energies than hitherto. Thus in the metallic bar (Figure 71 (a)) electrons travel up the bar under a thermal gradient carrying excess thermal enegy. To preserve the requirement of no net current flow (since this is an open circuit electrically), a return flow of electrons carrying their normal charge '$-e$' but no excess thermal energy, takes place. This return flow is produced by an electrical driving force, a potential difference ΔE, called the absolute thermoelectric force of the metal. The absolute thermoelectric power is then defined as

$$S = \frac{\Delta E}{\Delta T}.$$

In practice it is usually convenient and necessary to measure the difference in absolute thermoelectric power between two metals. Thus in the situation of Figure 71 (b) two dissimilar metals A and B have their junctions at temperatures T_1 and T_2. By measuring the thermoelectric voltage E_{12}, we have a thermometric indicator available for establishing the difference between T_1 and T_2. If A or B are not particularly suitable metals for constructing long strain-free connecting leads to the measuring instruments, then two junctions at a common temperature T_2 between A and a suitable third metal C, and between B and C (Figure 71 (c)) are made; the potential difference E_{12} at the ends of the leads C is still a direct measure of the thermoelectric potential difference between junctions AB at T_1 and AB at T_2. In practice T_1 is usually an unknown temperature, T_2 is an ice pot (or in some low-temperature applications a bath of liquid helium or liquid nitrogen), and the leads C are of copper.

It appears obvious that in a complete circuit of one homogeneous metal, irrespective of the presence of temperature gradients, no net thermoelectric current flows nor will a thermoelectric e.m.f. be observed on breaking the circuit at a point provided the two adjacent ends are at the same temperature. It follows that the reproducibility and general accuracy of thermoelectric thermometry depends largely on the homogeneity —both chemical and physical—of the metals in the circuit. Any chemical inhomogeneities or physical strains which are present may generate a spurious thermal e.m.f. if exposed to a temperature gradient.

Useful accounts of the history, application, and limitations of thermoelectric thermometry have been given in the proceedings of the 1939 Symposium on 'Temperature' by Roeser (1941), Aston (1941), Scott (1941), and Roeser and Wensel (1941).

Thermocouple materials

The article by Scott (1941) discusses the calibration of a large number of copper-constantan thermocouples against a platinum resistance thermometer over the range from 0° to −200° C, and the intercomparison of these e.m.f.s with tabulated values for a representative copper-constantan thermocouple. The normal variation ranges from 0 at the ice point (the reference temperature is the ice point) to ±50 μV (±100 μV in the most extreme cases) at −200° C. These deviations represent about ±1 per cent, so that errors of ±1 per cent in estimating temperature might be expected in comparing any copper-constantan thermocouple with a standard table.

However, by using a formula of the type

$$E = at + bt^2 + ct^3 \quad \text{for} -200° \text{ C} < t < 0° \text{ C} \tag{39}$$

and determining the constants a, b, c by measuring E at three different temperatures, the values of t subsequently obtained by measuring $E(t)$ at intermediate temperatures should not be in error by more than about 2 μV, representing less than 0·1° C. The three calibration temperatures may be the oxygen point, the carbon-dioxide point, and a point in the region from −30° to −50° C where the thermocouple may be calibrated in a stirred alcohol bath against an available resistance thermometer or liquid-in-glass thermometer. A slightly better fit is obtained by calibrating every 50° C and producing a graphical tabulated error function to represent the difference between E (experimental) and $E(t)$ calculated from (39).

It is an interesting sidelight on the possible accuracy of thermocouples to note that Giauque and collaborators (see Giauque, Buffington, and Schulze, 1927) used six copper-constantan thermocouples—originally calibrated from 15° to 283° K by reference to a hydrogen gas thermometer—as low-temperature secondary standards for many years. On checking their calibration after some years, they were found to be correct within limits of ±0·05° K. Thus by observing the necessary precaution of selecting the original wire carefully and not subjecting the thermocouples to mechanical straining, thermocouples can provide a practical secondary temperature scale suitable for most low-temperature applications down to below 10° K. They have the merits of being extremely localized in so far as the temperature-sensitive junction is concerned, of having a very small heat capacity, and they generate negligible heat in the process of measurement.

As Giauque *et al.* (1927) pointed out, serious errors which may arise due to having inhomogeneous lengths of wire in a temperature gradient largely come from wires in alloy form rather than from wires of a pure metallic element; in making a copper-constantan thermocouple, the copper (if annealed) produces insignificant spurious e.m.f.s but the constantan should be tested for chemical inhomogeneity; Giauque used the simple procedure of connecting the ends of each length of constantan being tested, to a potentiometer and passing the wire slowly through a glass U-tube immersed in liquid nitrogen. He then selected samples which did not give e.m.f.s over any regions of their length, greater than, say, 1 μV. For the samples of constantan tested by Giauque, the average thermoelectric e.m.f. developed in this test varied from 0·24 μV in 25 B. & S. wire to 1·84 μV in 40 B. & S. wire, maximum deflexions varying from 0·7 to 3·1 μV respectively. In his thermocouples, the effect of inhomogeneities was partly cancelled by using five constantan wires in parallel, each of 30 B. & S. silk-covered wire.

Values of the thermoelectric e.m.f.s down to about 80° K for representative copper-constantan, iron-constantan, and chromel-alumel thermocouples are available in National Bureau of Standards publications, e.g. *Reference Tables for Thermocouples* (1955), N.B.S. Circular 561, U.S. Government Printing Office, Washington, D.C.

In Figures 72, 73, and 74 are reproduced graphically thermoelectric force values for a copper-constantan thermocouple (Basinski and Swenson, private communication, 1956), an iron-constantan thermocouple (National Bureau of Standards Circular 561, 1955), a gold+cobalt:silver+gold thermocouple (Basinski and Swenson, private communication, 1956) made from wire obtained from Secon Metals Corporation of New York, and a gold+cobalt:silver+gold alloy thermocouple (Pearson, White, and Woods, private communication, 1956) made from Messrs. Johnson Matthey's wire. It may be observed that while the thermoelectric power of copper-constantan has already fallen to less than $4\,\mu V/^{\circ}K$ at $10^{\circ}\,K$, the $Au+2\cdot11$ atomic per cent

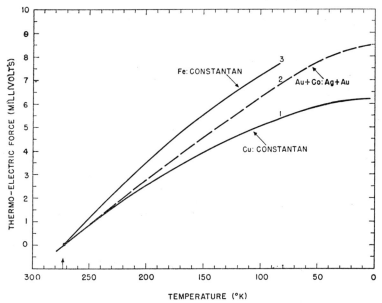

FIG. 72. Thermoelectric force versus temperature (reference junction at $0^{\circ}\,C$) 1 is copper:constantan (Basinski and Swenson); 2 is $Au+Co:Ag+Au$ (Basinski and Swenson); 3 is iron:constantan (N.B.S. Circular 561).

$Co:Ag+0\cdot37$ atomic per cent Au (approximate compositions for Johnson Matthey alloy) couple still has a thermoelectric power of $4\,\mu V/^{\circ}K$ at $5^{\circ}\,K$; this latter thermocouple was proposed originally by Keesom and Matthijs (1935) and has found considerable application recently as a thermometric element for actuating very sensitive electronic temperature controllers (see, for example, Dauphinee, MacDonald, and Preston-Thomas, 1954). Such gold and silver alloys have been obtainable from Messrs. Johnson Matthey Ltd. As in any alloy thermocouple wire, it is important to ensure that the alloy has been completely homogenized before being drawn into wire form.

The extensive researches of Borelius, Keesom, Johansson, and Linde (1930) revealed that many dilute alloys might be used for sensitive low-temperature thermocouples, in particular pure copper against a very dilute copper-iron alloy. Recently, as a result of investigations by Pearson on the effect of different

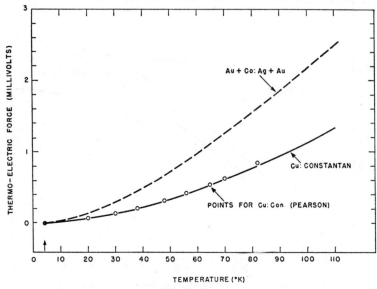

FIG. 73. Thermoelectric force below 100° K (reference junction at 4·2° K)

———— Copper : constantan (Basinski and Swenson);
—o—o Copper : constantan (W. B. Pearson, private communication);
– – – – Au+Co : Ag+Au (Basinski and Swenson).

specific impurities on the resistance minimum in copper, it appeared that traces of elements such as iron, tin, germanium, etc., produce not only a marked minimum in the electrical resistance but also modify the thermoelectric power very considerably at low temperatures. Figure 75 from Dauphinee, MacDonald, and Pearson (1953) shows that below 50° K the effect of traces of tin changes the thermoelectric power by orders of magnitude; above 50° K the thermoelectric power, i.e. the slope of the thermoelectric force versus temperature curve, approaches that of pure copper. Hence Cu versus Cu+0·003 atomic per cent Sn is a sensitive couple in the range below 50° K.

When working at low temperatures there are often considerable advantages in having the reference function immersed in liquid nitrogen or in liquid helium. Depending on the experi-

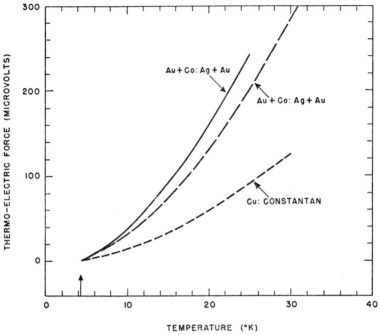

FIG. 74. Thermoelectric force below 30° K (reference junction at 4·2° K)

————— Au+Co:Ag+Au (Basinski and Swenson; alloys from Secon Metals Corp.);
— — — Au+2·11% Co:Ag+0·37% Au (Pearson, White, and Woods; alloys from Johnson Matthey Ltd.);
– – – – Copper:constantan (Basinski and Swenson).

mental arrangement, this may decrease considerably the spurious effects arising from inhomogeneities when wires of an alloy are brought out from a low-temperature cryostat to room temperature and into an ice pot. Suppose we are measuring a temperature of $T \simeq 22°$ K to $\pm 0·2°$ K with a copper-constantan thermocouple; if one function is in melting ice a total e.m.f. of about 6,000 μV must be measured to ± 1 μV. On the other hand, if measured with reference to a surrounding helium bath ($4\cdot2^\circ$ K), then the total e.m.f. which must be measured to ± 1 μV is only about 60 μV.

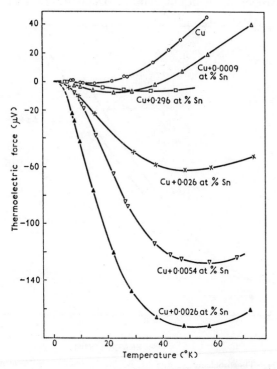

Fig. 75. Low-temperature variation of absolute thermoelectric force of some dilute copper-tin alloys (after Dauphinee, MacDonald, and Pearson, 1953).

In Chapter VII, the section dealing with electronic temperature control of experimental cryostats gives some details of the use of differential thermocouples for accurate temperature control.

Finally, as a point in favour of thermocouples for temperature measurement, it may be pointed out that the temperature-sensitive signal which they provide is easily recorded on the available commercial recorders.

REFERENCES

As has been mentioned in the text, the proceedings of the symposia arranged by the American Institute of Physics in 1939 and 1954, on 'Temperature, Its Measurement and Control in Science and Industry' are valuable works of reference. These proceedings have been published by the Reinhold Publishing Corporation, N.Y. in the form of vol. i (1941), and vol. ii (1955).

ARMSTRONG, G. T. (1954). *J. Res. Nat. Bur. Stand.* **53**, 263.

ASTON, J. G. (1941). *Temperature*, vol. i, p. 219, Reinhold, N.Y.

BABBITT, J. D., and MENDELSSOHN, K. (1935). *Phil. Mag.* **20**, 1025.

BARBER, C. R. (1950). *J. Sci. Instrum.* **27**, 47.

—— (1955). Ibid. **32**, 416.

BEATTIE, J. A. (1955). *Temperature*, vol. ii, p. 63, Reinhold, N.Y.

BERMAN, R. (1954). *Rev. Sci. Instrum.* **25**, 94.

—— and SWENSON, C. A. (1954). *Phys. Rev.* **95**, 311.

BORELIUS, G., KEESOM, W. H., JOHANSSON, C. H., and LINDE, J. O. (1930). *Leiden Comm.* 206a, 206b.

BRICKWEDDE, F. G. (1955). 'Conférence de Physique des Basses Températures', p. 608, Annexe 1955-3, *Suppl. Bull. Inst. int. Froid*, Paris.

BROWN, A., ZEMANSKY, M. W., and BOORSE, H. A. (1951). *Phys. Rev.* **84**, 1050.

CLEMENT, J. R., and QUINNELL, E. H. (1950). Ibid. **79**, 1028.

—— —— (1952). *Rev. Sci. Instrum.* **23**, 213.

—— —— STEELE, M. C., HEIN, R. A., and DOLECEK, R. L. (1953). Ibid. **24**, 545.

—— LOGAN, J. K., and GAFFNEY, J. (1955). *Phys. Rev.* **100**, 743.

—— —— —— (1955). *Rep. U.S. Naval Res. Lab.*, No. 4542.

DAUNT, J. G. (1955). *Temperature*, vol. ii, p. 327, Reinhold, N.Y.

DAUPHINEE, T. M., MACDONALD, D. K. C., and PEARSON, W. B. (1953). *J. Sci. Instrum.* **30**, 399.

—— and PRESTON-THOMAS, H. (1954). *Rev. Sci. Instrum.* **25**, 884.

—— MACDONALD, D. K. C., and PRESTON-THOMAS, H. (1954). *Proc. Roy. Soc.* A, **221**, 267.

DUGDALE, J. S., and MACDONALD, D. K. C. (1957). *Canad. J. Phys.* **35**, 271.

DUTTA, A. K. (1953). *Phys. Rev.* **90**, 187.

FAIRBANK, H. A., and LANE, C. T. (1947). *Rev. Sci. Instrum.* **18**, 525.

—— and WILKS, J. (1955). *Proc. Roy. Soc.* A, **231**, 545.

FRIEDBERG, S. A. (1955). *Temperature*, vol. ii, p. 359, Reinhold, N.Y.

GEBALLE, T. H., MORIN, F. J., and MAITA, J. P. (1955). 'Conférence de Physique des Basses Températures', p. 425, Annexe 1955-3, *Suppl. Bull. Inst. int. Froid*, Paris.

GERRITSEN, A. N., and LINDE, J. O. (1951). *Physica*, **17**, 573, 584.

GERRITSEN, A. N., and LINDE, J. O. (1952). *Physica*, **18**, 877.

GIAUQUE, W. F., BUFFINGTON, R. M., and SCHULZE, W. A. (1927). *J. Amer. Chem. Soc.* **49**, 2343.

—— STOUT, J. W., and CLARK, C. W. (1938). Ibid. **60**, 1053.

DE HAAS, W. J., DE BOER, J., and VAN DEN BERG, G. J. (1933–4). *Physica*, **1**, 1115.

HALL, J. A. (1955). *Temperature*, vol. ii, p. 115, Reinhold, N.Y.

—— (1956). *Brit. J. Appl. Phys.* **7**, 233.

HOGE, H. J., and BRICKWEDDE, F. G. (1939). *J. Res. Nat. Bur. Stand.* **22**, 351.

—— (1941). *Temperature*, vol. i, p. 141, Reinhold, N.Y.

—— (1950a). *J. Res. Nat. Bur. Stand.* **44**, 321.

—— (1950b). *Rev. Sci. Instrum.* **21**, 815.

HUDSON, R. P. (1955). *Temperature*, vol. ii, p. 185, Reinhold, N.Y.

HULM, J. K. (1950). *Proc. Roy. Soc.* A, **204**, 98.

KAMERLINGH ONNES, H., and HOLST, G. (1914). *Leiden Comm.* 142a.

KANNULUIK, W. G., and LAW, P. G. (1946). *J. Sci. Instrum.* **23**, 154.

KEESOM, P. H., and PEARLMAN, N. (1956). *Handb. der Physik.* **14**, 282.

KEESOM, W. H., and VAN DEN ENDE, J. N. (1930). *Leiden Comm.* 203c.

—— and MATTHIJS, C. J. (1935). *Physica*, **2**, 623.

—— and BIJL, A. (1937). Ibid. **4**, 305.

—— (1942). *Helium*, Elsevier, Amsterdam.

KELLER, W. E. (1956). *Nature*, **178**, 883.

KUNZLER, J. E., GEBALLE, T. H., and HULL, G. W. (1957). *Rev. Sci. Instrum.* **28**, 96.

LINDER, C. T. (1950). Westinghouse Research Laboratories, Report R–94433–2–A.

LOS, J. M., and MORRISON, J. A. (1951). *Canad. J. Phys.* **29**, 142.

MACDONALD, D. K. C., and PEARSON, W. B. (1955). *Acta Met.* **3**, 392, 403.

—— (1956). *Handb. der Physik*, **14**, 137.

MARKHAM, A. H., NETZEL, R. G., and DILLINGER, J. R. (1957). *Rev. Sci. Instrum.* **28**, 382.

MENDELSSOHN, K., and PONTIUS, R. B. (1937). *Phil. Mag.* **24**, 777.

—— and RENTON, C. A. (1955). *Proc. Roy. Soc.* A, **230**, 157.

MEYERS, C. H. (1932). *J. Res. Nat. Bur. Stand.* **9**, 807.

MOESSEN, G. W., ASTON, J. G., and ASCAH, R. G. (1954). *J. Chem. Phys.* **22**, 2096.

MORRISON, J. A., PATTERSON, D., and DUGDALE, J. S. (1955). *Canad. J. Chem.* **33**, 375.

MUELLER, E. F. (1941). *Temperature*, vol. i, p. 162, Reinhold, N.Y.

NICOL, J., and SOLLER, T. (1957). *Bull. Amer. Phys. Soc.* ser. ii, **2**, 63.

PARKINSON, D. H., and QUARRINGTON, J. E. (1954). *Proc. Phys. Soc.* B **67**, 644.

PARKINSON, D. H., and ROBERTS, L. M. (1955). *Proc. Phys. Soc.* **B 68**, 386.

PEARCE, D. C., MARKHAM, A. H., and DILLINGER, J. R. (1956). *Rev. Sci. Instrum.* **27**, 240.

RAYNE, J. A. (1956). *Aust. J. Phys.* **9**, 189.

ROBERTS, T. R., and SYDORIAK, S. G. (1956). *Phys. Rev.* **102**, 304.

ROESER, W. F. (1941). *Temperature*, vol. i, p. 180, Reinhold, N.Y.

—— and WENSEL, H. T. (1941). *Temperature*, vol. i, p. 284, Reinhold, N.Y.

RUHEMANN, M. and B. (1937). *Low Temperature Physics*, Cambridge University Press.

SCHWAB, F. W., and SMITH, E. R. (1945). *J. Res. Nat. Bur. Stand.* **34**, 360.

SCOTT, R. B. (1941). *Temperature*, vol. i, p. 206, Reinhold, N.Y.

—— (1955). *Temperature*, vol. ii, p. 179, Reinhold, N.Y.

SIMON, F. E., PARKINSON, D. H., and SPEDDING, F. (1951). *Proc. Roy. Soc.* A, **207**, 137.

STIMSON, H. F. (1955). *Temperature*, vol. ii, p. 141, Reinhold, N.Y.

VAN DIJK, H. (1952). *Maintenance of Standards Symposium*, p. 51, H.M.S.O., London.

—— (1951). *Proc. Int. Conf. Low Temp. Phys.*, p. 49, Oxford.

—— and DURIEUX, M. (1955). 'Conférence de Physique des basses Températures', p. 595, Annexe 1955–3, *Suppl. Bull. Inst. int. Froid*, Paris.

WERNER, F. D., and FRAZER, A. C. (1952). *Rev. Sci. Instrum.* **23**, 163.

WHITE, G. K. (1953). *Proc. Phys. Soc.* **A66**, 559.

—— and WOODS, S. B. (1957). *Rev. Sci. Instrum.* **28**, 638.

WOODCOCK, A. H. (1938). *Canad. J. Res.* **A16**, 133.

WOOLLEY, H. W., SCOTT, R. B., and BRICKWEDDE, F. G. (1948). *J. Res. Nat. Bur. Stand.* **41**, 379.

ZEMANSKY, M. W. (1943). *Heat and Thermodynamics*, 2nd edn. McGraw-Hill, New York.

Added in proof. Thermocouple wire of gold $+$ 2·1 atomic per cent cobalt alloy has recently become available from the Sigmund Cohn Manufacturing Company of New York, in both bare and insulated forms. Calibration tests, made from 2° to 300°K at the N.B.S. Boulder Laboratories, are described by M. D. Bunch and R. L. Powell in the *Proceedings of the 1957 Cryogenic Engineering Conference*, p. 269 (published Jan. 1958, Boulder, Colorado).

THE RESEARCH CRYOSTAT

CHAPTER V

INTRODUCTION TO CRYOSTAT DESIGN

1. General considerations

PART II of this book deals largely with the topic of cryostat design and is intended to detail the principles involved and some of the means by which particular physical measurements at low temperatures are made. It is clearly impossible to cover all the eventualities that do and will arise in the plans of the low-temperature experimenter but it is hoped that the discussion of general principles, heat transfer, methods of temperature control, etc., together with those chapters on temperature measurement and physical data, may help the experimentalist.

It is difficult to conceive of any single cryostat which is suitable for all possible physical measurements on a substance at all temperatures in the range we call 'low'. Even if possible, the complexity of such an apparatus would be considerable, to say the least. As a result it is necessary to formulate clearly the primary experimental problem to be tackled, and try to solve it as simply as possible, always consistent with the fact that a little extra difficulty in construction may allow a much wider range of usefulness or increased accuracy. Whether the primary aim is to measure the electrical resistance of an alloy, the X-ray lattice spacing in a solid or its heat capacity, a decision regarding the range of temperature over which measurements are needed is important in so far as the design is concerned.

With the aid of liquid refrigerants commonly available in a cryogenic laboratory, viz. liquid oxygen, nitrogen, and helium (and possibly liquid hydrogen), the following temperature ranges are immediately available by controlling the pressure at which the liquefied gas boils:

(a) $1°-4\cdot2°$ K (liquid helium);

   (b) 54°–90° K (liquid oxygen);

   (c) 63°–77° K (liquid nitrogen);

(and (d) 10°–20·4° K (by pumping liquid hydrogen to temperatures ranging from its normal boiling-point to well below the triple point)).

Provided that vacuum pumps of the required speed are available, temperatures in these ranges can be attained within the liquefied gases boiling in a dewar and therefore in any experimental chamber immersed in the liquid. With a manostat connected on the pumping tube, they can be maintained with fluctuations of less than one part in a thousand; over much of each range, temperature fluctuations as small as one part in five thousand can be maintained for a long period of time. This accuracy, of course, occurs in the temperature at the surface of the boiling liquid as calculated from the vapour pressure and does not mean that much larger temperature inhomogeneities cannot exist in the liquid itself, and particularly in the solid if pumped below the triple point.

If temperatures other than those within the accessible vapour-pressure range of the available liquefied gases are required, other methods must be used. These other methods generally maintain temperatures within the experimental space that are above the temperature of the surrounding bath; then a balance between the loss of heat (by radiation, conduction, etc.) from the experimental chamber and the supply of heat from a manually or automatically controlled source to the chamber must be produced. The degree of ease or difficulty with which this balance, and therefore relative constancy of temperature, is produced depends ultimately on the type of physical investigation being pursued; for example it depends on whether a steady drift of 1° K/min or an irregular oscillation of 2° or 3° K in temperature is unimportant, or whether on the other hand the temperature must be maintained to ±0·005° K for an hour or more. This degree of difficulty not only depends on the type of experiment but also on the approximate temperature at which it is being carried out: at temperatures below say 20° K, heat capacities are small and the time required to attain thermal equilibrium is usually short, so that the response to the manual control of an electrical heater is quite rapid; but at 150° K equilibrium times are much longer and the difficulty of finding manually a particular heat input necessary to produce ultimate temperature equilibrium is more tedious.

Another important and related factor is whether adiabatic conditions are required. To illustrate this, consider a measurement of heat capacity or heat conductivity. In these measurements stray temperature drifts and spurious heat inputs to the specimen under investigation must be eliminated as completely as possible. The specimen or its immediate container must be in a high vacuum enclosure and the surroundings must be temperature controlled to varying degrees of constancy. On the other hand, a measurement of the Hall effect, electrical resistance, or magnetic susceptibility may be made in a short time with the specimen kept in equilibrium with its surroundings by the presence of exchange gas so that a slight change in temperature will not affect the validity of the experimental value obtained, although it may make the precise temperature at which the value is obtained somewhat uncertain. Therefore before laying plans for a cryostat these questions must be answered:

    (i) Will results in the range from 1°–4° K and 55°–90° K give all the information needed, or are measurements, perhaps, only required at 90° K, 77° K, and 4·2° K?

  (ii) If the answers to these first questions are no, then how constant must the temperature be maintained and for how long at say 8° K, 40° K, 115° K?

 (iii) Can the experimental space be kept filled with a low-pressure gas which will assist in preserving temperature equilibrium within this space?

 (iv) What form of access to the experiment is required, i.e. are ten or twenty fine copper wires as electrical leads all that are necessary, or do we need special windows for an infrared or X-ray beam? Is some mechanical movement necessary in the experimental space, e.g. a mechanical switch or a suspension to a microbalance?

Having answered these questions—most of them with very

obvious answers in a particular investigation—the problem of designing and making a suitable apparatus has to be faced. One of the major problems in this, apart from the obvious ones of available materials, workshop facilities, and a necessary mechanical lifetime, is that of heat transfer.

In any apparatus designed to operate at temperatures considerably different from its surroundings, and perhaps designed to measure properties which are strongly influenced by the inflow or outflow of heat and/or change in temperature, this factor is a vital one. As a result a large part of the success or failure of an apparatus to give accurate results can often be traced to the care taken in reducing stray heat inflows due to (i) conduction through low-pressure gas when the vacuum is not sufficiently good, (ii) radiation, (iii) conduction of heat along the tubes or electrical leads, or (iv) Joule heating or eddy current heating.

Chapter VI deals with the calculation of heat inflows that may be expected and compares the magnitude of the heat transferred by radiation between surfaces of various emissivities with that conducted through low-pressure gas or conducted down electrical lead wires and supporting tubes. However, there seems to be merit in first showing some schematic diagrams, and in some cases more detailed illustrations of cryostats which have been and are being used to measure physical properties, before considering the problems of heat transfer and temperature control in more detail. This may help the reader to understand some of the practical methods of tackling these problems, and he may refer back to them again after reading other chapters.

2. Cryostats for specific-heat measurements

Most specific heat measurements at low temperatures have been made with the adiabatic calorimeter—originally introduced by Nernst and Eucken in 1910—and the ensuing discussion is restricted to examples of this type. In the simple form illustrated schematically in Figure 76 (a) the specimen S, with heater H and thermometer T (combined as one in some cases) attached, is suspended by nylon or cotton threads in an evacuated enclosure X, which in turn is surrounded by a liquefied gas A. The specimen may be in the form of a solid block of metal with T and H cemented to its surface or embedded in it; or the specimen may be in a solid, powder, or liquid form contained in a thin-walled calorimeter vessel of known heat capacity in which case T and H are usually attached to the calorimeter; a small pressure of

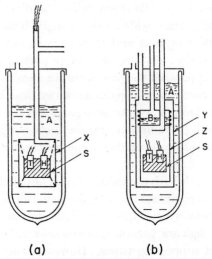

(a)   **(b)**

FIG. 76. Types of cryostat suitable for specific-heat
determinations.

helium exchange gas may then be used to ensure temperature equilibrium within the calorimeter. If the vacuum is sufficiently good and conduction down the leads is small, such a simple apparatus can adequately provide specific heat data over a quite wide range of temperature, provided that the temperatures of the wall X and the specimen S are not widely different, otherwise radiation and lead conduction become large. As a result this simplest form may be used at temperatures below 20° K, and at temperatures within the range of say 55°–90° K covered by liquid oxygen, provided that $T_S - T_X$ is kept small. At temperatures above 20° K, an adiabatic shield in the space beween S and X usually becomes necessary.

Silvidi and Daunt (1950) and Pearlman and Keesom (1952) have described the use of comparatively simple cryostats of this type (see also descriptions of the specific heat apparatus used at Leiden by Keesom and Van den Ende, 1930; Keesom and Clark, 1935; and review by Keesom and Pearlman, 1956). They use heaters of manganin or constantan, and measure temperature in the helium range with leaded phosphor-bronze wires and at higher temperatures with a resistance thermometer of pure lead wire.

The second cryostat (Figure 76 (b)) is more complex than 76 (a) in that it has an intermediate wall Z which is attached to the copper chamber B, and can therefore be controlled at temperatures different from that of the outer liquid bath A; either by reducing the pressure over a liquid in B or electrically heating the chamber B, its temperature and the temperature of Z can be controlled so as to preserve only a small temperature difference between Z and the specimen S.

An example of a cryostat of type (b) in which liquid can be drawn into the inner chamber B from the dewar bath itself, is illustrated in Figure 77 (after Rayne, 1956; Rayne and Kemp, 1956). Liquid in the dewar A is at atmospheric pressure and can be admitted through the needle valve E into the chamber F. The vessel D is of brass and F is of copper, both being supported by thin-walled (0·1 and 0·2 mm wall thickness) German silver tubes from the top plate. In this cryostat both vessels are evacuated separately and the use of helium exchange gas at low temperatures is avoided by using a mechanical thermal switch similar to that described by Ramanathan and Srinivasan (1955). Quoting Rayne, 'within the working space, the specimen J is suspended by nylon threads from the disk K, which is thermally anchored to the bath F by a flexible copper strap L. Movement of the disk is made by a stainless steel tube M, connected to a bellows N which can be actuated by the screw mechanism P ...'. By lowering the disk and pressing the specimen against the flat bottom of the can, J may be cooled to the temperature of F. The avoidance of the use of exchange gas, particularly at liquid-helium temperatures, reduces the 'starting-up' time considerably and ensures that no heat leak through residual exchange gas can occur. Rayne used a manganin heater wound on a copper

former Q, screwed into the top of the specimen, and a 10-ohm
Allen–Bradley carbon thermometer in a copper sleeve R for
temperature measurement.

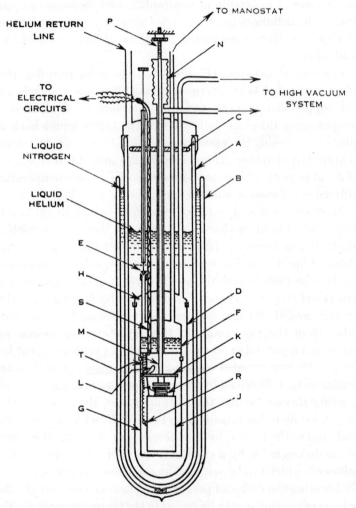

FIG. 77. Schematic diagram of cryostat (after Rayne, 1956).

A variant of this pattern, but closely related to the type 76 (*b*)
is the apparatus described by Hill (1953) and shown in Figure 78.
The use of exchange gas can again be avoided by admitting

liquid helium or liquid hydrogen to the compartment *E*. This cryostat, designed and built at the Clarendon Laboratory at a time when supplies of liquid helium were by no means plentiful,

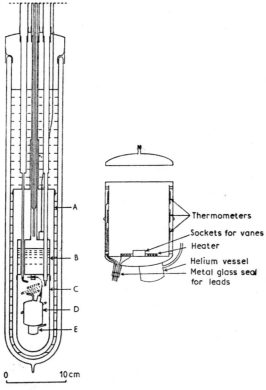

FIG. 78. A cryostat and calorimeter (after Hill, 1953).

uses (i) liquid helium in *B* with liquid hydrogen in the outer dewar, or (ii) for higher temperature operation, liquid hydrogen in *B* and liquid air in the surrounding dewar. The helium evaporation rate is of the order of 10 cm³/hour, compared with a total rate of about 100 cm³/hour which would be encountered if the outer dewar were also filled with liquid helium. The section of the helium or hydrogen transfer siphon which leads into *B* may be seen in the figure, and the details of the calorimeter in which the specimen is placed are shown in the inset. Hill (1953) has also described an alternative cryostat, similar in principle but in which chamber B is the expansion vessel of a Simon liquefier. This latter cryostat is similar to that of Parkinson, Simon, and Spedding (1951) although in their calorimeter liquid helium or hydrogen for cooling purposes was admitted directly into the calorimeter rather than into the separate small helium vessel E used by Hill. In either case, the calorimeter or the compartment E may be used both for cooling and for resistance thermometer calibration by using the helium-filled volume as a vapour-pressure thermometer below 4·2° K and as a gas thermometer above 4·2° K. Resistance thermometers consisting of (i) platinum, (ii) constantan, and (iii) leaded phosphor-bronze or leaded brass wires are wound onto the light copper inner frame of the calorimeter vessel.

Another cryostat in which a gas thermometer is attached to the calorimeter and is used for temperature measurement over the range 4°–15° K has been described by Aven, Craig, and Wallace (1956). Their calorimeter-thermometer unit is suspended below a copper plate on which an electrical heater is wound, and a radiation shield is attached to the copper plate so as to surround the calorimeter. This is all enclosed in an evacuated metal can, surrounded by a dewar of liquid helium. Adiabatic conditions are produced by controlling the shield temperature in response to a Au+Co:Ag+Au thermocouple which measures the temperature difference between shield and calorimeter. In terms of the models in Figure 76, the apparatus of Aven *et al.* might be considered as type (a) with a shield interposed between S and X or as type (b) without the small liquid chamber B.

The most serious criticism that might be levelled at a specific heat apparatus of the general pattern of Figure 76 (b) is that at comparatively high temperatures where, for example, T_A may be 90·1° K, and T_B approximately 150° K, adiabatic conditions are not sufficiently well established. That is, due to radiation transfer and to heat flow along electrical leads, serious temperature inequalities may be produced between different points on the shield Z and thereby cause small temperature drifts in the calorimeter, sufficient to adversely affect high-precision calorimetry. Two good examples of adiabatic calorimeters designed for use at temperatures up to room temperature, and to give values of specific heat correct to within about $\pm 0\cdot 2$ per cent, are those of Morrison and his collaborators (Morrison, Patterson, and Dugdale, 1955; Morrison and Los, 1950) and of Dauphinee, MacDonald, and Preston-Thomas, 1954. In both

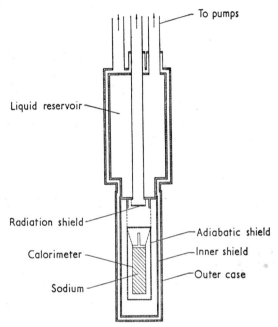

FIG. 79. A cryostat for specific-heat measurements. Heaters and thermocouples are not shown (after Dauphinee, MacDonald, and Preston-Thomas, 1954).

cases an apparatus rather similar to type 76 (*b*) has an additional temperature-controlled copper shield interposed between Z and S. In Morrison's apparatus the electrical heating of the shield is manually controlled in response to the temperature difference between shield and calorimeter, indicated by a sensitive chromel P-constantan thermocouple; using a three-junction couple, a signal of about 180 μV per degree of temperature difference is realized.

In the semi-automatic apparatus of Dauphinee *et al.*, of which the principal parts are shown in Figure 79, Au+Co:Ag+Au differential thermocouples are used to actuate an electronic temperature controller. Great care is taken to ensure temperature equilibrium over the adiabatic shield, and to a lesser extent on the outer shield, as their method of measurement consists of continuous heating of the calorimeter and calculation of heat capacity from the continuously recorded temperature-time chart. In such a continuous process in which constant electrical heating produces a temperature rise of about 5° K/hour, no corrections for spurious temperature drift can be made; hence the temperature drift must be negligible. In more conventional specific heat determinations, the heat input to the calorimeter is essentially discontinuous—occupying perhaps 10–30 seconds—and temperature drift rates are carefully ascertained before and after the brief heating period.

3. Cryostats for measurement of thermal conductivity and thermoelectric power

In the solid rod shown in Figure 80, the axial heat flow $\dot{Q}$ is given by

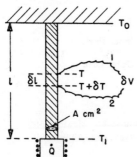

$$\lambda(T) = \frac{\dot{Q}}{A}\frac{\delta l}{\delta T}$$

where $\lambda(T)$ is a function of T expressing the thermal conductivity of the material. Thus the total heat conduction

$$\dot{Q} = \frac{A}{l}\int_{T_0}^{T_1}\lambda(T)\,dT.$$

FIG. 80. Heat flow through a solid rod.

If the rod is metallic (or a semiconductor), a thermoelectric potential difference is produced along the rod and the thermoelectric power with respect to the metal of which the potential leads 1 and 2 are made is $S = \delta V/\delta T$; the thermoelectric force, denoted by V or E, is

$$E = \int_{T_0}^{T_1} S(T)\,dT.$$

In principle and in practice the thermoelectric power $S(T)$ may be determined either (i) by measuring δV and δT, where $\delta T \ll T$

and hence it may be assumed $S(T) \simeq S(T+\delta T)$; then, varying T_1 and T_0, a series of values for $S(T)$ may be obtained; or (ii) by keeping T_0 fixed and measuring the total thermoelectric force $E(T_1-T_0)$ as T_1 is changed; $S(T)$ is then obtained by differentiating the curve $E(T)$.

Similarly, in the case of thermal conductivity, an integrated conductivity is obtained by measuring $\dot{Q}$ and T_1 for different values of $\dot{Q}$, and differentiating the resultant function $\dot{Q}(T_1)$ to obtain $\lambda(T)$. Alternatively, by keeping T_1-T_0 small, values of δT and $\dot{Q}$ are obtained at various temperatures and a graph of $\lambda(T)$ obtained directly from these.

Since the major interest in thermoelectricity has been practical thermometric interest in the thermoelectric e.m.f. E produced by a thermocouple junction with respect to a second junction fixed at a reference temperature (often $0°$ C but sometimes $4 \cdot 2°$ or $77°$ K), the integrated quantity E is usually measured. This quantity has greater practical value and since it is normally a simple monotonic function of T, S can be derived by differentiation if required. In recent years, however, there has been an increased fundamental interest in thermoelectric power and many differential measurements giving S directly have been made (see, for example, Frederikse, 1953; and Jan, Pearson, and Templeton, 1955). In these latter measurements the procedure is almost identical with the measurement of thermal conductivity except that a potential difference δE ($= \delta V$) must be obtained corresponding to δT and the heat flow $\dot{Q}$ need not be known.

In thermal conductivity measurements, the interest has been a largely fundamental interest in $\lambda(T)$ and so the differential measurement giving $\lambda(T)$ directly has been used. Since $\lambda(T)$ is frequently not a simple monotonically increasing function of T but a rather complicated function, and also since δT can be measured with a fairly high degree of accuracy with a differential thermometer system, this yields more reliable results than the 'integral' method.

In certain cases (see Wilkinson and Wilks, 1949) where, for technical reasons, values of the total heat $\dot{Q}$ conducted by a rod of a material when the ends of the rod are at quite different temperatures (e.g. 4·2° and 20° K) are needed, the 'integral' method has been used; in these cases values of $\dot{Q}l/A$ for certain specific values of T_0' and T_1' have been required, and not any detailed knowledge of $\lambda(T)$.

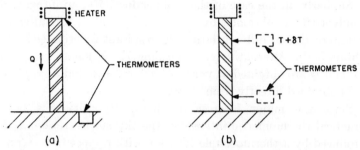

FIG. 81. Thermal-conductivity determination by the axial flow method; figure (b) represents the more reliable *potentiometric* form.

We shall confine our discussion below to cryostats in which values of $\lambda(T)$ can be obtained, and if desired $S(T)$ can be measured at the same time. In some of the early low-temperature measurements on heat conduction at Leiden, one end of the specimen was soldered directly to a 'heat sink', e.g. copper plate of which the opposite surface was in contact with liquid helium or hydrogen, and the heater was wound directly onto or adjacent to a thermometer attached by a solder connexion to the other end of the specimen. The accuracy of this method depends on the contact thermal resistance of the solder junctions being small in comparison with that of the specimen, which is frequently not the case.

In an interesting paper on the heat conductivity of steels de Nobel (1951) has described the use of the type of assembly shown in Figure 81 (a) and also the subsequent adoption of the 'potentiometric' form of measurement (Figure 81 (b)), which is largely used today. This latter form, provided that the heat flow along the thermometer connexions is negligible when equilibrium is established, represents a thermal potentiometer; measurement of T and $T+\delta T$ at the thermometers is a true indication of the respective temperatures at the points on the specimens where

the thermometer 'probes' are attached. de Haas and Rademakers (1940) first used helium-gas thermometers—attached to
a mercury differential manometer by fine contracid† capillaries
—in a thermal conductivity measurement by the 'potentiometer' method. Since the introduction of the butyl phthalate

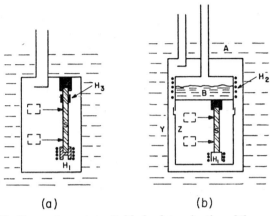

(a)   (b)

FIG. 82. Types of cryostat suitable for determination of thermal conductivity and thermoelectric power.

oil-filled manometer by Hulm (1950), this gas thermometric
method of measurement has proved most popular for use over an
extended temperature range. Berman (1951), Olsen (1952),
Estermann and Zimmerman (1952), Andrews, Webber, and
Spohr (1951), White (1953), and Rosenberg (1955), have all used
this general method, although the details of the differential
manometry have varied slightly.

Leaving the details of temperature measurement (discussed
in Chapter IV), we turn to the type of experimental cryostat
suited to measurements of $\lambda(T)$. The simple form of Figure 82 (a)
shows the specimen S thermally anchored to an evacuated metal
chamber which is immersed in a liquid refrigerant A; S has a
heater H_1 attached to its lower end. This cryostat is very suitable
for measurements in the range of temperature covered by the
liquid A and measurements may often be extended to slightly
higher temperatures by having an additional heater H_3 to raise

† A low-conductivity alloy containing about 60% Ni, 15% Cr, 16% Fe,
7% Mo, and 2% Mn.

the temperature of the rod S above T_A. Such a relatively simple type of cryostat has been used very successfully in the liquid-helium and liquid-hydrogen temperature regions by de Haas and Rademakers (1940), Hulm (1950), and others; at these temperatures radiation heat transfer is not a serious problem.

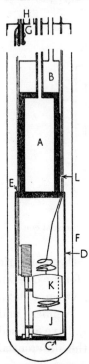

For working at temperatures outside the range covered by liquefied gases, the more complicated type of cryostat in Figure 82 (b) has been widely used. In this the inner chamber B may contain a liquefied gas boiling at atmospheric or some other controlled pressure or it may be controlled by the heater H_2 at a temperature above that of the surrounding liquid A. The wall Z acts as a radiation shield and is normally of copper, frequently silver- or gold-plated to reduce its emissivity. Since the specimen is thermally anchored by a solder joint (or in some cases cemented to a metal collar which can be soldered) to B, and the spaces between S and Z, and between Z and Y are evacuated, Z itself need not be a vacuum-tight enclosure; by leaving a hole in Z, both spaces can be evacuated easily through a common pumping line, and electrical leads can be more easily taken out from H_1 (for example) and then thermally anchored both around chamber B and to a copper post attached to Y.

FIG. 83. A thermal conductivity cryostat associated with a Simon expansion liquefier (after Berman, 1951).

Figure 83 from Berman (1951) shows a thermal conductivity cryostat similar in principle to 82 (b), but in which the inner liquid chamber is the expansion vessel of a Simon liquefier. As is discussed in Chapter VII, such an expansion vessel can be temperature controlled below 4·2° K by pumping on liquid helium, between 10° and 4·2° K by controlled expansion, and from 10° to 33° K by admitting liquid hydrogen into B and letting it boil at a controlled pressure.

Details are given below (with Figures 84, 85) of a cryostat similar to that described briefly by White and Woods (1955), and based on that of White (1953). Such cryostats have been found useful not only for measurements of thermal conductivity, thermoelectric power, and electrical resistance of specimens in rod form, but also for the electrical resistance of fine wires (using exchange gas in the inner container which is then made vacuum tight), and has been adapted for use in measuring mechanical properties over the temperature range from 2° K to room temperature; one has been in operation for nearly six years and has given no trouble, the only vacuum leaks having been occasional ones due to leaking glass stop-cocks or careless soldering of the Wood's alloy joint which seals the outer vacuum jacket.

With a voltage signal from a Au+Co:Ag+Au thermocouple (see Chapter IV) a chopper-amplifier can be used to regulate the power fed to the electrical heater attached to the inner experimental chamber, so that its temperature may be controlled (see White and Woods, 1955; Dauphinee and Woods, 1955) to a constancy of about 0·001° K at temperatures outside the range of available liquids. In experiments not involving such precise temperature control the heater (H_2 in Figure 84) could be manually controlled. H_2 has normally been a 1,000-ohm resistor of constantan or manganin wound onto a baked Formel varnish on the copper chamber and then revarnished and baked; however, a 1,000-ohm carbon resistor (I.R.C. resistor) in a copper sleeve soldered to the inner chamber seems to work adequately.

The Au+Co:Ag+Au junction of the control thermocouple is soldered to the copper bush at t_1; the Au+Co:Cu (40 B. & S. enamelled copper wire) and Ag+Au:Co junctions are thermally anchored to the re-entrant copper bush t_2, with cigarette paper and nail polish as insulation and cement respectively.

The outer can is of 3 in. diameter brass tube ($\frac{1}{16}$ in. wall thickness) and is suspended by the German silver pumping tubes (0·2 mm wall thickness) from the main top plate. These German silver tubes are soft soldered (marked S) through bushes of brass or copper which are hard soldered into the plates. The two joints marked X are Wood's metal joints by means of which the outer brass can and inner copper shield (gold-plated) can be easily removed and replaced after the mounting of specimens. The valve for inlet of liquid from the dewar into the small copper

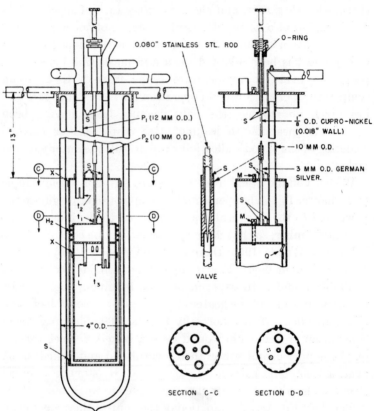

FIG. 84. A temperature-controlled cryostat used at the National
Research Council (Ottawa).

inner chamber, is a stainless steel needle of 10° total taper seating in a brass shoulder and is operated by turning the knurled head above the main top plate.

For measurements of the conductivity of a sample in rod form, the rod is fitted with small copper end-pieces (shown in Figure 85) which are soldered to or, if soldering is not possible, are cemented to the rod. One copper end-piece is then fixed by Wood's metal into the 0·040 in. hole in the copper pillar L (seen in Figure 84) and the heater H_1 is similarly fixed to the other end-piece on the specimen. For potential leads, thermal and electrical, two short lengths of copper wire (about 0·030 in. diameter) are tightly wrapped around the specimen, then soldered or cemented to it. The copper gas-thermometer bulbs (Figure 85) are gold-plated

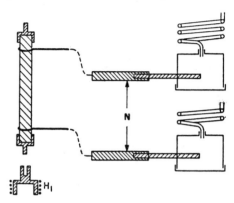

FIG. 85. Method of mounting thermal conductivity specimens.

to prevent tarnishing and hence to keep the radiation corrections small and constant; they are connected by lengths of 0·5 mm outer diameter (0·3 mm inner diameter) German silver capillary tubing to the external manometer system, the two capillaries passing through small holes in the bushes marked M on Figure 84. In many experiments it is necessary to prevent a partial electrical short-circuit through these thermometers and their supporting capillaries, so that a linkage N (Figure 85) which is electrically insulating but thermally conducting must be made. This is done by covering the copper strip ($\frac{1}{16}$ in. $\times \frac{1}{64}$ in.), which would otherwise connect the thermometers via a Wood's metal joint to the copper potential leads from the specimen, with a layer of Formel varnish and cigarette paper, baking the varnish, adding fresh varnish and then wrapping this layer with copper foil (0·003 in.–0·004 in. thick) and baking again to harden the varnish. The copper potential leads are then attached by Wood's metal to this foil, when the specimen is in position in the cryostat.

As mentioned, both inner and outer containers (Figure 84) are evacuated during thermal conductivity measurements through a common pumping line P_1. In this case two holes at the bottom of the inner shield are left open, the inner shield is merely attached at X by a heavy vacuum grease, the second pumping tube P_2 is sealed at its top end and all electrical leads

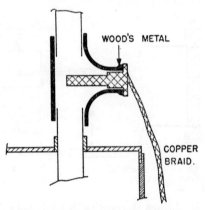

WOOD'S METAL

COPPER BRAID.

FIG. 86. A modification to the cryostat (Figure 84) which allows electrical leads to be thermally anchored at the bath temperature.

are brought down the pumping tube P_1. This is convenient since the leads may be thermally anchored at the temperature of the bath by wrapping them around the copper bush t_2 (holding them by cotton thread and nail polish), and then bringing them into the inner experimental space through the holes at Q and anchoring them again to the copper bush t_3.

However, when the electrical resistance of fine wire specimens is being measured, it is essential to have exchange gas in the inner space to preserve thermal equilibrium. In this case the inner shield is made vacuum-tight and electrical leads are brought in through pumping tube P_2 and thermally anchored at t_3; so that these leads may not conduct too much heat to the inner chamber, they are thermally anchored at the temperature of the liquid in the surrounding dewar via a copper pillar inserted into the pumping tube P_2 (see Figure 86).

In either case the electrical leads emerging from the top of the pumping tubes are taken through short lengths of ceramic tubing which rest in a brass bush (not shown); a vacuum wax, Apiezon W, is used to seal the top of the tube where the leads emerge.

The operation of such a cryostat is as follows:

(a) Below 4·2° K: liquid helium is at atmospheric pressure in the surrounding dewar and boils under controlled pressure in the inner chamber.

(b) 4·2°–54° K: with liquid helium in the surrounding dewar, electronically controlled heating of the inner vessel maintains the required temperature.

(c) 55°–90° K: liquid oxygen is at atmospheric pressure in the surrounding dewar, boils under controlled pressure in the inner chamber. Similarly, with liquid nitrogen the range 63°–78° K can be controlled.

(d) Above 90° K: with liquid nitrogen or oxygen in dewar, the inner vessel is electronically temperature controlled.

Note that in measurements of thermal conductivity or thermo-electric power, temperature drifts which are comparable with the difference δT being measured, over a period of time of the order of the equilibrium time of the specimen and thermometer assembly, must be eliminated; with specimens which are poor heat conductors, this 'equilibrium' time may vary from minutes ($\sim 10°$ K) to hours ($\sim 100°$ K). As a result few measurements of these quantities have been carried out above 150° K in cryostats of this type, as it is usually less time-consuming and more accurate to use specimens of very different shape factor, i.e. of much smaller l/A, and to use thermometers such as thermocouples which respond more rapidly. However, for measurements of electrical resistance in which exchange gas can be used in the inner space to promote rapid thermal equilibrium, the range from 150° to 300° K can be adequately covered.

Another variation of the method of thermal conductivity measurement is that used very successfully by Powell and his collaborators at the National Bureau of Standards (Powell *et al.*, 1957). They use a rather extensive length of specimen in rod form, attach eight thermocouples at points along its length and automatically record the eight different temperatures when a temperature gradient has been established. This yields seven values of thermal conductivity, each at a slightly different temperature, from which in practice a weighted mean is obtained. Their thermocouples of Au+2·1 per cent Co: Cu give a thermo-electric power of about 40 μV/° K above 100° K, falling to 30 μV/° K at 50° K, 20 μV/° K at about 30° K, and 10 μV/° K at about 12° K.

4. Cryostats for electrical resistance or Hall-effect measurements

From the cryogenic viewpoint electrical resistance and such quantities as magneto-resistance or Hall effect are among the properties whose measurement presents no great difficulties. For one thing such determinations require the entry of only a limited number of electrical leads and are unaffected by exchange of thermal energy with the surroundings; the specimen may be kept in thermal equilibrium with a thermometer either by direct contact, by exchange gas, or by immersion of specimen and thermometer in a common refrigerating bath. Equally impor-tant is the fact that slow drifts in temperature of the specimen and its surroundings do not directly affect the determination as they do in calorimetric or thermal conduction measurements, except in so far as they introduce a small uncertainty as to the precise temperature of the specimen at the particular time that the measurement is made.

It is relatively difficult to measure the specific heat or heat conductivity of a solid at low temperatures, even when a com-paratively crude estimate is required. But by merely attaching current and potential leads to a wire or rod and immersing it in a dewar of liquid helium, hydrogen, oxygen, etc., a reliable value of its electrical resistance may be obtained provided that there is a suitable electrical measuring circuit.

Of course, for precise calibration of electrical-resistance thermometers as secondary standards many precautions must be observed in the temperature determination as we discussed in Chapter IV. Frequently the resistance thermometer in capsule form is placed in good thermal contact with a copper block, which also houses a vapour-pressure bulb and gas thermometer.

More generally, values of electrical resistance of a metal in wire or rod form are determined at certain fixed temperatures or over limited ranges of temperature by immersion in a series of liquefied gas refrigerants—boiling at atmospheric pressure or under controlled pressure.

For values over the whole range from about 1° K to room temperature, a cryostat of the type described in some detail in § 2 (Figure 84) may be used. In this cryostat several specimens, in the form of wires or rods, are suspended in a strain-free manner from the copper pillar in the inner experimental vessel. To each specimen current and potential leads are attached, and the inner vessel is filled with a small pressure of helium exchange gas ($\sim$ 1 mm Hg) to preserve temperature equilibrium. By controlling the pressure over the evaporating liquid in the small inner chamber or by controlled electrical heating of this chamber, temperatures over the range 1° K to room temperature can be attained; temperatures are measured by the gas thermometers in the inner space, by the vapour pressure of the evaporating liquid, or with a platinum resistance thermometer in the inner space. At temperatures above, say, 170° K, a convenient alternative to the use of liquid oxygen (or nitrogen) in the dewar and electrical heating of the inner chamber, is the use of a well-stirred bath of alcohol or other low-freezing-point liquid, cooled by an immersed copper coil with a slow stream of liquid nitrogen passing through it.

Commonly available liquids which are used for such a low-temperature bath are methyl alcohol (melting-point at −98° C), ethyl alcohol (melting-point at about −116° C), and *iso*pentane (melting-point at −160° C). However, their highly inflammable nature may make it preferable to use a non-flammable mixture of organic liquids, if such baths are to be used frequently. As suggested by Scott (1941; see also Kanolt, 1926, for recommended non-flammable mixtures), a non-flammable eutectic

mixture of carbon tetrachloride and chloroform may be used
down to $-75°$ C, and a five-component system $(14.5\%$ chloroform, 25.3% methylene chloride, 33.4% ethyl bromide, 10.4%
trans-dichloroethylene, and 16.4% trichloroethylene) may be
used to below $-140°$ C.

5. Cryostats for investigating mechanical properties

Recently there has been an awakened experimental interest in
the low-temperature aspects of such metallurgical problems as
the mechanism of flow stress, brittle fracture, and in the hardness
and tensile strength of materials. No doubt a number of factors
have contributed to this interest, among them the relatively
greater accessibility of liquid helium as a refrigerant, the
importance of more knowledge of these properties for purposes
or large-scale cryogenic engineering and the considerable
advances in fundamental knowledge of the character of dislocations which affect mechanical properties so significantly.

From the point of view of designing a suitable cryostat for
measurement of stress-strain relations, no very new cryogenic
problem is presented as the material may be surrounded by
exchange gas to preserve thermal equilibrium and its temperature may therefore be easily measured by a suitable
low-temperature thermometer; the only slightly different
requirement is a means of transmitting stress to the body under
examination.

The diagram of Figure 87 illustrates the adaptation of the
cryostat described in some detail in § 2 (Figure 84) above, for
flow-stress measurements by Z. S. Basinski of the National
Research Council in Ottawa (private communication).

The chief alterations to the design of the cryostat are that a
heavy wall ($\frac{5}{8}$ in. outer diameter, $\frac{1}{4}$ in. inner diameter) stainless
steel tube is taken centrally from the top plate down into the
inner experimental space and to this is rigidly fixed a stainless
steel 'cage'; one end of the specimen is clamped by a grip at the
bottom of this 'cage' and the other is clamped bo the bottom of
a $\frac{3}{16}$ in. stainless steel rod which is located freely in the centre of
the stainless steel tube. At the top the tube is attached to a fixed

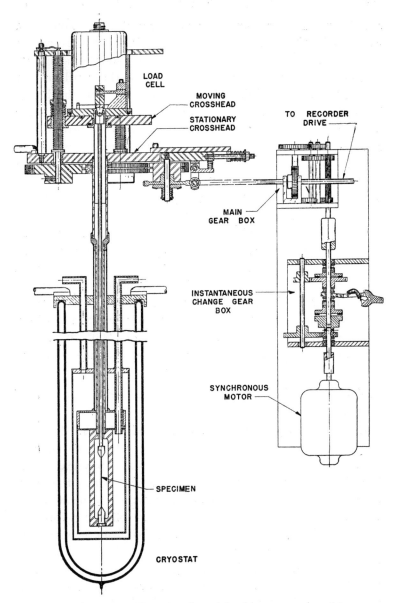

LOAD
CELL

MOVING
CROSSHEAD

STATIONARY
CROSSHEAD

TO RECORDER
DRIVE

MAIN
GEAR BOX

INSTANTANEOUS
CHANGE GEAR
BOX

SYNCHRONOUS
MOTOR

SPECIMEN

CRYOSTAT

Fig. 87. Cryostat of Figure 84 adapted for the measurement of flow-
stress of materials.

crosshead; on a screw-driven moving crosshead is mounted a vacuum-tight load cell in which a 24S aluminium cantilever beam is used to register the tension in the central stainless steel rod; four resistance strain gauges are mounted on the cantilever and form a Wheatstone bridge network, the output from this bridge being amplified and applied to a Speedomax recorder. The chart of the Speedomax recorder is driven from the gearbox and synchronous motor which also operate the moving crosshead of the tensile tester, so that a direct load-elongation curve is recorded.

Basinski's cryostat† has proved suitable for determining stress-strain relations at temperatures from about 2°–300° K.

Among cryostats for low-temperature mechanical testing, are that of Wessel (1954) and the large cryostat cooled by expansion engines used by Collins at M.I.T. A considerable amount of research of technical interest on the mechanical properties of metals has been carried out by Kropschot and his collaborators at the N.B.S. Boulder Laboratories; their results have been obtained over the temperature range from 300°–20° K (see, for example, Kropschot, 1955, and Kropschot and Graham, 1956 a, 1956 b).

6. Cryostats for optical and X-ray examination of materials

In the past few years there has been a greatly increased interest in the properties of materials at low temperatures, not only by physicists but also by physical chemists and physical metal-lurgists. One particular avenue of research which the wider availability of refrigerants like liquid helium has encouraged is the measurement of optical properties of solids, e.g. infra-red and ultra-violet transmission; closely linked from the viewpoint of cryostat design are X-ray diffraction studies, whether they be an investigation of phase change or measurement of expansion coefficient from the measured lattice spacing. In all these cases, solids must be cooled, maintained at specified low

---

† A brief description of a similar tensile testing machine, temperature controlled at low temperatures by the Swenson Method (see § 7.5) has been published (Basinski, 1957).

temperatures, and subjected to electromagnetic radiation, which must therefore have free access to and exit from the experimental region of the cryostat.

Usually temperature control need not be precise in experiments of this type as fluctuations of one or two degrees in temperature are unimportant. However, the necessity for providing unrestricted passage to a beam of infra-red radiation or X-radiation poses its own special problems.

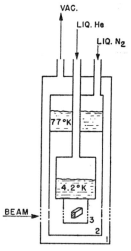

A suitable type of cryostat is shown schematically in Figure 88. The radiation beam in its passage from source to specimen must pass through three barriers: (1) the outer wall of the vacuum jacket which is at room temperature; hence the required type of window, e.g. beryllium or cellophane for X-radiation, silica for ultra-violet, or rock salt for infra-red radiation, may be cemented with Araldite or sealed with a flange and rubber O-ring; (2) the liquid-nitrogen-cooled radiation shield—usually of polished copper—which need not be

FIG. 88. Schematic diagram of the type of cryostat which may be used for optical or X-ray examination of materials.

vacuum-tight, as the regions on both sides of (2) may be pumped through a common line, and therefore holes or slits may be freely cut in it to act as windows for the beam; (3) the final wall, which may or may not require a vacuum-sealed transmission window depending on whether the specimen must be surrounded by exchange gas or can be supported in good thermal contact with the liquid-helium chamber to maintain temperature equilibrium.

Since the windows providing access for the beam must necessarily transmit some thermal radiation from surfaces at room temperature and at 77° K to the specimen, the latter must be in quite close thermal contact with the helium vessel if it is to be at a temperature within a few tenths of a degree of the helium bath. Experience has shown that with most pressure contacts and many cemented contacts the equilibrium temperature of a specimen may be many degrees above that of the low-temperature vessel to which it is fixed. This is particularly so in the case of solids which are poor thermal conductors, as their surface temperatures may be raised considerably by absorption of incident radiation. Of course, in the case of a solid metallic

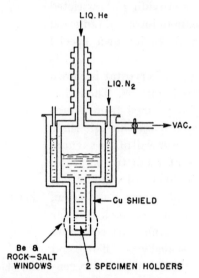

FIG. 89. Schematic diagram of a cryostat, similar to that used by Duerig and Mador (1952) for optical measurements.

X-ray specimen which is solder-bonded to a heavy copper pillar, itself in contact with liquid helium, temperature equilibrium may be preserved quite well.

Two examples of low-temperature optical cells are shown in Figures 89 and 90. In the first schematic diagram is a cryostat similar to that of Duerig and Mador (1952) in which no exchange gas is used around the specimen; they find that by thermally bonding their crystal to a copper holder with silicone grease (impregnated with silver dust) or a silver conducting paste or indium, the crystal reaches a temperature of about 5°–8° K. A thermocouple of Au+Co: copper is attached to the crystal surface to check its temperature. The 1-litre helium vessel is copper plated and polished to reduce radiation inflow and is suspended by a ⅝ in. outer diameter (0·028 in. wall) stainless steel tube; a polished copper radiation shield surrounds the section of the helium chamber and specimen chamber which

are below the annular liquid-nitrogen vessel. A sylphon bellows and a rack and pinion arrangement (not shown) allow vertical movement of the specimens in order that they may be aligned with the optical beam.

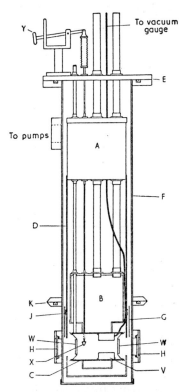

FIG. 90. Low-temperature absorption cell (after Roberts, 1955).

In the absorption cell of Roberts (1955) shown in Figure 90, a rock salt window is used to seal the specimen compartment so that it can be filled with helium gas and the specimen kept within 1° K of the cooling bath at temperatures from 4·2°–330° K. This cryostat is rather similar to that described in 1949 by McMahon, Hainer, and King (1949) who used special dome-shaped silver chloride windows sealed with a spring washer and lock nut arrangement. Roberts (1954) found that a rather simpler seal, capable of withstanding repeated cooling, could be made by cementing a thin flexible diaphragm of copper (0·003 in. thick) to the window with thermo-setting Araldite. The outer edge of the copper shim is soldered to the copper chamber (see Figure 91). In Roberts's cryostat, the temperature of the gas-filled specimen chamber is measured by a gas thermometer which occupies the annular volume V (Figure 90) surrounding the radiation beam.

The method of construction used in Roberts's cryostat in

which the two liquid chambers are directly above one another
has advantages, in so far as the construction and maintenance
of high vacuum-tight joints are concerned. The container B is
of copper and A is of brass or copper; brass bushes are hard
soldered into these containers and thin-walled cupro-nickel (or
German silver) tubes are soft soldered through these. The
radiation shield D should be of polished
copper sufficiently thick-walled (say
$\sim 0{\cdot}050$ in.) to ensure adequate heat
conduction along it and be well soldered
to chamber A; then temperatures within
a few degrees of the liquid nitrogen in A
should be maintained over the entire
shield. A simple and effective alternative to polishing or plating the containers and shields, is to wrap them with
thin aluminium foil which has an emissivity of about 0·04.

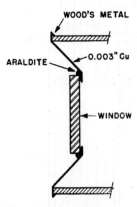

FIG. 91. An optical win-
dow for low-temperature
use (after Roberts, 1954).

An interesting development in optical
windows was described by Warschauer
and Paul (1956), who tested a thin polyethylene window and found it remained vacuum-tight after
repeated cooling to 4·2° K and warming to room temperature.
They milled a window aperture from brass or copper stock about
$\frac{1}{8}$ in. thick, leaving a flat area about $\frac{1}{4}$ in. wide surrounding the
opening. The polyethylene film, 0·005 in. thick, was stuck to this
supporting area with a thin film of silicone grease. A greased flat
retaining plate was then clamped down tightly onto the polyethylene by four screws. Under a one-atmosphere pressure
difference the film window assumed a domed shape but remained
vacuum-tight.

Other cryostats for study of absorption spectra, etc., at low
temperature have been described by Taylor, Smith, and
Johnston (1951), and Geiger (1955).

As we mentioned at the outset, problems in design of low-
temperature X-ray cameras are rather similar to those arising
in optical cells. The cryostat for X-ray diffraction studies of the

alkali metals at low temperatures used by Barrett and his
collaborators at Chicago was described at the Oxford conference
on low-temperature crystallography (Barrett, 1956) and is
illustrated in Figure 92. The specimen in this case is cooled by

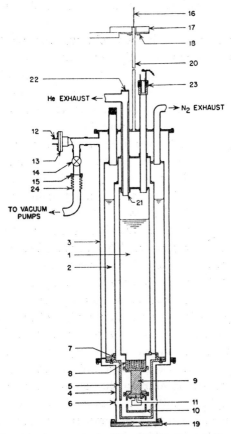

FIG. 92. A cryostat for X-ray diffraction studies
(after Barrett, 1956).

conduction through the bar (9) which is in close thermal contact
with the bottom of chamber 1. Chamber 1 holds about 2 litres
of liquid helium (or hydrogen or nitrogen). The specimen can be
changed by opening the O-ring joint between (3) and (4) and the
conical joint (7). Another X-ray camera, described by Pearson
(1956) at this conference, is basically similar in design but allows

for rotation of the cryostat with respect to the external X-ray tube and casette. Both this camera and that described by Figgins, Jones, and Riley (1956) were intended for the accurate measurement of lattice spacings by X-ray diffraction methods, thus determining the thermal expansion coefficient of a solid at low temperatures.

Finally, returning to the general form of cryostat sketched in Figure 88 at the beginning of this section, there arises the problem

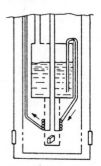

FIG. 93. Possible method of temperature control for a low-temperature camera.

of controlling specimen temperatures outside the easily accessible ranges $1°–4°$ K, $55°–90°$ K, and $10°–20°$ K. One way of solving this problem is to separate the specimen cavity from the lower liquid reservoir by a metal post of carefully chosen material and dimensions. Then with the aid of an electrical heater attached to the cavity or on the post adjacent to the cavity, it can be raised to temperatures above that of the liquid boiling in the reservoir. This method has obvious drawbacks if it is desired to operate at temperatures over the entire range from $2°$ K to room temperature; no single choice of connecting post is likely to allow temperature control at both $5°$ and $40°$ K with liquid helium in the lower reservoir, or at both $60°$ and $150°$ K with liquid oxygen, and yet preserve a relatively low rate of evaporation of the refrigerant in each case.

Perhaps something akin to that shown diagrammatically in Figure 93 might be suitable. This modification of Figure 88 is based on the Swenson type of temperature controller (see § 7.5 for more details) in which liquid is drawn slowly from the reservoir through a narrow copper tube which is closely wound around and solder-bonded to the copper specimen chamber. The evaporated gas is then led to a needle valve at room temperature, through which a mechanical vacuum pump extracts it; by using a fine control needle valve, the rate of flow can be varied sufficiently to control the chamber over a wide temperature range.

7. Magnetic susceptibility cryostats

The many methods of measuring magnetic susceptibilities can be divided into two broad classes—static and induction methods. The latter involve a measurement or comparison of mutual or self-inductances. Using an a.c. inductance bridge or a ballistic throw method, they have been widely used for the measurement of susceptibilities of paramagnetic salts at temperatures near 1° K and below but have not been greatly used for absolute measurements at higher temperatures (see, however, inductance bridge of Erickson, Roberts, and Dabbs, 1954, for use in measuring susceptibilities below 77° K and the development of an improved inductance method by McKim and Wolf, 1957).

Of the static methods generally used, those involving a weight determination and therefore classed as balance methods appear to be the most precise. The various methods and their relative merits have been discussed in standard texts such as Bates (1948), Casimir (1940), Stoner (1934), and Van Vleck (1932). The balance methods depend on the force exerted on a body placed in a non-homogeneous magnetic field; this force is measured by suspending the body from a sensitive balance. In the so-called Faraday method of measurement, a sample is used which is sufficiently small that the field H does not vary appreciably within the dimensions of the body, but is nevertheless sufficiently inhomogeneous to exert a measurable force given by

$$\mathbf{F} = \mathbf{M} \wedge \operatorname{grad} \mathbf{H},$$

where $\mathbf{M}$ is the magnetic moment. Hence, if χ_m is the mass susceptibility and m the mass, then

$$F_y = m\chi_m H_x \frac{\partial H_x}{\partial y}$$

is the vertical force exerted by an inhomogeneous field of strength H_x in a horizontal direction and gradient $\partial H_x/\partial y$ in the vertical direction.

An alternative balance method is that of Gouy in which the specimen is in the form of a long cylindrical rod. If the lower end is in a homogeneous field H and the upper end in a much weaker field H_0, then the force acting on a sample of cross-sectional area A is

$$F = \frac{\chi_v - \chi_g}{2}(H^2 - H_0^2),$$

where χ_v is the volume susceptibility of the sample and χ_g is the susceptibility of the gas medium.

In either method a critical requirement is a sensitive balance of which many types have been described over the years. The reader who may be interested is referred to the description of the Leiden balance (Kamerlingh Onnes and Perrier, 1913; Oosterhuis, 1914), the general descriptions of other types with references by Bates (1948), and papers by Gulbransen (1944), Hutchison and Reekie (1946), Dawson and Lister (1950), and Bowers and Long (1955) among others.

Returning to the cryogenic aspects of the problems associated with susceptibility measurement by a balance method, we note two distinctive features:

(a) the sample must be freely suspended with no mechanical constraint from a microbalance;

(b) vibrations of the sample or balance should be avoided as much as possible.

The result is a narrow vertical tube in which the sample is suspended; the tube and balance (or part of them) are filled with exchange gas to keep the sample in temperature equilibrium with the nearby tube wall. The tube is then immersed in a dewar which, to ensure maximum field strength, is narrow in the region that is in the pole gap of the magnet. The requirement of no constraint prevents any thermometer being attached to the sample under investigation unless perhaps a thermocouple is attached to the sample and the two thermocouple leads form the suspension.

A common type of susceptibility cryostat is that illustrated schematically in Figure 94 (cf. Kamerlingh Onnes and Perrier, 1913; McGuire and Lane, 1949). The dewar containing liquid helium or liquid nitrogen may be pumped to control the temperature of the liquid bath if care is taken to avoid vibration from the mechanical pump being transmitted to the dewar and balance.

The chief problems arise when control of temperatures outside those covered by a liquefied gas is required. One method of controlling temperature at say 30° or 110° K has been used by Hedgcock (submitted *Rev. Sci. Instrum.*, 1958) and is illustrated

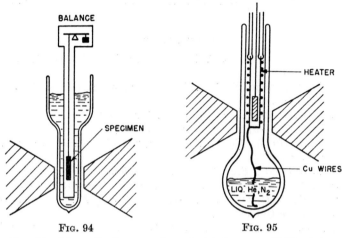

FIG. 94.

FIG. 95.

FIG. 94. Schematic diagram of a cryostat for susceptibility determinations.

FIG. 95. Cryostat used by F. T. Hedgcock for the measurement of magnetic susceptibility.

in Figure 95. The lower section of the sample tube is of copper of sufficient wall thickness to ensure a relatively small temperature gradient along the length of the specimen. This copper tube has an electrical heater and thermometers (carbon thermometer and a copper resistance thermometer) attached to it, and a heavy copper wire (six strands of no. 24 B. & S.) acts as a partial thermal link between the copper tube and the liquid in the wide tail of the dewar vessel. By carefully selecting the dimensions of this thermal link and varying the heater power, temperatures above that of the liquid refrigerant can be maintained around the specimen.

An alternative to this might be the use of a 'Swenson' type of control (see Chapter VII) in which copper tubing about $\frac{1}{8}$ in.

outer diameter, 0·015 in. wall) is closely wound around the copper specimen tube; one end of this fine tubing extends to the bottom of the dewar while the other leads to a needle valve and mechanical pump. By controlling the setting of the needle valve, liquid is drawn up through the fine copper tube to cool the specimen chamber. Again a thermometer and a resistance heater would be attached to the chamber in the vicinity of the specimen.

REFERENCES

ANDREWS, F. A., WEBBER, R. T., and SPOHR, D. A. (1951). *Phys. Rev.* **84**, 994.

AVEN, M. H., CRAIG, R. S., and WALLACE, W. E. (1956). *Rev. Sci. Instrum.* **27**, 623.

BARRETT, C. S. (1956). *Brit. J. Appl. Phys.* **7**, 426.

BASINSKI, Z. S. (1957). *Proc. Roy. Soc.* A, **240**, 229.

BATES, L. F. (1948). *Modern Magnetism*, 2nd edn., Cambridge University Press.

BERMAN, R. (1951). *Proc. Roy. Soc.* A, **208**, 90.

BOWERS, R., and LONG, E. A. (1955). *Rev. Sci. Instrum.* **26**, 337.

CASIMIR, H. B. G. (1940). *Magnetism and Very Low Temperatures*, Cambridge University Press.

DAUPHINEE, T. M., MACDONALD, D. K. C., and PRESTON-THOMAS, H. (1954). *Proc. Roy. Soc.* A, **221**, 267.

—— and WOODS, S. B. (1955). *Rev. Sci. Instrum.* **26**, 693.

DAWSON, J. K., and LISTER, M. W. (1950). *J. Chem. Soc.*, p. 2177.

DUERIG, W. H., and MADOR, I. L. (1952). *Rev. Sci. Instrum.* **23**, 421.

ERICKSON, R. A., ROBERTS, L. D., and DABBS, J. W. T. (1954). Ibid. **25**, 1178.

ESTERMANN, I., and ZIMMERMAN, J. E. (1952). *J. Appl. Phys.* **23**, 578.

FIGGINS, B. F., JONES, G. O., and RILEY, D. P. (1956). *Phil. Mag.* **1**, 747.

FREDERIKSE, H. P. R. (1953). *Phys. Rev.* **92**, 248.

GEIGER, F. E. (1955). *Rev. Sci. Instrum.* **26**, 383.

GULBRANSEN, E. A. (1944). Ibid. **15**, 201.

DE HAAS, W. J., and RADEMAKERS, A. (1940). *Physica*, **7**, 992.

HILL, R. W. (1953). *J. Sci. Instrum.* **30**, 331.

HULM, J. K. (1950). *Proc. Roy. Soc.* A, **204**, 98.

HUTCHISON, T. S., and REEKIE, J. (1946). *J. Sci. Instrum.* **23**, 209.

JAN, J. P., PEARSON, W. B., and TEMPLETON, I. M. (1955). 'Conférence de Physique des Basses Températures', p. 418, Annexe 1955–3, *Suppl. Bull. Inst. int. Froid*, Paris.

KAMERLINGH ONNES, H., and PERRIER, A. (1913). *Leiden Comm.* 139a.

KANOLT, C. W. (1926). *Bur. Stand. Sci. Paper*, 520, March.

KEESOM, P. H., and PEARLMAN, N. (1956). *Handb. der Physik*, **14**, 282.

KEESOM, W. H., and CLARK, C. W. (1935). *Physica*, **2**, 698.

—— and VAN DEN ENDE, J. N. (1930). *Leiden Comm.* 203d.

KROPSCHOT, R. H. (1955). *Proc. 1954 Cryogenic Engng. Conf.*, N.B.S. Report No. 3517, p. 164.

—— and GRAHAM, W. F. (1956a). N.B.S. Report No. 5009, U.S. Dept. of Commerce.

—— —— (1956b). Ibid. No. 5024, U.S. Dept. of Commerce.

McGUIRE, T. R., and LANE, C. T. (1949). *Rev. Sci. Instrum.* **20**, 489.

McKIM, F. R., and WOLF, W. P. (1957). *J. Sci. Instrum.* **34**, 64.

McMAHON, H. O., HAINER, R. M., and KING, G. W. (1949). *J. Opt. Soc. Amer.* **39**, 786.

MORRISON, J. A., and LOS, J. M. (1950). *Faraday Soc. Disc.* No. 8, p. 321.

—— PATTERSON, D., and DUGDALE, J. S. (1955). *Canad. J. Chem.* **33**, 375.

DE NOBEL, J. (1951). *Physica*, **17**, 551.

OLSEN, J. L. (1952). *Proc. Phys. Soc.* **A65**, 518.

OOSTERHUIS, E. (1914). *Leiden Comm.* 139b.

PARKINSON, D. H., SIMON, F. E., and SPEDDING, F. H. (1951). *Proc. Roy. Soc.* A, **207**, 137.

PEARLMAN, N., and KEESOM, P. H. (1952). *Phys. Rev.* **88**, 398.

PEARSON, W. B. (1956). *Brit. J. Appl. Phys.* **7**, 427.

POWELL, R. L., ROGERS, W. M., and COFFIN, D. O. (1957). *J. Res. Nat. Bur. Stand.* **59**, 349.

RAMANATHAN, K. G., and SRINIVASAN, T. M. (1955). *Phil. Mag.* **46**, 338.

RAYNE, J. A. (1956). *Aust. J. Phys.* **9**, 189.

—— and KEMP, W. R. G. (1956). *Phil. Mag.* **1**, 918.

ROBERTS, V. (1954). *J. Sci. Instrum.* **31**, 251.

—— (1955). Ibid. **32**, 294.

ROSENBERG, H. M. (1955) *Phil. Trans. Roy. Soc.* **247**, 441.

SCOTT, R. B. (1941). *Temperature*, p. 206, Reinhold, N.Y.

SILVIDI, A. A., and DAUNT, J. G. (1950). *Phys. Rev.* **77**, 125.

STONER, E. C. (1934). *Magnetism and Matter*, Methuen, London.

TAYLOR, W. J., SMITH, A. L., and JOHNSTON, H. L. (1951). *J. Opt. Soc. Amer.* **41**, 91.

VAN VLECK, J. H. (1932). *Theory of Electric and Magnetic Susceptibilities*, Clarendon Press, Oxford.

WARSCHAUER, D. M., and PAUL W. (1956). *Rev. Sci. Instrum.* **27**, 419.

WESSEL, E. T. (1954). *Proc. 1954 Cryogenic Engng. Conf.*, N.B.S. Report No 3517, p. 170.

WHITE, G. K. (1953). *Proc. Phys. Soc.* **A66**, 559; *Aust. J. Phys.* **6**, 397.

—— and WOODS, S. B. (1955). *Canad. J. Phys.* **33**, 58.

WILKINSON, K. R., and WILKS, J. (1949). *J. Sci. Instrum.* **26**, 19.

CHAPTER VI

HEAT TRANSFER

1. Introduction

A DETERMINATION of the physical properties of materials at temperatures considerably different from the ambient temperature requires some degree of thermal isolation of the material from its surroundings; the degree of isolation must be sufficient to meet the demands of temperature control, temperature measurement, and in the case of low-temperature research, the available refrigerating capacity of the coolant. In a measurement such as the determination of heat capacity by the adiabatic method, the sample must also be thermally isolated from its immediate environment—the cooling medium. These conditions imply that an important factor in the design of a successful cryostat is the ability to predict the degree of thermal isolation or in other words, to calculate the transfer of heat that will take place between the specimen and its surroundings; then materials and methods of construction must be used which will ensure this heat transfer being within or below certain allowable limits.

In general, heat may be transferred by conduction, convection, and radiation. In most low-temperature applications, thermal isolation is assisted by partial evacuation of gas from the interior of the cryostat so that convection is eliminated. Then effective heat transfer takes place by conduction through the residual low-pressure gas, conduction through the solids that interconnect the various parts of the cryostat, and by radiation. In addition such factors as Joule heating in electrical leads, eddy current heating, mechanical vibration, adsorption or desorption of gases may contribute to the heat transfer.

Of the three major processes responsible for heat conduction at low temperatures that due to conduction by solids can be estimated generally with a fair degree of accuracy; low-pressure gas conduction and radiation transfer may be estimated with rather less accuracy, the uncertainty depending on our lack of knowledge of the accommodation coefficient and emissivity respectively. However, it is usually possible to estimate an upper bound for the heat transfer by these processes and therefore ensure that materials, degree of high vacuum, etc., used are sufficient to meet the required demands.

The remainder of this chapter deals in some detail with the methods of calculating heat transferred by these processes.

2. Conduction of heat by a gas

An elementary treatment on the basis of kinetic theory indicates that in a gas at normal pressures the thermal conductivity λ and viscosity η are given by (see, for example, Roberts, 1940, or Jeans, 1948)

$$\lambda = \tfrac{1}{3}mln\bar{v}C_v, \quad \eta = \tfrac{1}{3}mln\bar{v},$$

where m = mass of one molecule,

         l = mean free path,

         n = number of molecule per cm³,

         $\bar{v}$ = mean velocity,

         C_v = specific heat per gm.

Thus if ρ is the density,

$$\lambda = \tfrac{1}{3}\rho l\bar{v}C_v, \quad \eta = \tfrac{1}{3}\rho l\bar{v},$$

and $\lambda = \eta C_v.$

Since the mean free path $l \propto 1/p$, both λ and η are seen to be pressure independent at least to a first approximation, and to depend on the temperature through their dependence on the mean velocity $\bar{v}$.

Experiment (and a more detailed theory) indicates that $\lambda = \text{constant}.\eta C_v$ where the constant has a value of 1·5–2·5 for most common gases. As may be seen from Figures 50 and 51 (Chapter III), λ and η increase monotonically with increasing temperature as T^n where the exponent n has experimental values in the range 0·6–0·9 for hydrogen, helium, nitrogen, and oxygen.

However, as we have pointed out before, the residual gas pressure in a cryostat is nearly always reduced to a point where the mean free path becomes comparable with the dimensions of the system; at room temperature a pressure of $\sim 10^{-4}$ mm Hg is sufficiently low that the mean free path is ~ 100 cm. At such pressures, the average molecule may travel from a hot wall to a cold wall without collision with another gas molecule, and the thermal conductivity becomes a function of the number of molecules present (and also their mean velocity), i.e. at low pressures $\lambda \propto n \propto p$.

For approximately parallel surfaces at temperatures T_1 and T_2, the heat transferred, $\dot{Q}$, by conduction through a gas at low pressure p dynes cm^{-2} is given by (see Kennard, 1938):

$$\dot{Q} = \frac{a_0}{4} \frac{\gamma+1}{\gamma-1} \sqrt{\left(\frac{2R}{\pi M}\right)} p \frac{T_2 - T_1}{\sqrt{T}} \text{ ergs cm}^{-2} \text{ sec}^{-1}, \qquad (40)$$

where M is the molecular weight and γ is the ratio of specific heats of the gas, R is the gas constant in ergs mole^{-1} deg^{-1}; a_0 is related to the individual accommodation coefficients a_1 and a_2 and the areas A_1 and A_2 of the two surfaces by

$$a_0 = \frac{a_1 a_2}{a_2 + (A_2/A_1)(1-a_2)a_1},$$

so that if $A_1 \simeq A_2$, then

$$a_0 = \frac{a_1 a_2}{a_1 + a_2 - a_1 a_2};$$

if also
$$a_1 = a_2 = a, \quad a_0 = \frac{a}{2-a}$$

$$\simeq \tfrac{1}{2}a \text{ for } a \to 0$$

$$\simeq a \quad \text{for } a \to 1.$$

Accommodation coefficients are normally measured for the case of a wire at temperature T_2 slightly higher than a surrounding gas at temperature T_1. In this case molecules colliding with the wire have an average energy corresponding to T_1 so that T in the denominator of (40) may be identified with T_1. The molecules leave the wire with an energy corresponding to a temperature T_2' intermediate between T_1 and T_2; then

$$(T_2' - T_1) = a(T_2 - T_1)$$

defines the accommodation coefficient a.

In many low-temperature applications the molecules may travel from one wall to the other without collision and it is impossible to identify T in (40) with either T_1 or T_2. Also the value of p used in equation (40) must be considered very carefully, since at low pressures (under molecular or Knudsen conditions) the thermal transpiration or thermo-molecular pressure effect arises and the local pressure and temperature vary together as expressed by

$$p/(T)^{\frac{1}{2}} = \text{constant}.$$

R. J. Corruccini of the National Bureau of Standards (Boulder Laboratories) has examined recently this question of gaseous heat conduction at low pressures and low temperatures. He points out† that p and T are associated in the derivation of (40), and that p is observed by a vacuum gauge usually at room temperature. Under low-pressure conditions $l \gg d$, the diameter of the tube connecting the gauge to the cryostat chamber, and if the system is in equilibrium, $p/(T)^{\frac{1}{2}}$ is constant. Therefore, if a value of p obtained from the gauge is inserted in (40), the appropriate value for T is the temperature at the pressure gauge.

Equation (40) may be simplified to

$$\dot{Q} = 0{\cdot}243\,\frac{\gamma+1}{\gamma-1}\,a_0\,\frac{T_2-T_1}{\sqrt{(MT)}}\,p_{\text{mm}}\ \text{W cm}^{-2}, \qquad (41)$$

and using $T = 295°$ K,

$$\dot{Q} = 0{\cdot}014\,\frac{\gamma+1}{\gamma-1}\,a_0\,\frac{T_2-T_1}{\sqrt{M}}\,p_{\text{mm}}$$

$$= \text{constant}\ a_0 . p_{\text{mm}}(T_2-T_1)\ \text{W cm}^{-2}, \qquad (42)$$

where the constant has approximate values of $0{\cdot}028$, $0{\cdot}059$, and $0{\cdot}016$ for helium, hydrogen, and air respectively. The chief uncertainty in calculating the heat conducted by a low-pressure gas lies in the accommodation coefficient a. As an upper limit $a = 1$, but experimental research has shown that with a clean metallic surface exposed to helium gas, a may be as low as $0{\cdot}025$.

---

† I am very grateful to Dr. Corruccini for his kindness in giving me a draft of this interesting paper, which was presented in part at the 1957 Cryogenic Engineering Conference (Boulder, Colorado) and which is also expected to be submitted to a suitable journal in the near future, e.g. *Vacuum*, Edwards High Vacuum Ltd., Sussex.

Keesom (1942) has given a number of values for a for helium gas obtained by measuring the heat loss from a wire stretched along the axis of a tube. Some of the values found (original references may be found in Keesom, 1942) are given in Table XIV below.

TABLE XIV

Accommodation Coefficient for Helium Gas

Metal

Platinum	0·49 (90° K, 153° K); 0·38 (34°–264° C)
Bright platinum . .	0·44 (50°–150° C)
Blackened platinum . .	0·91 (50°–150° C)
Clean fresh tungsten . .	0·025 (79° K); 0·046 (195° K); 0·057 (22° C)
Gas-filled tungsten . .	0·19 to 0·82
Gas free nickel . .	0·048 (90° K); 0·060 (195° K); 0·071 (273° K)
Nickel (gas layer adsorbed).	0·413 (90° K); 0·423 (195° K); 0·360 (273° K)
Glass	0·67 (12° K) 0·38 (77° K); 0·34 (273° K)

The experimental figures suggest that for a metal surface in the usual condition encountered in a cryostat, exposed to helium gas at low pressure, a value

$$a \leqslant 0.5$$

should provide a useful upper limit for calculating heat transfer.

Available data for the accommodation coefficient of other gases on various metallic surfaces seems rather meagre. Values quoted in the *International Critical Tables* (1929) for the accommodation coefficients at about room temperature for He, H_2, air, N_2, O_2, and argon at a platinum surface range from 0·2 to 0·9.

More recent experimental work on accommodation coefficients (for example, Bremner, 1950; Eggleton, Tompkins, and Wanford, 1952; Thomas and Schofield, 1955; Schäfer, 1952) deals principally with surfaces of tungsten which are clean and gas free. The results, of fundamental rather than practical cryogenic interest, serve to confirm some of the experimental disagreements and the considerable experimental difficulties that are faced in these determinations. In contrast to Roberts (1930), Thomas and Schofield find very little change in accommodation coefficient with temperature for helium on a clean gas-free tungsten filament; from 80° to 300° K they find a has a value of 0·015–0·017 but increases to ~ 0.2 when the surface is contaminated by gas (oxygen). Eggleton, Tompkins, and Wanford report values of $a \simeq 0.056$ after flashing a tungsten wire, but find $a \simeq 0.3$ when the surface has adsorbed gas layers on it.

Generally for clean gas-free surfaces, a increases with molecular weight: for example, from Bremner (1950) for flashed tungsten at 90° K, $a = 0.041$ for He, 0.081 for Ne, 0.16 for A, 0.09 for H_2 0.20 for O_2. For heavy polyatomic molecules (e.g. organic gases) it appears that generally $0.8 < a < 0.9$.

3. Heat transfer through solids

As we mentioned in the last chapter, the heat flow $\dot{Q}$ through a solid of cross-section A cm² under a temperature gradient $\partial T/\partial x$ is given by

$$\dot{Q} = \lambda(T)A\,\frac{\partial T}{\partial x}. \qquad (43)$$

Thus, if the ends of a solid bar of uniform cross-section and length l are at temperatures T_1 and T_2,

$$\dot{Q} = \frac{A}{l}\int_{T_1}^{T_2} \lambda(T)\,dT. \qquad (44)$$

$\lambda(T)$ is the temperature-dependent thermal conductivity of the solid, of which some typical examples are shown in the graphs of Figure 96. In Chapter XI are summarized experimental data (with references to compiled tables) of the thermal conductivity of the various typical groups of solids: (i) glasses, (ii) metallic alloys, (iii) pure metallic elements, (iv) crystalline dielectric solids.

In the case of metallic alloys, e.g. brass, German silver, monel, stainless steel, available data enable us to give a fairly accurate estimate of $\lambda(T)$ at any temperature and therefore of the integrated heat conductivity $\int \lambda(T)\,dT$, provided that the alloy composition is not markedly different from that of alloys already investigated and that we know the physical state, e.g. strained or annealed. In the case of pure metallic elements, however, the conductivity at low temperature is very sensitive to small traces of chemical impurities and physical defects; but as discussed in Chapter XI, a comparatively simple measurement of the

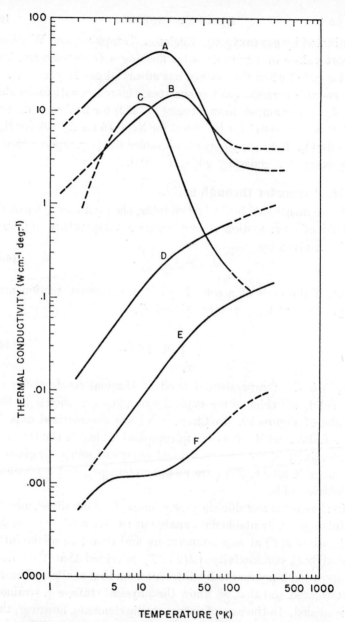

FIG. 96. Thermal conductivity of some solids, from data in Powell and Blanpied (1954). *A*, a metallic element, Al (high purity); *B*, a metallic element, Cu (electrolytic tough pitch); *C*, a dielectric crystal, quartz; *D*, an alloy, annealed brass (70 Cu, 30 Zn); *E*, an alloy, stainless steel; *F*, a glass, quartz glass.

residual electrical resistance (normally at about 4·2° K) enables
a good estimate of the heat conductivity to be made.

The knowledge most often needed for practical cryogenic
calculations is the effective heat conductance of a solid bar of a
few common materials, with certain end temperatures. Commonly encountered pairs of end temperatures may be 300° K
(room temperature) and 77° K, 300° and 4·2° K, 77° and 20° K,
77° and 4·2° K, 4·2° and 2° K. In Table XV are given values for
the mean heat conductivity,

$$\bar{\lambda} = (T_2 - T_1)^{-1} \int_{T_1}^{T_2} \lambda(T) \, dT,$$

under these temperature conditions for a number of common
materials, e.g. Pyrex glass, stainless steel, inconel (hard-drawn),
monel (annealed), German silver, constantan, brass, phosphorus
deoxidized copper (representing the material from which many
copper items are frequently made: pipe, tube, and some rod and
bar), electrolytic tough pitch copper (representing the type of
copper frequently used in commercially available spools of wire).
The values in the table, with the exception of those on coppers
and brass, were calculated from the data compiled by Powell
and Blanpied (1954). The values for the copper specimens were
based on measurements by Powell, Rogers, and Roder (1957) and
those for brass were taken from Kemp, Klemens, Tainsh, and
White (1957).

It is well to note that values for $\bar{\lambda}$ for most commercial glasses
appear to be close (within 30 per cent) to those given for Pyrex
glass in the table. Similarly, values for manganin approximate
to the constantan values given. Values for annealed inconel and
annealed K-monel will approximate to those for annealed monel,
and values for hard-drawn monel and K-monel will be not more
than about 20 per cent greater than those given for hard-drawn
inconel.

For comparatively pure metallic elements such as commercial
copper, small variations in chemical or physical purity may
affect the conductivity considerably, particularly at low
temperatures. This is discussed more fully in Chapter XI. Data

TABLE XV

Mean values of Thermal Conductivity expressed in watts/cm °K

	λ $T_2 = 300°K$ $T_1 = 77°K$	λ $T_2 = 300°K$ $T_1 = 20°K$	λ $T_2 = 300°K$ $T_1 = 4°K$	λ $T_2 = 77°K$ $T_1 = 20°K$	λ $T_2 = 77°K$ $T_1 = 4°K$	λ $T_2 = 20°K$ $T_1 = 4°K$	λ $T_2 = 4°K$ $T_1 = 2°K$
Pyrex glass	0·0082	0·0071	0·0068	0·0028	0·0025	0·0012	0·0007
Stainless steel†	0·123	0·109	0·103	0·055	0·045	0·009₇	0·0022
Inconel (c. 72 Ni, 14–17 Cr, 6–10 Fe, 0·1 C) hard-drawn	0·125	0·111	0·106	0·061	0·051	0·012	0·003
Monel (c. 66 Ni, 2 Fe, 2 Mn, 30 Cu) annealed	0·207	0·192	0·183	0·133	0·113	0·040	0·007
German silver (47 Cu, 41 Zn, 9 Ni, 2 Pb) as received	0·20	0·19	0·18	0·14	0·12	0·039	0·005
Constantan (60 Cu, 40 Ni) wire as received	0·22	0·21	0·20	0·16	0·14	0·04₆	0·006
Brass (30 Zn, 70 Cu) as received	0·81	0·70	0·67	0·31	0·26	0·078	0·015
Copper (phosphorus deoxidized) as received	1·91	1·71	1·63	0·95	0·80	0·25	0·07
Copper (electrolytic tough pitch) as received	4·1	5·4	5·7	9·7	9·8	10	4

† These figures for stainless steel are calculated from thermal conductivity data which are representative of the behaviour of types 303, 304, 347, and therefore an appropriate composition could be 18% Cr, 9% Ni, traces of Mn, Nb, Si, Ti totalling 2–3% with remainder Fe.

for $\lambda(T)$ of materials such as nylon, Teflon, Perspex, soft solder, Wood's metal, and a silicon bronze† are also given in tabular form in this later chapter.

The values in this table make it evident why alloys of the cupro-nickel family (copper-nickel, constantan, German silver) or of the monel and stainless steel group are so frequently chosen for the tubes in a cryostat where low thermal conductivity is a requirement. Stainless steel and inconel have somewhat lower heat conductivities than the cupro-nickel alloys although the latter are often preferred due to the greater ease with which they may be soft-soldered.

4. Heat transfer by radiation

A perfect black body may be defined as one which absorbs all radiation falling upon it. For such a body the absorptivity a and emissivity ϵ are unity, and so its reflectivity

$$R = 1-\epsilon = 1-a$$

is zero.

It may be shown (see, for example, Roberts, 1940) that for a black body at a temperature T the total radiant energy emitted per second per unit area is given by

$$E = \sigma T^4,$$

where the constant σ, Stefan's constant, has an experimental value of $5 \cdot 67 \times 10^{-12}$ W cm^{-2} deg^{-4}. Such radiant energy is distributed over a range of wavelengths, the energy $E(\lambda)\,d\lambda$ emitted over a narrow interval λ, $\lambda + d\lambda$ being a function of λ and T. The function $E(\lambda)$ at any temperature T has a maximum value for $\lambda = \lambda_m$, and it may be shown that

$$\lambda_m T = \text{constant (Wien's constant)} \tag{45}$$

for which the experimental value is $0 \cdot 290$ cm deg.

Thus for
$$T = 300° \text{ K}, \quad \lambda_m = 9 \cdot 67\ \mu,$$
$$T = 200° \text{ K}, \quad \lambda_m = 14 \cdot 5\ \mu,$$
$$T = 77° \text{ K}, \quad \lambda_m = 37 \cdot 7\ \mu,$$
$$T = 4 \cdot 2° \text{ K}, \quad \lambda_m = 690\ \mu.$$

† A useful low-conductivity alloy which is non-magnetic at low temperatures; contains 96% Cu, 3% Si, 1% Mn.

Most calculations dealing with the radiant heat transfer in low-temperature equipment are not restricted to black bodies but deal with metallic surfaces whose emissivity may be anywhere between 0·01 and 1·0.

Most non-metallic surfaces, of which glass and perhaps baked varnishes are the most important from our viewpoint, do approximate to black bodies in that their emissivities are in the neighbourhood of 0·9. However, for a particular metallic conductor the emissivity or the reflectivity depends on the wavelength of incident radiation and the physical state of the surface.

The classical theory of Drude yields a relation between the reflectivity R, the wavelength λ (microns), and the d.c. electrical resistivity of the metal ρ (ohm cm):

$$1 - R = \epsilon = 36 \cdot 5 (\rho/\lambda)^{\frac{1}{2}}. \qquad (46)$$

Evidence for the experimental validity of this formula has been discussed by Worthing (1941), Blackman, Egerton, and Truter (1948), Reuter and Sondheimer (1948), and Ramanathan (1952), etc. At relatively high temperatures the experimental agreement is reasonably good in many instances.

At low temperatures, however, the theoretical relation might be expected to fail even with smooth uncontaminated metallic surfaces, as the relaxation time of the electrons (period of the electron mean free path) becomes comparable with the period of vibration of the incident radiation.

The validity of the Hagen–Rubens equation (46) depends on the assumption that $\nu\tau < 1$ where ν is the frequency of the radiation and τ is the electron relaxation time. In a typical monovalent metal at room temperature the electron velocity (Fermi velocity) and mean free path are respectively about 1×10^8 cm/sec and 1 to 5×10^{-6} cm, so that $\tau \sim 3 \times 10^{-14}$ sec (assuming $l \sim 3 \times 10^{-6}$ cm). For room-temperature incident radiation, $\lambda_m \simeq 10^{-3}$ cm, whence $\nu \sim 3 \times 10^{13}$ (assuming velocity $c = 3 \times 10^{10}$ cm/sec). Therefore $\nu\tau \sim 1$. Therefore for radiation in the visible region of the spectrum we should expect a calculation of the reflection coefficient to require us to take electron relaxation into account. This yields a relation for R or ϵ which is independent of the wavelength λ (see, for example, Mott and Jones, 1936, Chapter III). Agreement with available experimental evidence appears tolerably good for optical wavelengths when relaxation is considered. The discrepancy is still very marked for infra-red radiation at low temperatures, and it is difficult to believe that surface roughness or a surface electrical resistance higher than the bulk resistance is sufficient to explain discrepancies of a factor of 100 or more which occur with annealed electro-polished specimens at helium temperatures. Reuter and Sondheimer (1948; see also review on electron mean free paths in metals by Sondheimer, 1952) treated theoretically the problem of the anomalous skin effect, i.e. the effect on surface resistance when electron mean free paths become so long that at high frequencies the applied electric field may change appreciably within the extent of an electron mean free path. They assumed specular reflection of electrons at the metal surface and deduced a formula for the reflectivity or absorptivity in considerably better agreement with low-temperature experiments (e.g. Ramanathan, 1952). Dingle, in a series of papers in *Physica* in 1952–3 (see particularly Dingle, 1953 b, but also Dingle, 1952, 1953 a, c, d) deduced a slightly simpler expression and by assuming diffuse reflection showed that reasonable agreement with experiment could be obtained. In Table XVI (Dingle, 1953 b) are compared experimental values of the *percentage* absorptivity for 14 μ radiation on electro-polished copper, with theoretical values.

TABLE XVI

Temperature	Experimental	Classical theory (incl. relaxation)	Anomalous skin effect (diffuse reflection)
Room temp. . .	1·2	0·5	0·8
Liquid-oxygen temp. .	0·8	0·09	0·5
Liquid-helium temp. .	0·6	0·003	0·4

Returning to our practical problem of calculating the approximate radiant heat transfer between surfaces, it is apparent that despite the partial success of more sophisticated theoretical analyses, it is generally necessary to select experimental data which may be considered most appropriate for the particular surfaces in question. In Table XVII below are collected experimental values for the emissivity of a number of commonly used metals; as indicated in the table these values have been obtained on surfaces in various physical conditions, e.g. electro-polished, normally smooth and clean, highly oxidized, etc. By some intelligent guessing, the most suitable value of ϵ, or a probable

TABLE XVII

Experimental Values of Emissivity

Material	Fulk, Reynolds, & Park (1955) 300° K radn. on 78° K surface	McAdams (1954) room temp.	Ramanathan (1952) 14μ radn. on 2° K surface	Blackman, Egerton, & Truter (1948) 293° K radn. on 90° K surface	Ziegler & Cheung (1957) 273° K radn. on 77°K surface
Al-clean polished foil .	0·02	0·04	0·011†	0·055	0·043‡
Al-plate .	0·03	..	..	..	..
Al-highly oxidized .	..	0·31	..	..	..
Brass-clean polished .	0·029	0·03	0·018†	0·046	0·10‡
Brass-highly oxidized .	..	0·6	..	..	..
Cu-clean polished .	0·015–0·019	0·02	0·0062–0·015†	0·019–0·035	..
Cu-highly oxidized .	..	0·6	..	..	..
Cr-plate .	0·08	0·08	..	0·065	0·084‡
Au-foil .	0·010–0·023	0·02–0·03	..	0·026	..
Au-plate .	0·026	..	..	..	..
Monel .	..	0·2	..	..	0·11‡
Ni-polished .	..	0·045	..	..	..
Rh-plate .	0·078	..	..	..	..
Ag-plate .	0·008	0·02–0·03	..	0·023–0·036	..
Stainless steel .	0·048	0·074	..	..	..
Sn-clean foil	0·013	0·06	0·013†	0·038	..
Soft solder .	0·03	..	..	..	0·047‡
Glass . .	..	0·9	..	0·87	..
Wood's metal	..	..	..	..	0·16

† These surfaces were electro-polished (Ramanathan).

‡ These surfaces were neither highly polished nor heavily oxidized, but as encountered in normal practice (Ziegler). Ziegler observed that a thin layer of oil or Apiezon grease on a low-emissivity surface raised the emissivity to 0·2 or 0·3. He also found that varnishes such as GEC adhesive no. 7031 and bakelite lacquer gave an emissivity $e \simeq 0·87$; similarly, Scotch tape (Sellotape) had an emissivity of about 0.88.

upper limit for ϵ, must then be selected for calculation of heat transfer.

For two plane parallel surfaces each of area A, and emissivities ϵ_1 and ϵ_2, and at respective temperatures T_1' and T_2', the heat transfer by radiation per unit time is

$$\dot{Q} = \sigma A(T_1^4 - T_2^4)\frac{\epsilon_1 \epsilon_2}{\epsilon_1 + \epsilon_2 - \epsilon_1 \epsilon_2}, \tag{47}$$

whence $\qquad \dot{Q} \simeq \sigma A(T_1^4 - T_2^4) \quad$ for $\epsilon_1 = \epsilon_2 \simeq 1.$ $\qquad$ (48)

In the case where $\epsilon_2 \ll \epsilon_1$, (47) reduces to

$$\dot{Q} = \sigma A(T_1^4 - T_2^4)\epsilon_2. \tag{49}$$

Similarly, if $\epsilon_1 = \epsilon_2 = \epsilon$, and $\epsilon \ll 1$, (47) becomes

$$\dot{Q} = \sigma A(T_1^4 - T_2^4)\epsilon/2. \tag{50}$$

5. Other causes of heat transfer

While the processes of heat transfer discussed in the preceding sections, viz. low-pressure gas conduction, heat conduction by solids, and radiation transfer, are those chiefly encountered, other less common but quite troublesome sources of energy often arise.

Joule heating

Joule heating in connecting leads and in resistance thermo-meters, giving rise to a heat input $\dot{Q} = I^2 R = V^2/R$ is not difficult to estimate but may be overlooked as a source of temperature drift or temperature inhomogeneity in a cryostat. The opposing demands of low thermal conduction along electrical leads, and insignificant heat dissipation in these same leads often presents a problem. At temperatures below $7°$ K this has frequently been solved by using wires of a poor thermal conductor such as constantan, and tinning the surface with a thin lead coating; this becomes superconducting below $7°$ K and the wire remains a poor heat conductor. As is discussed in a later chapter (XI), most alloys (excluding superconducting alloys) exhibit an electrical resistance which does not decrease appreciably as the temperature falls from room temperature to liquid-helium temperatures, but their heat conductivity usually decreases by a factor of 10–100. On the other hand, pure metallic elements have an electrical resistance which may fall by a factor of a hundred or more as the temperature is changed from 300°–4·2° K; over the same range the thermal conductivity of the pure metallic element normally increases as T falls below 100° K, passes through a maximum at a temperature in the vicinity of $\theta_D/20$ (say 10°–20° K), and falls linearly towards zero at the absolute zero. As a result a piece of copper wire may have approximately the same heat conductivity at 4° and 300° K while its electrical resistance is different by a factor of 100; a wire of constantan may have approximately the same electrical resistance at 4° and 300° K but a heat conductivity which has changed by a factor of 100. It may be noted that at both low temperatures ($\sim$ 4° K) and high temperatures ($\sim$ 300° K) the ratio $\rho\lambda/T$ for most metals has a value which at least approximates to the theoretical Lorenz value of $2\cdot45 \times 10^{-8}$ W ohm/deg². In selecting electrical lead wires to place in a cryostat, these factors should be borne in mind.

Gas adsorption

Another cause of temperature drift of concern to the low-temperature calorimetrist is the adsorption or desorption of residual gas. The thermal energy required to desorb a layer of adsorbed gas from a surface is of the same order of magnitude as the latent heat of vaporization. As the temperature of the solid surface is raised, e.g. crystals in a calorimeter vessel, gas desorption begins and part of any electrical energy fed to the calorimeter is employed in this desorption process. Keesom (1942, p. 127) has given some adsorption data for helium gas on surfaces of glass and charcoal at low temperatures. Between 2° and 3° K glass adsorbs about 30×10^{-10} mole/cm² for which the heat of adsorption is $\sim$ 70 cal/mole. A simple calculation indicates that the desorption of such a layer from 100 cm² of glass requires energy of $\sim$ 1,000 ergs. It appears likely that with surfaces of baked lacquers and powdered materials, the amount of adsorption is very much greater than with a clean glass or metal surface. Thus it has been found by some experimenters that in high-precision calorimetry at low temperatures, it is undesirable to expose the sample or calorimeter to exchange gas at temperatures below about $10°$ K, because of the adsorption which occurs and subsequent slow temperature drifts which may be attributed to gradual desorption of the helium layer when the space is pumped to a high vacuum. This process has also been named as a contributing factor to 'heat leaks' in adiabatic demagnetization cryostats; when a salt pill is cooled to a temperature of $\frac{1}{100}°$ K and is surrounded by a $1°$ K wall, helium gas (remaining from exchange gas used in cooling) slowly desorbs and becomes adsorbed on the colder pill, transferring thermal energy in an amount which may cause a serious temperature rise, owing to the small heat capacities of the system.

Mechanical vibration

In most cryogenic experiments gas desorption is not a very serious factor, nor is mechanical vibration. Quantitative information on the amount of heat released in an otherwise thermally isolated system by its being in mechanical vibration—a result of mechanical linkage to its surroundings, i.e. external vibrations of pumps, building vibration, etc.—is rather lacking. However, it has been frequently noted by workers in the field of temperature below $1°$ K, where heat inputs of 100 erg/min may be considered excessive, that the rate of temperature rise of their salt pills after demagnetization was affected by the operation of pumps. In a recent interesting series of experiments on thermal contact and insulation below $1°$ K, Wheatley, Griffing, and Estle (1956) mechanically coupled their cryostat to a motor whose speed could be adjusted to vary the vibration frequency from 0 to 13 per second; they found at the maximum frequency a heat leakage to a pill (mounted on a rather rigid support) of 235 erg/min, compared with about 10 erg/min when the motor was switched off. It is apparent that a fairly rigid suspension, e.g. glass rods as opposed to nylon or cotton threads, is less susceptible to external vibrations as its resonant frequency is much higher than the frequency of most normal building or pump vibrations. A salt pill suspended by fine threads is much more likely to be set in resonant vibration by the action of external sources, and heat leaks of the order of 1,000 erg/min have been encountered in some such instances.

Darby *et al.* (1951) reported that in their two-stage de-magnetization equipment, in which the two pills were suspended by nylon threads, vacuum pumps produced a serious vibrational heat source; even the action of mercury 'bumping' in a diffusion pump attached to the cryostat caused 'heat leaks' in excess of 300 erg/min to the upper salt pill. On the other hand, Malaker (1951) used a nylon thread suspension and calculated the heat leak to be only ~ 4 erg/min at very low temperatures. The exact process of such energy release in the pill, although presumably frictional, appears somewhat obscure.

An excellent discussion of the problems of thermal insulation at very low temperatures was given some years ago by Cooke and Hull (1942).

6. Example of heat-transfer calculation

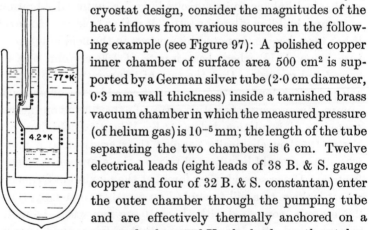

As an illustration of the calculations that may be necessary in cryostat design, consider the magnitudes of the heat inflows from various sources in the following example (see Figure 97): A polished copper inner chamber of surface area 500 cm^2 is supported by a German silver tube (2·0 cm diameter, 0·3 mm wall thickness) inside a tarnished brass vacuum chamber in which the measured pressure (of helium gas) is 10^{-5} mm; the length of the tube separating the two chambers is 6 cm. Twelve electrical leads (eight leads of 38 B. & S. gauge copper and four of 32 B. & S. constantan) enter the outer chamber through the pumping tube and are effectively thermally anchored on a copper bush at 77° K; the leads are then taken to the inner chamber, each lead having a length of about 12 cm between its points of attachment on the respective chambers.

Fig. 97. Diagram of a cryostat.

We require to calculate the following:

  (i) Radiant heat inflow from the brass to the copper chamber.

 (ii) Radiant heat inflow down the German silver tube to the inner chamber when no radiation baffle is present.

(iii) Heat conducted down the German silver tube from the outer to the inner chamber.

(iv) Heat conducted down the electrical leads from one chamber to the other.

 (v) Heat conducted through the low-pressure helium gas in the inter-chamber space.

(vi) And to examine whether Joule heating due to a current of 5 mA in the electrical leads is serious in view of the other heat inflows.

Firstly,

  (i) Assuming that for tarnished brass $\epsilon_1 \rightarrow 1$, and for polished copper $\epsilon_2 \simeq 0.03$,

from (49) $\qquad \dot{Q}_r = \sigma A (T_1^4 - T_2^4) 0.03$

$$\simeq 5.67 \times 10^{-12} \times 500 \times 0.03 \times (77)^4$$

$$= 3 \times 10^{-3} \text{ W}.$$

  (ii) Any calculation of the radiant heat reaching the inner space by 'funnelling' of room temperature radiation down the German silver tube must yield a very crude approximation to the true experimental result, at best. An upper limit $\dot{Q}_f(\text{max})$ may be calculated easily, assuming 'complete funnelling' i.e. perfect specular reflection from the inner wall of the tube, so that all the radiation $\dot{Q}$ $(= \sigma \pi 1^2 (295)^4)$ reaches the inner space.

$$\dot{Q}_f(\text{max}) = 5.67 \times 10^{-12} \times \pi \times (295)^4$$

$$= 0.135 \text{ W}.$$

Alternatively, if we assume almost complete absorption of the radiation which reaches the inner wall of the tube, $\dot{Q}_f(\text{min})$ is merely the radiation from a small solid angle subtended by the lower exit of the tube at its upper (room temperature) end. If the length of the tube be about 30 cm between $4 \cdot 2°$ K end and that part at room temperature

$$\dot{Q}_f(\text{min}) \simeq \frac{\pi \cdot 1^2}{2\pi \cdot (30)^2} \times \sigma A (295)^4$$

$$\sim 10^{-4} \text{ W}.$$

In practice this minimum value for radiant heat inflow via the pumping tube may be approached by painting the inner wall of the German silver tube with an optical black paint, 'Aquadag', etc. More complete isolation from room-temperature radiation is usually obtained by means of a bend in the tube or insertion of a small radiation baffle. By this means the room-temperature radiation is adsorbed by the tube wall near the bend or at the baffle and transmitted into the liquid-nitrogen bath; the inner experimental space then only sees radiation emitted from a relatively small area of surface at $77°$ K which is transmitted by a direct path or successive internal reflections down the tube.

(iii) For the heat conducted by the German silver tube

$$\dot{Q}_c = \lambda \frac{A}{l} \Delta T$$

$$= 0 \cdot 12 \times \frac{2\pi \times 0 \cdot 03 \times 73}{6} \quad (\lambda = 0 \cdot 12 \text{ from Table XV})$$

$$= 0 \cdot 275 \text{ W}.$$

(iv) The heat conducted down the electrical leads is given by $\dot{Q}_c^* = \dot{Q}$ (eight copper leads of $0 \cdot 010$ cm diameter)$+ \dot{Q}$ (four constantan leads of $0 \cdot 020$ cm diameter); using data from Table XV, λ (copper) $= 9 \cdot 8$, λ (constantan) $= 0 \cdot 14$, therefore

$$\dot{Q}_c^* = 8 \times 9 \cdot 8 \times \frac{0 \cdot 786}{12} \times 10^{-4} \times 73 + 4 \times 0 \cdot 14 \times \frac{0 \cdot 314}{12} \times 10^{-3} \times 73$$

$$= 6 \cdot 08 (0 \cdot 00616 + 0 \cdot 000176)$$

$$= 0 \cdot 0385 \text{ W}.$$

(v) For gas conduction $\dot{Q}_g$ is given by (42), which in the case of helium gas reduces to

$$\dot{Q}_g = 0 \cdot 028 p_{\text{mm}} a_0 \Delta T \text{ W cm}^{-2}.$$

Assuming that the respective surface areas are approximately equal and parallel, and that

$$a_{max} \simeq 0.5 = a_1 = a_2,$$

then
$$a_0 = 0.5/(2-0.5)$$
$$= 0.333.$$

Since $\Delta T = 73°$ K, $p = 10^{-5}$ mm,

therefore $\dot{Q}_g = 0.028 \times 0.333 \times 73 \times 10^{-5}$ W cm^{-2},

and since $A \simeq 500$ cm^2,

$$\dot{Q}_g = 0.0034 \text{ W}.$$

(vi) (a) Eight copper leads of 38 B. & S. wire each have an approximate room-temperature resistance of 0·024 ohm/cm. Hence, assuming for normal commercial wire that $\rho_r/\rho_{0\ °C} \simeq 10^{-2}$, the resistance will be about 0·0046 ohm/cm at 77° K and 0·0003 ohm/cm at 4·2° K.

If the mean resistance is 0·0025 ohm/cm, the total heat produced by 5 mA is

$$(5 \times 10^{-3})^2 \times 0.0025 \times 12 = 0.75 \times 10^{-6} \text{ W per wire.}$$

A rather crude calculation based on a mean thermal conductivity of 10 W/cm °K shows that the temperature rise in the wire will be $< 0.01°$ K at any point. If all the Joule heat were transferred to the inner chamber this would only amount to about 6 μW.

(b) In the case of constantan (four wires of 32 B. & S.) the electrical resistance of each wire is about 0·14 ohm/cm and is not particularly sensitive to change in temperature.

Total Joule heat produced is

$$4 \times (5 \times 10^{-3})^2 \times 12 \times 0.14 = 1.68 \times 10^{-4} \text{ W}.$$

Again, assuming $\bar{\lambda} \simeq 0.14$ W/cm deg, it may be calculated that the temperature rise will not be greater than about 5° K.

Summarizing, we note that the major source of heat leakage is via the supporting tube, and provided that precautions are taken to prevent room-temperature radiation entering the inner chamber via the tube this leak amounts to about 0·275 W. Radiant heat of 10^{-3} W reaches the inner chamber from the surrounding 77° K chamber and heat leakage through the residual 10^{-5} mm pressure of helium gas is less than 0·004 W; by comparison a 5 mA current through each electrical lead could contribute a maximum heat inflow of about 100 μW.

The total heat leak of about 0·28 W is equivalent to 240 cal/hour, which would evaporate nearly 400 cm³ of liquid helium per hour; this assumes that the cold evaporating gas does not play any useful role in cooling the wall of the German silver tube and thereby reduce the heat leak.

7. Heat transfer through pressed contacts

Elsewhere we make passing reference to the problem of heat transfer across the boundary between two solid surfaces in contact. This has a direct application to at least two practical cryogenic problems, namely to the design of mechanical heat switches (for example, as applied to calorimetry by Westrum, Hatcher, and Osborne, 1953; Webb and Wilks, 1955; Ramanathan and Srinivasan, 1955; and Rayne, 1956) and in the design of insulating supports for low-temperature equipment (as applied to the internal supporting members in large dewar vessels by Birmingham *et al.*, 1955).

The first comprehensive investigation of thermal contact has been that of Berman† (1956) who studied the thermal conductance of various solid contacts at liquid-helium and liquid-nitrogen temperatures, using loads of 50–250 lb. His results suggest that:

(i) The measured thermal conductance is always greater than that calculated by the Wiedemann–Franz–Lorenz law from the measured electrical conductance. This discrepancy, often a factor of 100 or more, is as high as 10^5 when contact and measurement are made at 4·2° K. The only possible conclusion seems to be that the majority of the heat is carried across the interface by thermal waves rather than by electrons.

(ii) The thermal conductance varies nearly linearly with the pressure, and hence is not sensitive to change in area for a given total load.

† In this paper Berman includes a brief account of some earlier work in this field by Jacobs and Starr, Fulton, Zavaritski, etc.

(iii) At liquid-helium temperatures (1°–4° K), the conductance varies as T^2 but becomes less temperature-sensitive at higher temperatures, the change in conductance between 64° and 77° K being only about 10 per cent.

(iv) Some typical figures given by Berman for the thermal conductance of the contact between (a) two copper rods, (b) two 0·001 in. steel disks are:

(a) $1·02 \times 10^{-2}$ W deg^{-1} at 4·2°K; $32·5 \times 10^{-2}$ W deg^{-1} at 77°K;

(b) $0·54 \times 10^{-2}$ W deg^{-1} at 4·2° K; 26×10^{-2} W deg^{-1} at 77° K;

in each case the contact was made at room temperature and the load applied was 100 lb.

The recent experimental work on heat conduction through insulating supports by Mikesell and Scott (1956) is of less fundamental interest than Berman's experiments but of great practical significance in cryogenic design. Their work was concerned with the internal support of large dewar vessels by using stacks of thin disks. Although the mechanical strength of the stack is great, the thermal contact resistance between disks is such that the total thermal resistance of a stack may be a hundred times greater than that of a solid rod of the same material and dimensions. For example, measurements of the thermal conductance of a stack of about 315 stainless steel plates of thickness 0·0008 in. under a pressure of 1,000 p.s.i. showed that: with end temperatures of 296° and 76° K, the conductance is 0·93 W cm^{-2} and with end temperatures of 76° and 20° K it is 0·062 W cm^{-2}; assuming the length of the stack is $315 \times 0·0008$ in. $= 0·25$ in., these figures correspond to effective mean conductivities of 2·7 mW/cm °K and 0·71 mW/cm °K respectively. These may be compared with values of $\bar{\lambda} = 123$ mW/cm °K (300°–77° K) and $\bar{\lambda} = 55$ mW/cm °K (77°–20° K) from Table XV (§ 6.3) for stainless steel in solid form. Mikesell and Scott found that the conductance of the stack of disks could be decreased substantially by using a thin layer of manganese dioxide dust between each pair of plates.

Such stacked disks provide an excellent means of transmitting high pressures into a cryostat, as a stack can have very high compressional strength, and yet retain a low heat conductivity (see, for example, their use by Berman, 1956).

The use of the mechanical contact as a heat switch for cooling specimens prior to a specific heat determination has already been mentioned (§ 5.2). Such a 'switch' obviates the necessity for using exchange gas at low temperature with the entailed problems of slow gas desorption. Cone and socket contacts have been used for this purpose but they appear to generate considerable frictional heat on breaking the contact and the double-jaw type (Webb and Wilks, 1955) or flat plates (Ramanathan and Srinivasan, 1955; Rayne, 1956) seem more successful. Webb and Wilks report that the heat flow across their closed contact was of the order of 10^{-2} J/deg min, this being sufficient to cool their specimens from 4° to 1° K in a few minutes. It is probable that the conductance of the flat-plate type of switch is somewhat greater.

Experiments on contact resistance also confirm the reasons for the frequent difficulties that are encountered in thermally anchoring electrical leads effectively at low temperatures. When wires are brought down through a pumping tube into a cryostat, they are often wrapped around a copper post or tube which is in close thermal contact with the refrigerant; despite this, they often seem to be the source of heat inflow into a specimen (calorimeter, etc.) to which they are connected and which is otherwise isolated. The only method of avoiding this trouble appears to be to wrap as great a length of the wire as possible in close contact with the anchoring pillar and then to cement it firmly in place; glyptal, bakelite varnish, Formel varnish, or nail polish are all useful cements for this purpose.

Although the heat transfer between liquid helium and a solid is not properly a problem of pressed contacts, it seems appropriate to mention here some experimental values obtained for the flow of heat $\dot{Q}$ across a liquid-solid interface. As part of an investigation of the heat conductivity of liquid helium below 1° K, Fairbank and Wilks (1955) observed that between copper and the liquid helium, $\dot{Q}$ was proportional to the temperature gradient and varied nearly as the square of the temperature; in fact

$$Q = 2 \cdot 20 \times 10^{-2} T^2 \text{ W cm}^{-2} \text{ deg}^{-1}.$$

REFERENCES

BERMAN, R. (1956). *J. Appl. Phys.* **27**, 318.

BIRMINGHAM, B. W., BROWN, E. H., CLASS, C. R., and SCHMIDT, A. F. (1955). *Proc. 1954 Cryogenic Engng. Conf.* N.B.S. Report No. 3517, p. 27.

BLACKMAN, M. B., EGERTON, A., and TRUTER, E. V. (1948). *Proc. Roy. Soc.* A, **194**, 147.

BREMNER, J. G. M. (1950). Ibid. A, **201**, 305, 321.

COOKE, A. H., and HULL, R. A. (1942). Ibid. A, **181**, 83.

DARBY, J., HATTON, J., ROLLIN, B. V., SEYMOUR, E. F. W., and SILS- BEE, H. B. (1951). *Proc. Phys. Soc.* A, **64**, 861.

DINGLE, R. B. (1952). *Physica*, **18**, 985.

—— (1953a) Ibid. **19**, 311.

—— (1953b). Ibid. 348.

—— (1953c). Ibid. 729.

—— (1953d). Ibid. 1187.

EGGLETON, A. E. J., TOMPKINS, F. C., and WANFORD, D. W. B. (1952). *Proc. Roy. Soc.* A, **213**, 266.

FAIRBANK, H. A., and WILKS, J. (1955). Ibid. A, **231**, 545.

FULK, M. M., REYNOLDS, M. M., and PARK, O. E. (1955). *Proc. 1954 Cryogenic Engng. Conf.* N.B.S. Report No. 3517, p. 151.

JEANS, SIR JAMES (1948). *An Introduction to the Kinetic Theory of Gases*, Cambridge University Press.

KEESOM, W. H. (1942). *Helium*, Elsevier, Amsterdam.

KEMP, W. R. G., KLEMENS, P. G., TAINSH, R. J., and WHITE, G. K. (1957). *Acta Met.* **5**, 303.

KENNARD, E. H. (1938). *Kinetic Theory of Gases*, McGraw-Hill, New York.

McADAMS, W. H. (1954). *Heat Transmission*, 3rd edn., McGraw-Hill, New York.

MALAKER, S. F. (1951). *Phys. Rev.* **84**, 133.

MIKESELL, R. P., and SCOTT, R. B. (1956). *J. Res. Nat. Bur. Stand.* **57**, 371.

MOTT, N. F., and JONES, H. (1936). *Theory of the Properties of Metals and Alloys*, Clarendon Press, Oxford.

POWELL, R. L., and BLANPIED, W. A. (1954). *Nat. Bur. Stand. Circular* 556, U.S. Govt. Printing Office, Washington, D.C.

—— ROGERS, W. M., and RODER, H. M. (1957). *Proc. 1956 Cryogenic Engng. Conf.* N.B.S., Boulder, Colorado, p. 166.

RAMANATHAN, K. G. (1952). *Proc. Phys. Soc.* **A65**, 532.

—— and SRINIVASAN, T. M. (1955). *Phil. Mag.* **46**, 338.

RAYNE, J. A. (1956). *Aust. J. Phys.* **9,** 189.

REUTER, G. E. H., and SONDHEIMER, E. H. (1948). *Proc. Roy. Soc.* A, **195,** 336.

ROBERTS, J. K. (1930). Ibid. A, **129,** 146.

—— (1940). *Heat and Thermodynamics,* 3rd edn., Blackie & Sons, London.

SCHÄFER, K. (1952). *Z. Elektrochem.* **56,** 398.

SONDHEIMER, E. H. (1952). *Phil. Mag. Suppl.* i. 1.

THOMAS, L. B., and SCHOFIELD, E. B. (1955). *J. Chem. Phys.* **23,** 861.

WEBB, F. J. and WILKS, J. (1955). *Proc. Roy. Soc.* A, **230,** 549.

WESTRUM, E. F., HATCHER, J. B., and OSBORNE, D. W. (1953). *J. Chem. Phys.* **21,** 419.

WHEATLEY, J. C., GRIFFING, D. F., and ESTLE, T. L. (1956). *Rev. Sci. Instrum.* **27,** 1070.

WORTHING, A. G. (1941). *Temperature—Its Measurement and Control in Science and Industry,* vol. i, p. 1164, Reinhold, N.Y.

ZIEGLER, W. T., and CHEUNG, H. (1957). *Proc. 1956 Cryogenic Engng. Conf.* N.B.S., Boulder, Colorado, p. 100.

CHAPTER VII

TEMPERATURE CONTROL

1. Introduction

CONTROL of temperature may be achieved by a variety of methods and with various degrees of efficiency, a desirable efficiency depending on the particular investigation for which a cryostat is intended. A measure of the efficiency is the width of the temperature region over which control can be maintained and the smallness of the temperature fluctuation achieved at any temperature in this region. In general terms temperature control demands an effective balance within the 'experimental space' between the supply and loss of thermal energy.

The various methods may be divided into two broad categories: firstly, those in which the experimental space (temperature T) is thermally linked (preferably by a 'poor' thermal link) to surroundings at a higher temperature, T_0, and heat is continuously extracted from the experimental space; secondly, those in which the surroundings or a thermal reservoir to which the 'space' is loosely thermally connected, are at a lower temperature (T_0) than the desired control temperature, T, in which case heat is supplied to the 'space' to maintain control. Examples of the first are the use of controlled gas desorption, controlled adiabatic expansion of a gas, and Joule–Thomson throttling; evaporation of a liquid under a controlled reduced pressure might also be considered to belong to this category, as might the 'Swenson' method of control. In the second class belong the common methods of electrical heating by which a chamber or specimen is raised to a temperature above that of the surroundings by supply of electrical current to a resistance element, the current being controlled either manually or automatically in response to a temperature signal.

The two means most commonly used—vapour-pressure control and electrical heating—are discussed in §§ 2 and 3 below, followed in §§ 4 and 5 by descriptions of the 'controlled refrigeration' systems and the 'Swenson' method.

2. Control of vapour pressure

The relation between the temperature and the vapour pressure of a liquefied gas was discussed in Chapter IV (Temperature Measurement) and the importance of the vapour pressure of liquid helium, hydrogen, oxygen, etc., as secondary thermometers was stressed. Here we shall consider 'manostats' or pressure-

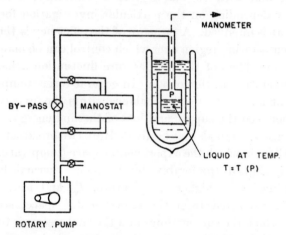

FIG. 98. Control of the pressure above a boiling liquid.

control devices by which the vapour pressure of a boiling liquid may be controlled to within certain limits.

The usual arrangement (Figure 98) has a manostat in the pumping tube from the liquid whose boiling pressure is to be controlled. The 'by-pass' valve enables the vapour to be pumped directly, e.g. when initially reducing the pressure over the liquid from atmospheric to near the control pressure, or when pumping to pressures below the lower limit of the manostat.

In the writer's experience, the most convenient pressure controller for most cryogenic applications is the Cartesian manostat. The history and theory of the application of the Cartesian diver to automatic pressure control has been discussed in some detail by Gilmont (1946, 1951); such manostats, suitable for use both above and below atmospheric pressure, have been commercially available for some years (e.g. from the Emil

Greiner Company of New York). However, a glass Cartesian manostat similar to that shown in Figure 99 can be very easily made. A number of these glass devices—made by a competent glass-blower in two or three hours—have been used by the writer for controlling the vapour pressure of liquid helium, liquid nitrogen, and liquid oxygen from atmospheric pressure down to

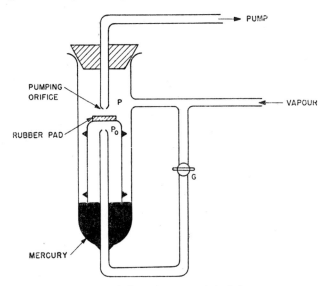

Fig. 99. A Cartesian manostat of glass.

2 or 3 mm Hg. The glass diver of about 1 in. diameter is about $\frac{1}{4}$ in. smaller in outside diameter than the internal diameter of the main tube, and has six glass pips attached for centring; these pips allow the diver to move freely up and down. A valve is formed by the glass orifice seating and unseating against a rubber pad (preferably gum rubber of $\frac{1}{16}$–$\frac{1}{8}$ in. thick sheet) or a rubber bung. In operation, the pressure P above the liquid is reduced by pumping through the by-pass valve (Figure 98) and keeping the glass tap G open until P is near the desired control pressure; then the by-pass valve and G are both closed, and P will fluctuate with a small amplitude ΔP about the control pressure P_0. As shown by Gilmont (1951) and found experimentally, the fluctuation $\Delta P/P_0$ depends on the size of the orifice and varies slightly

with P_0. With an orifice of about 1 mm diameter the expected pressure variation is about 0·5 per cent. In practice, the variation or fluctuation is sufficiently rapid that it is difficult to observe any variation in the vapour pressure above the liquid surface, as recorded by a mercury manometer. Over the greater part of the range from 760 mm to 2 mm Hg pressure, such manostats are

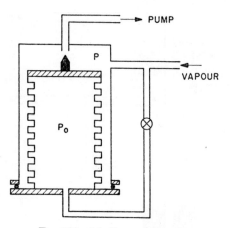

FIG. 100. A bellows manostat.

quite capable of reducing the temperature fluctuations to the order of 0·001° K for liquid helium and 0·01° K for liquid nitrogen or oxygen.

Very similar in its performance characteristics is the bellows type of aneroid manostat, illustrated schematically in Figure 100. Provided that the sylphon bellows used is sufficiently sensitive to pressure change, and the orifice is comparable in diameter with that used in the Cartesian manostat, the pressure and hence temperature fluctuations are not very different. In the model used by Croft and the writer (Croft and White, 1949, unpublished) at the Clarendon Laboratory, a stainless steel needle and brass orifice constituted the control valve but a rubber pad (cf. Cartesian manostat) could easily be substituted for the needle.

An interesting modification of the bellows manostat due to Simon (1949) has a microswitch instead of a valve attached to the end of the bellows; this microswitch relay opens and closes a mechanical valve through a simple thyratron circuit; this valve itself is adapted from a standard relay by replacing the two contacts by a $\frac{3}{32}$ in. nozzle and by a rubber-lined anvil. When used for controlling helium vapour pressure over the range 2 cm Hg to 1 atmosphere this gives a pressure oscillation of less than 0·3 mm Hg with a period of about one second. The temperature fluctuation is thus reduced to $\sim 0\cdot0004°$ at 4° K and $\sim 0\cdot004°$ at 2° K.

Rather different is the bubbler device used by Mendelssohn (1936) and his collaborators for controlling vapour pressure. The liquid used for setting the hydrostatic pressure head, which is the control pressure, is either mercury or butyl phthalate oil depending on the pressure range over which it is required to operate. This 'bubbler' will control the temperature of a liquid-helium bath to a few thousandths of a degree for a considerable period of time, but is somewhat more bulky and difficult to construct than the Cartesian or aneroid type.

Andrew (1948) has described a vapour-pressure controller used at the Mond Laboratory in which a liquid column—registering the vapour pressure—interrupts a light beam, from which an amplified photoelectric signal drives a shaft mechanically coupled to a needle valve. Andrew reports that temperature fluctuations of only 0·001° K are obtained over the range from 1·9° to 4·2° K.

The problem sometimes arises in investigations within the liquid-helium range of providing temperature control rather more precise than the $\pm 0\cdot001°$ K which is the usual magnitude obtained with the manostats described above. Boyle and Brown (1954) overcame this difficulty by using a needle valve to set a constant pumping speed, and then obtaining a temperature balance by automatic electrical heating. Taking advantage of the high temperature sensitivity of a carbon resistor (Allen–Bradley 56 ohm), they amplified the out-of-balance signal from an a.c. bridge, of which the carbon resistor immersed at the bottom of the helium bath was one arm, and fed it to an electrical resistance heater placed close to the detecting resistor in the bath. By this means the temperature was controlled to closer than 10^{-4} °K.

It should be noted that in pumping liquid oxygen vapour, some care should be taken in choosing the type of mechanical pump and pump oil to use. Pumps of the Kinney type should not be used for oxygen as the explosion risk is great. The usual type of rotary vane pump has been used by the writer for pumping oxygen for many years, without any trouble, although it is considered advisable by some competent authorities (e.g. Professor S. C. Collins, private communication) to replace the normal pump oil by tricresyl phosphate.

3. Control by electrical heating

As we have stressed before, regulation of temperature outside the ranges covered by the vapour pressures of available liquefied

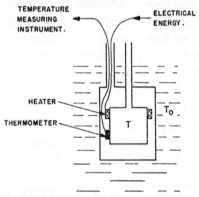

Fig. 101. Temperature-control by electrical heating.

gases, presents difficulties; the magnitude of these difficulties depends on the required degree of precision of the temperature regulation. The usual method is by controlling the supply of electrical energy to preserve a temperature T in the space which is above that of the surroundings (at T_0). As the loss of heat, $-\dot{Q}$, to the surroundings by radiation, conduction, etc., is a monotonically increasing function of $T-T_0$, so the electrical input, $\dot{Q}$ must increase similarly with $T-T_0$. The situation is represented schematically in Figure 101, where a temperature detector, e.g. gas thermometer, thermocouple, or resistance thermometer, provides information by which manual or automatic regulation of the electrical current to a heater is determined.

Manual control of the heating current often meets the experimental demands, when physical measurements may be done quickly and when they are not very sensitive to temperature drift; particularly at low temperatures, where heat capacities are small and the time for establishment of thermal equilibrium is short, a correct adjustment of heating current may be found quickly. Unfortunately, any change in the heat loss to the surroundings—due to change in pressure of residual exchange gas, for example—must affect the temperature and await manual adjustment of the heating current.

Most automatically controlled heating systems used at low temperatures are based on continuous control, as opposed to the simple on-off type of controller operated by a bimetallic spiral or expanding mercury column which is often used as a thermostat at higher temperatures. Such continuous controllers are usually actuated by the signal from a thermocouple or resistance thermometer; they amplify this signal and feed it back into the electrical heater. The degree of amplification required depends on the sensitivity of the detector, i.e. the magnitude of the signal, and on the precision required in the control of temperature.

A comparison of a resistance thermometer and thermocouple thermometer as temperature detectors shows each to have certain advantages and disadvantages. As was pointed out in Chapter IV, no available resistance thermometer has a high sensitivity over the entire range from $4 \cdot 2°$–$300°$ K; also by its very nature the resistance thermometer is itself a source of thermal energy which can be a serious disadvantage when it is desired to control T very close to T_0. But resistance thermometers may be operated on a.c. and therefore supply an a.c. signal (e.g. out-of-balance e.m.f. when the detector is one arm of an a.c. bridge) which can be amplified more easily than the d.c. signal from a thermocouple. For temperatures in the range $4°$–$20°$ K, a carbon resistance provides a very sensitive thermometric element; for

the range from 20°–300° K, a copper resistance winding is suitable and for the range from 150° down to 4° K, manganin wire
can provide a means of high-precision control even though its
sensitivity is rather less than that of a copper thermometer.
Turning to the thermocouple we observe that there is negligible
heat dissipation due to the couple itself and a suitable thermocouple, e.g. Au+2 per cent Co : Cu, will provide a useful signal
at temperatures down to 4° K. Although the thermocouple is
often less reliable as a thermometer than a resistance element
due to the presence of strains and inhomogeneities producing
spurious signals, it is nevertheless quite stable for long periods
of time when fixed in position in a cryostat and not subject to
violent changes in temperature. The major disadvantage is that
a high-gain d.c. amplifier is required for precision control.
Fortunately, reliable chopper-amplifiers for this purpose have
been described and the mechanical choppers required to modulate the d.c. signal before amplification are now commercially
available.

A good example of precision control by the thermocouple
method is that of Dauphinee and Woods (1955); the regulator
shown schematically in Figure 102 below is based on a chopper-
type d.c. amplifier suitable for detecting thermocouple signals
as small as 10^{-8} V. Choppers described by them and now
available commercially (Tinsley of Canada Ltd.) modulate the
signal from a differential thermocouple; it is then amplified
about 10^7 times and the output demodulated by further choppers,
the input and output choppers being synchronous. The amplifier
described is a fairly conventional low audio-frequency amplifier,
preceded and followed by high-quality transformers. With a
Ag+Au : Au+Co thermocouple, this chopper-amplifier has been
used (e.g. Dauphinee, MacDonald, and Preston-Thomas, 1954;
White and Woods, 1955) to control temperatures over the range
from 4·2°–300° K to a precision of a few ten-thousandths of a
degree. As described in § 5.3 (see Figure 84) the Ag+Au : Au+Co
junction is soldered to an inner copper experimental chamber
and the Ag+Au : Cu and Au+Co : Cu junctions are thermally
anchored to a surrounding vessel which is at 4·2° K, 77° K, or

90° K. The signal resulting when the temperature of the inner chamber is $(T-T_0')$ °K above the outer chamber, is suppressed by passing current through a fixed thermal-free resistor in series with the thermocouple; the out-of-balance signal is chopped, amplified, unchopped, and used to control the current through a bank of tubes connected in series with a 1,500-ohm constantan

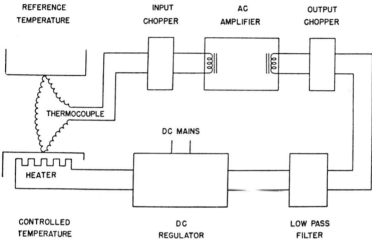

FIG. 102. The temperature regulator (after Dauphinee and Woods, 1955).

heater, wound onto the inner chamber. If less precise control is required it is possible to use chopper-amplifiers that are available commercially, although most are rather expensive and have a lower limit of about 10^{-7} V.

An alternative method of amplification is the use of the galvanometer-amplifier principle; a d.c. signal may be fed directly to a galvanometer and the light beam from the galvanometer mechanically chopped by a sector disk before falling on a split photo-cell. The modulated photo-cell output may then be amplified, passed through a phase-sensitive device and fed to the heater. A thermostat for controlling temperatures to 0·01° C between −40° C and −150° C, using a thermocouple-galvanometer-photomultiplier-amplifier sequence, has been described by Gilchrist (1955). An automatic temperature controller for a calorimeter shield which is also based on a difference thermocouple-galvanometer-photomultiplier sequence has been described by Zabetakis, Craig, and Sterrett (1957).

As we mentioned above, the resistance thermometer operated on an a.c. voltage lends itself to a rather more simple control circuit than the thermocouple. The writer (White, 1953) has used a cryostat over the range from 4°–150° K in which a 2,000-ohm manganin resistance non-inductively wound on the experimental chamber forms one arm of an a.c. Wheatstone bridge. The bridge is fed with a few volts at standard frequency, and has a small variable capacitance in one arm to balance the capacitance of the manganin thermometer. Any temperature fluctuation in the thermometer produces an out-of-balance signal which is amplified in a high-gain audio amplifier, then passed through a phase detector, power-amplifier, and into the heater. This control unit was originally designed and built by Wylie (1948) (similar to the electronic controllers of Sturtevant, 1938, and Penther and Pompeo, 1941) for use with a copper thermometer element, to control liquid baths to $\pm 0 \cdot 001°$ C at or near room temperature. Apart from the different thermometer element, only one minor modification was made to Wylie's controller to fit it for low-temperature control: the output heating current was taken direct from the cathode lead of the power stage rather than from a power transductor—used by Wylie to give the high power output of 5–500 W necessary to control large oil baths. One difficulty, however, is the residual power developed in the thermometer which makes control below about 6° K difficult, due to the very small heat input required to maintain thermal balance at such temperatures.

Wilson and Stone (1957) have described a precision bath thermostat designed for use at room temperature, as was that of Wylie; their controller, which includes an a.c. bridge, amplifier, and phase-sensitive radio valve, also might be adapted usefully for cryogenic problems.

4. Controlled refrigeration

By 'controlled refrigeration' we mean those methods by which an experimental chamber is maintained at a temperature below its general surroundings, using controlled expansion or desorption of a gas. Such methods have been most widely used to bridge the temperature interval between $4\cdot2°$ K and that which can be attained with liquid hydrogen.

In the Clarendon Laboratory at Oxford, Simon expansion helium liquefiers have been an integral part of a number of research cryostats; physical investigation of properties in the region between $4°$ and $10°$ K is done by carefully controlling the adiabatic expansion of the compressed helium gas (initially at $10°$ K and about 120 atmospheres) so as to maintain temperatures of say $8°$, $7°$, or $6°$ K before the expansion and liquefaction is complete. The high thermal capacity of the compressed gas makes it relatively easy to cool to $7°$ K and maintain this temperature quite closely for a period of many minutes. Examples of the use of this method of control are afforded by the work of Berman (1951) and Rosenberg (1955) on thermal conductivity, and of MacDonald and Mendelssohn (1950) on electrical resistance.

Simon's desorption liquefier has also been used as an effective temperature controller in the range between $4°$ and $10°$ K (see, for example, Simon, 1937). The process is very similar to that of controlled expansion, except that the helium-gas pressures involved are much smaller. Instead of controlling the expansion of the compressed helium gas, the rate at which the helium is pumped from its charcoal adsorbent is carefully controlled; the relatively large heat capacity of the adsorbed gas also acts as a thermal reservoir, the temperature of which is therefore insensitive to small changes in heat transfer. Measurements by de Haas, de Boer, and Van den Berg (1933–4) on electrical resistance, and by Bijl (1950) on paramagnetic resonance, were made with the help of this method of maintaining steady temperatures.

It might be thought that in a laboratory equipped with a large central helium liquefier and well-filled storage dewars but with little or no liquid hydrogen available, the above methods would be impracticable. This may be so, but a recent paper by Rose-Innes and Broom (1956) shows that an ingenious modification of the Simon desorption liquefier enables temperatures to be controlled from 4·2° K up to liquid-oxygen temperatures without the use of hydrogen. Figure 103 illustrates their 'reversed' Simon procedure; after completing their calorimetric measurements at 4·2° K and below, liquid helium is evaporated by the heater R so that only helium adsorbed on the charcoal (in copper can D) remains. The experimental chamber can be warmed up to a temperature of say 20° or 30° K and then maintained there by pumping away some of the adsorbed gas; the heat capacity of the charcoal and gas is sufficient that the bottom of the dewar can be kept, for example, at 21° K for more than 30 minutes with 100 mW being dissipated in the calorimeter vessel.

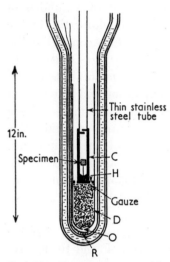

FIG. 103. Temperature control by the desorption method of Rose-Innes and Broom (1956).

It is uncommon to use Joule–Thomson or Linde liquefiers for the control of temperatures above the liquefaction temperature of the gas being circulated. In principle it is clearly possible by regulating the rate of flow of gas through the expansion valve, or perhaps more effectively by regulating the input pressure of the gas stream (regulation at the compressor) to prevent liquid being formed at the valve; reducing the flow rate sufficiently allows the inflow of heat from the surroundings to balance the Joule–Thomson cooling at a desired control temperature; alternatively, reducing the pressure of the incoming gas stream reduces the cooling efficiency (of the throttling process), so that again, a balance may be obtained.

An obvious drawback to this type of control is that fine adjustment of flow rate or input pressure is difficult; in particular the flow rate may change quite abruptly due to a small particle of some solid impurity (e.g. solid air in a cold helium-gas stream) collecting at or being dislodged from the throttling valve. Since the available heat capacity of the 'region' near the throttling valve is usually small (in contrast to the heat capacity of the compressed gas in a Simon expansion liquefier or of the adsorbed gas in a desorption apparatus), small fluctuations in the rate-of-flow or input pressure will result in a fairly rapid change in temperature. It has proved possible in the Collins type of helium liquefier to 'halt' the temperature in the space below the expansion valve, before the liquefaction temperature is reached; in this machine adjustment may be made to the cam-settings which control the time of opening of the expansion engine valves, as well as adjustment of flow-rate or input pressure. However, even in this case, it is unlikely that very accurate temperature control at say 10° and at 40° K can be achieved in an experimental space in the bottom of the 'liquefier'.

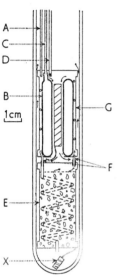

Fig. 104. A charcoal desorption cryostat (after Jackson and Preston-Thomas, 1951).

Despite these pessimistic observations on precision temperature control in Joule–Thomson liquefiers, Jackson and Preston-Thomas (1951) have shown that a small conventional Joule–Thomson helium liquefier of the Linde pattern can be adapted to obtain precise temperature control in the range between 4·2° and 14° K; they achieved this by attaching a small plastic container (E in Figure 104) filled with adsorbent charcoal in the tail of their helium liquefier. The cupro-nickel tube (A) carries cold helium gas from the expansion valve down past a soft-glass gas thermometer bulb B, through the coil in the charcoal to the bottom of the dewar; the gas then passes back through the charcoal and around the gas thermometer and specimen (in the centre of the thermometer bulb) taking the path shown by the arrows. When this section of the cryostat has been cooled to the desired temperature, the Joule–Thomson valve is closed, and the heat influx is balanced by desorbing gas from the charcoal. The rate of desorption is controlled by a needle valve in a line leading to a mechanical pump. They found that a temperature of 5° K could be maintained for about 1½ hours while the pressure over the charcoal was reduced from 1 atmosphere to 10 cm Hg. With sufficiently sensitive temperature indication, the temperature could be controlled to a constancy of ±0·01° K.

5. Swenson's method of control

A rather efficient method of regulating temperature was evolved by Swenson at the Massachusetts Institute of Technology a few years ago (described in a paper by Swenson and Stahl, 1954), a method in which both the latent heat of vaporization of a liquefied gas and part of the heat capacity of the gas are used to balance the heat inflow to an experimental chamber. The principles may be seen from Figure 105 which illustrates a cryostat used for high-pressure investigations. Temperatures between 4° and 80° K were maintained in the experimental enclosure by drawing liquid helium from the reservoir through a ⅛ in. thin-walled cupro-nickel tube to the heat exchanger. The exchanger consists of three concentric layers of 3/16 in. outer diameter copper tubing, wound around and solder bonded to the

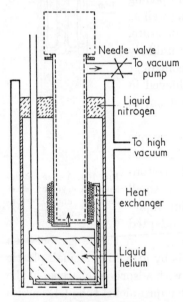

FIG. 105. Schematic diagram of a cryostat in which the temperature is controlled by the *Swenson* method (after Swenson and Stahl, 1954).

Needle valve
To vacuum pump
Liquid nitrogen
To high vacuum
Heat exchanger
Liquid helium

copper-walled enclosure which is to be kept at constant temperature. The rate at which the liquid helium is drawn through this tubing is controlled by the setting of a fine needle valve in the pumping tube between the heat exchanger and a mechanical pump. When controlling the enclosure at some temperature T ($> 4\cdot2°$ K), the liquid helium evaporates in the copper coil extracting about 20 cal/mole from the system; it is warmed up to a temperature close to the control temperature T as it circulates through the coil, extracting further heat equal to about $5\times(T-4\cdot2)$ cal/mole. It is found that to maintain temperatures of 20° or 30° K, a very careful setting of the needle valve is necessary to adjust the small pressure drop (< 1 cm Hg) between the inlet and outlet of the coil so that the flow rate of coolant is not too great. The addition of an electrical heater, e.g. a carbon resistor in a copper sleeve, cemented to the outside of the heat exchanger, simplifies the problem of control; the needle valve can then be used for comparatively coarse temperature adjustment and the heater current as a fine adjustment.

Temperatures between 80° K and room temperature can be regulated in the same manner, replacing liquid helium in the reservoir by liquid nitrogen and dispensing with the outer liquid-nitrogen shield.

Such a cryostat can hardly achieve the same precise degree of temperature regulation as an electronically controlled chamber of the type described in § 7.3 or as can be achieved by careful control of liquid-vapour pressure (§ 7.2). However, it does make efficient use of the cooling capacity of the refrigerant, and it would be quite possible to use automatically controlled electrical heating to counterbalance the somewhat coarse nature of the needle-valve flow-control mechanism.

References

Andrew, E. R. (1948.) *J. Sci. Instrum.* **25**, 416.
Berman, R. (1951). *Proc. Roy. Soc.* A, **208**, 90.
Bijl, D. (1950). *Proc. Phys. Soc.* A, **63**, 405.
Boyle, W. S., and Brown, J. B. (1954). *Rev. Sci. Instrum.* **25**, 359.
Dauphinee, T. M., MacDonald, D. K. C., and Preston-Thomas, H. (1954). *Proc. Roy. Soc.* A, **221**, 267.
—— and Woods, S. B. (1955). *Rev. Sci. Instrum.* **26**, 693.
Gilchrist, A. (1955). Ibid. 773.
Gilmont, R. (1946). *Industr. Engng. Chem. Anal. Ed.* **18**, 633.
—— (1951). *Anal. Chem.* **23**, 157.

DE HAAS, W. J., DE BOER, J., and VAN DEN BERG, G. J. (1933–4). *Physica*, **1**, 609, 1115.

JACKSON, L. C., and PRESTON-THOMAS, H. (1951). *J. Sci. Instrum.* **28**, 99.

MACDONALD, D. K. C., and MENDELSSOHN, K. (1950). *Proc. Roy. Soc.* A, **202**, 103.

MENDELSSOHN, K. (1936). Ibid. A, **155**, 558.

PENTHER, C. J., and POMPEO, D. J. (1941). *Electronics*, **14**, April, 20.

ROSE-INNES, A. C., and BROOM, R. F. (1956). *J. Sci. Instrum.* **33**, 31.

ROSENBERG, H. M. (1955). *Phil. Trans. Roy. Soc.* **247**, 441.

SIMON, F. E. (1937). *Physica*, **4**, 879.

SIMON, I. (1949). *Rev. Sci. Instrum.* **20**, 832.

STURTEVANT, J. M. (1938). *Rev. Sci. Instrum.* **9**, 276.

SWENSON, C. A., and STAHL, R. H. (1954). Ibid. **25**, 608.

WHITE, G. K. (1953). *Proc. Phys. Soc.* A **66**, 559.

—— and WOODS, S. B. (1955). *Canad. J. Phys.* **33**, 58.

WILSON, W., and STONE, N. W. B. (1957). *J. Sci. Instrum.* **34**, 327.

WYLIE, R. G. (1948). *Divn. of Physics Report* PA–2, C.S.I.R.O. Nat. Stand. Lab., Sydney.

ZABETAKIS, M. G., CRAIG, R. S., and STERRETT, K. F. (1957). *Rev. Sci. Instrum.* **28**, 497.

CHAPTER VIII

ADIABATIC DEMAGNETIZATION

1. Introduction

AT the beginning of this book it was pointed out that methods of cooling and entropy reduction are inextricably linked. Because the entropy or disorder of a gas is a function of volume as well as of temperature, the volume forms a useful physical variable by which the entropy of the gas can be reduced; if the initial alteration in volume V_1 to V_2 be made isothermally in a direction such as to reduce the entropy S, a subsequent adiabatic or isentropic change of V_2 to V_1 results in a drop in temperature.

To reach temperatures below that available by liquefying and pumping on helium, it is necessary to find some system which remains partially disordered and which can be ordered by a change in some available physical parameter. It was suggested by Giauque (1927) and independently by Debye (1926) that a disordered assembly of magnetic dipoles which may still occur in a paramagnetic substance at liquid-helium temperatures, should constitute such a system. Using the magnetic field H, as the variable quantity, successive processes of isothermal magnetization and adiabatic demagnetization should produce cooling. As is now well known, Giauque and MacDougall (1933) at Berkeley and de Haas, Wiersma, and Kramers (1933) at Leiden proved this experimentally; soon afterwards Kurti and Simon (1934) at Oxford also carried out successful demagnetizations.

The history of this field as well as later developments have been given in detail in the monographs of Casimir (1940), Garrett (1954), and reviews by Ambler and Hudson (1955), de Klerk and Steenland (1955), and particularly in the detailed review by de Klerk (1956). For the uninitiated, the published lectures delivered by Simon (1937) at the British Museum and by Kurti (1952) at the Royal Institution are very instructive introductions to the principles of magnetic cooling. The cooling process is illustrated in terms of entropy reduction by Figure 106. This figure shows what is happening thermodynamically during the isothermal magnetization (change from $H = 0$ to $H = H_1$ at T_0 and subsequent isentropic demagnetization (change from $H = H_1$ at T_0 to $H = 0$ at T_1). We may also ask what happens to the alignment of the individual magnetic dipoles during these

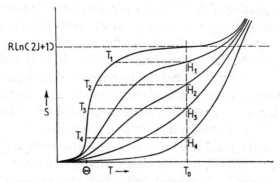

FIG. 106. Entropy of a paramagnetic salt used in cooling experiments (after de Klerk, 1956).

changes. Firstly, let us consider the dipoles initially at T_0 as a non-interacting assembly, or more properly as an assembly with such a small interaction that the dipoles have no preferred orientation. If the paramagnetic ion has a total angular momentum J, then its moment may take up any one of $2J+1$ directions with respect to the vanishingly small interaction field, the energy difference between adjacent orientations (or energy levels) being U, where U is assumed to be much less than kT_0. The probability of the magnetic moment of an ion having a certain orientation is governed by the Boltzmann distribution, i.e. the factor $\exp(U/kT)$; since $U = g\beta H_{\text{int}} \ll kT_0$, any of the $2J+1$ orientations are equally probable. However, on applying a field H_1 such that $g\beta H_1 \geqslant kT_0$, the ions will go into the lower energy levels which correspond to dipoles pointing in the direction of the applied field (see Figure 107). Here g is the Landé splitting factor

$$1 + \frac{J(J+1)+S(S+1)-L(L+1)}{2J(J+1)}$$

and β is the Bohr magneton. In Figure 107 the degree of occupation of the various energy levels (here $J = 5/2$ so $2J+1 = 6$) is indicated by the shading on the lines. On removing the applied field H_1 isentropically, the degree of order must remain constant but the difference U returns to its former small value. For this to occur the distribution functions involving $\exp(g\beta H_1/kT_0)$ ($H = H_1$ at $T = T_0$) and

$$\exp(g\beta H_f/kT_1)$$

($H = H_f \to 0$ at $T = T_1$)

must be equal, hence the final temperature

$$T_1 = \frac{H_f T_0}{H_1}.$$

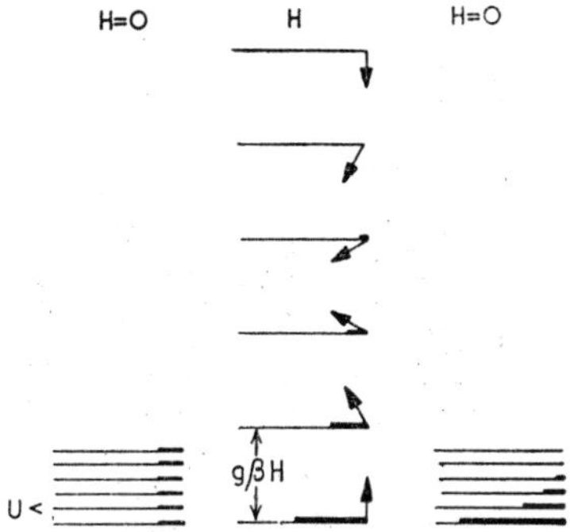

Lest it be supposed that on reducing the external field H to zero, T falls to zero and thereby violates the third law, it should be remembered that the dipoles do interact, just as atoms in a gas interact and eventually condense into a liquid or solid state at sufficient low temperatures. So the small interactions (which may be represented as producing an internal field, H_{int} or H_f) cause the fine splitting of levels by an amount U which is sufficient to give T_1 a finite value and prevent an 'attainability catastrophe'.

Fig. 107. Energy diagram of a paramagnetic ion (after Kurti, 1952).

A further condition for effective magnetic cooling is that the non-magnetic entropy of the system should be small in comparison with the magnetic entropy S_m, or more strictly in comparison with the possible reduction in magnetic entropy. This non-magnetic entropy comprises the vibrational entropy of the lattice, e.g.

$$S_0 = \int_0^{T_0} \frac{465(T/\theta_D)^3}{T}\, dT = 155\left(\frac{T}{\theta_D}\right)^3 \text{ cal/mole deg,}$$

which is usually negligible at or near $1°$ K in comparison with ΔS_m.

Summarizing for the paramagnetic ion:

(i) $S_m = R\log(2J+1)$ when $H = 0$,

(ii) ΔS_m should be appreciable in a field H, and

(iii) we require $S_{\text{lattice}} \ll \Delta S_m$.

Experimentally the magnetic cooling process may be represented schematically by Figure 108. The time spent at stage

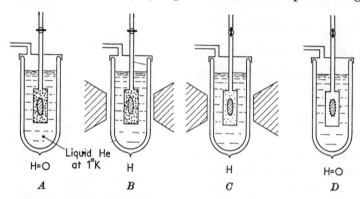

FIG. 108. Schematic diagrams of the experimental procedure used in magnetic cooling.

B must be sufficiently long for the heat of magnetization $Q = T_0\,\Delta S_m$ to be removed through helium exchange gas to the surrounding helium bath at temperature $T_0 \sim 1°$ K, i.e. for the magnetization to be effectively isothermal. C represents the period during which the exchange gas is removed. Whether or not this exchange gas is removed completely, the process of demagnetization to a temperature $T_1' \ll T_0$ is sufficiently rapid that residual gas is adsorbed onto the cold surface of the salt pill.

Provided that liquid helium and suitable pumps, dewar, magnet, etc., are available, cooling to $\frac{1}{10}°$ or $\frac{1}{100}°$ K can no longer be considered a particularly difficult or exclusive art, thanks to the pioneering efforts at Berkeley, Leiden, Oxford, and Cambridge. However, the problems of knowing what temperatures are attained by demagnetization, of maintaining those temperatures for appreciable periods, and of ensuring that the temperature at one point in a salt pill is also the temperature at another point or in some attached specimen are formidable.

2. Paramagnetic salts

Salts suitable for magnetic cooling must contain paramagnetic ions which have a non-zero resultant angular momentum or magnetic moment. The interaction between the magnetic ions (dipole-dipole or exchange interaction) should be sufficiently small that the energy level splitting U is much less than kT at $1°$ K; but in a field of a few thousand oersteds the splitting $g\beta H$ should be greater than kT. In addition, it is desirable that any higher energy levels should be already so high in zero external field that their influence on the distribution function is negligible, i.e. they should be 'quenched'.

Then we may assume that the entropy and magnetic moment M are functions of H/T only,

$$\text{e.g.}\quad M = \text{constant } H/T \quad \text{(Curie's law)}$$

or magnetic susceptibility $\chi = \text{constant}/T$ down to a temperature $T \sim \theta = U/k$. When temperatures in the neighbourhood of this characteristic temperature θ are reached, thermal energies have become comparable with the residual splitting or interaction energies, so that Curie's law is no longer obeyed; θ is the approximate limit of cooling and is also near the maximum of the magnetic specific heat anomaly. At temperatures appreciably above θ, the ion interaction is negligible and the magnetic specific heat $C_m = \text{constant}/T^2$.

Suitable magnetic ions come largely from the transition elements and the rare earth elements; that is, from those elements in which the atoms have a residual magnetic moment due to an unfilled but partially shielded inner shell. Of these, the most commonly used have been gadolinium and cerium among the rare earths and those transition elements with an unfilled $3d$ shell, viz. Ti, Cr, Mn, Fe, Co, Ni; certain cupric salts have also been found useful.

These elements, present in the form of magnetic ions, are normally used in mixed salts in which the interaction is reduced by the presence of non-magnetic ions and water of crystallization. For transition elements the energy levels of interest are generally the spin levels as the orbital magnetism—if present—

is quenched by the crystalline electric fields, i.e. Stark splitting of the orbital levels such that the energy gap between them is much greater than kT at 1° K. The magnetic moment due to electron spin is not directly affected by these electric fields but only via a coupling of the orbital and spin momenta.

The properties of a number of the most commonly used salts for which magnetic cooling experiments, susceptibility measurements, specific heat measurements, and paramagnetic resonance studies have provided data, are given by Garrett (1954), Cooke (1955), Ambler and Hudson (1955), and de Klerk (1956). For example, in the case of ferric ammonium alum, the chemical formula is $FeNH_4(SO_4)_2.12H_2O$. The ground state of the ferric ion is $^6S_{5/2}$ from which $2S+1 = 6$ and therefore the total spin entropy $S_m = R\log 6$. The susceptibility closely follows Curie's law with a Curie constant of 4·37 per mole and resonance studies give $g = 2·00$. Measurements of specific heat show

$$C/R \simeq 0·013_5/T^2.$$

Some of these salts are listed in Table XVIII below, with values for the temperature $T_1°$ K reached by adiabatic demagnetization from $T_0 \simeq 1·1°$ K, $H_1 \simeq 5,000$ oersteds (de Klerk,

TABLE XVIII

Magnetic Cooling with $H_1 = 5,000$ oersteds, $T_0 = 1·1°$ K

Salt	$T_1 °K$	$\theta_m °K$
$Cr(NO_3)_3.9H_2O$	0·21	..
$FeNH_4(SO_4)_2.12H_2O$	0·090	0·061
$Mn(NH_4)_2(SO_4)_2.6H_2O$	0·165	0·11
$CuK_2(SO_4)_2.6H_2O$	0·099	..
$Gd_2(SO_4)_3.8H_2O$	0·28	0·21
$CrK(SO_4)_2.12H_2O$	0·20	0·095
$†Cr(NH_3CH_3)(SO_4)_2.12H_2O$	0·21	..
$Ce_2Mg_3(NO_3)_{12}.24H_2O$	$\sim 0·01$	..

† Chromium methylamine alum.

1956). Also shown are some values of $\theta_m = U/k$ from Kurti and Simon (1935); they have assumed that the basic level of each ion is split into $2J+1$ levels, separated by equal energy differences due to interaction of $U = k\theta_m$. This characteristic temperature

θ_m then governs the final temperature that may be obtained by demagnetization:

$$\frac{T_1'}{T_0} = \frac{14\cdot9}{g}\frac{\theta_m}{H_1} \text{ where } H_1 \text{ is in kilo-oersteds.}$$

For many magnetic ions of interest, $g \simeq 2$, so that

$$\frac{T_1'}{T_0} \simeq 7\cdot5 \frac{\theta_m}{H_1}.$$

A property of obvious interest when using a salt as a cooling medium is its specific heat. Not only is this a fairly direct criterion of the splitting of the energy levels, and hence of the temperatures which may be obtained by demagnetization, but it also governs the warming-rate of the salt arising from a given 'heat leak'. If the electrical resistance of a material is to be investigated in the range $0\cdot3°$–$0\cdot5°$ K, it is pointless to use a cooling salt such as cerium magnesium nitrate which has a single maximum in the specific heat below $0\cdot01°$ K and hence a very small heat capacity between $0\cdot1°$ and $1\cdot0°$ K.

The specific heat curves shown in Figure 109 have been plotted from data given by de Klerk (1956) in his review. Not shown is that for cerium magnesium nitrate, for which $C/R = 6\cdot4\times10^{-6}T^{-2}$ (Daniels and Robinson, 1953); this may be compared with $C/R = 193\times10^{-4}T^{-2}$ for chromium methylamine alum. The specific heat of ferric ammonium alum has been taken from Kurti and Simon (1935). Many other paramagnetic salts have been used for cooling and countless others may be investigated and used in the future, but the salts mentioned in Table XVIII and Figure 109 include those which have received the greatest attention in the past twenty years and therefore about which we have the greatest knowledge of entropy, specific heat, energy levels, etc.

As suggested above, these properties may be altered by diluting a paramagnetic salt so as to increase the distance between magnetic ions, thereby decreasing the magnetic interaction and hence the splitting of the lower energy levels. As de Haas and Wiersma (1935) found, dilution of chromium potassium alum with aluminium potassium alum allows much lower values of T_1' to be obtained provided that H_1 is increased. But dilution also reduces the magnetic entropy S_m so that the total heat capacity per unit volume is reduced and likewise the capacity of the salt for cooling other objects is reduced. As we shall discuss further in §§ 4 and 5 below, the cooling salt is usually mounted in a cryostat in one of three forms: (i) single crystal, (ii) powder

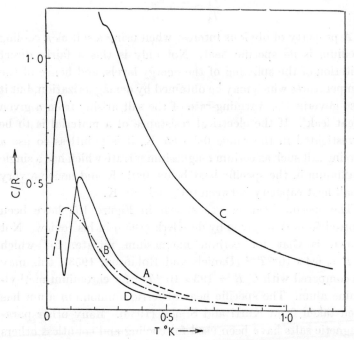

FIG. 109. Heat capacity of some salts used in magnetic cooling.
A, chromium methylamine alum; B, chromium potassium alum;
C, gadolinium sulphate; D, ferric ammonium sulphate.

compressed into a semi-solid rod, (iii) loose powder packed into a glass, plastic, or metal container. In any of these forms the salt must be protected against loss of its water of crystallization.

It is usually advisable to store 'salt pills' in a refrigerator or in liquid nitrogen, and never to pump a vacuum in the space around them until they have been cooled appreciably below room temperature. Ambler and Hudson (1956) suggested the use of salts which are not hydrated but which are sufficiently dilute magnetically that low temperatures may be reached with them; these suggested salts belong to a family having an $(NH_4)_3FeF_6$ structure e.g. $(NH_4)_3CrF_6$ for which preliminary results of demagnetization were given. Other water-free paramagnetics including acetonates and certain metal oxides have been suggested by Daunt and his collaborators at Ohio State University (e.g. pp. 158, 218 of 'Proceedings of Conférence de Physique des basses Températures', Paris, 1955, in the supplement to *Bull. Inst. int. Froid*).

3. Temperature measurement

Relationship between temperature and magnetic susceptibility

For paramagnetic salts there is an observable magnetic property, the susceptibility, which is temperature sensitive and provides a thermometric parameter. We may define a temperature scale T^* such that the observed volume susceptibility is related to it by

$$\chi = C/T^*,$$

where C is the Curie constant, since it is known that for a non-interacting assembly of magnetic dipoles (and for most magnetic cooling salts at temperatures $T \sim 1° \text{K} \gg \theta_m$) the magnetic susceptibility varies inversely as the absolute temperature. However, even at temperatures $T \gg \theta_m$ we cannot put $T^* = T$ due to the complicating influence of the shape-dependent demagnetizing field and the Lorentz internal field—due to magnetic interactions.

First consider the relation between the magnetic field within a paramagnetic salt and an external applied field H_{ext}. Following de Klerk (1956) we may define an internal field H_{int} which is the resultant of H_{ext} and a demagnetizing field. Confining the discussion to a spheroidal (ellipsoid of revolution) shaped salt pill

$$H_{int} = H_{ext} - \epsilon M/V,$$

where ϵ is the demagnetization coefficient, a function of the ratio of length to diameter. A convenient graph of ϵ as a function of l/d for ellipsoids is given by Kurti and Simon (1938a) which shows that ϵ has the following approximate values:

l/d	1	2	3	4	6	8	10
ϵ	4	2·2	1·4	1	0·5	0·3	0·2

In the particular case of a sphere $(l/d = 1)$, ϵ has the value $4\pi/3$. We may also define a 'local' field H_{loc} in the salt which is the sum of H_{int} and the field due to magnetic interaction between the ions, sometimes called the Weiss field:

$$H_{loc} = H_{int} + H_{weiss}$$
$$= H_{ext} + H_{weiss} - \epsilon M/V.$$

In the simplest case Lorentz has shown that the dipole interaction produces a field $4\pi M/3V$ (see, however, de Klerk, 1956, Ambler and Hudson, 1955, for more complete discussion of this and the Onsager and Van Vleck treatments of internal fields). To a first approximation in a cubic lattice the Lorentz treatment gives a correct answer, provided that the temperature is not so low as to be comparable with the characteristic temperature θ_m.

Thus
$$H_{loc} = H_{ext} + \left(\frac{4\pi}{3} - \epsilon\right) M/V,$$

from which
$$\chi_{loc} = \frac{\chi_{ext}}{1 + \left(\dfrac{4\pi}{3} - \epsilon\right)\chi_{ext}/V},$$

which for a spherical sample reduces to

$$\chi_{loc} = \chi_{ext}.$$

T^* was defined with respect to the external field

$$T^* = C/\chi_{ext},$$

which means that T^* values will be shape-dependent; Kurti and Simon introduced a quantity $T^{(*)}$ defined as

$$T^{(*)} = C/\chi_{loc},$$

so that for a spherical pill, $T^{(*)} = T^*$.

However, more generally using $\chi_{loc} = \chi_{ext} / \left[1 + \left(\dfrac{4\pi}{3} - \epsilon \right) \chi_{ext}/V \right]$
we have

$$T^{(*)} = \frac{C}{\chi_{ext}} \left[1 + \left(\frac{4\pi}{3} - \epsilon \right) \chi_{ext}/V \right]$$

$$= T^* + \left(\frac{4\pi}{3} - \epsilon \right) C/V$$

$$= T^* + \Delta.$$

For most paramagnetic salts used in cooling experiments it may be assumed that $T^{(*)} = T$ provided $T \gg \theta_m$.

Therefore $\quad \chi_{ext} = \dfrac{C}{T - \Delta} = \dfrac{C}{T - \left(\dfrac{4\pi}{3} - \epsilon \right) fC/V};$

here f is a filling factor which may be required, in the case of loosely packed salt pills, to take account of their density being appreciably less than the density of a single crystal. For example, let us consider potassium chrome alum. From Kurti and Simon (1938 a), the Curie constant per cubic centimetre is 0·0066 so that if a pill has an approximately spheroidal shape, ratio of length to diameter of four, and density about 97 per cent of the single-crystal density, then

$$\Delta = \left(\frac{4\pi}{3} - 1 \right) \times 0{\cdot}0066 \times 0{\cdot}97$$

$$= 0{\cdot}019_5,$$

so that the measured susceptibility $\chi \propto (T - 0{\cdot}02)^{-1}$. Some values of the Curie constant per cubic centimetre and Δ for an ellipsoid of $l/d = 3$, are given below (from Kurti and Simon, 1938 a).

TABLE XIX

Some values of the Curie constant and the quantity Δ
(assuming $f = 1$)

Substance	C/V	Δ° K
Gadolinium sulphate . .	$5{\cdot}85 \times 10^{-2}$	0·166
Manganous ammonium sulphate	$2{\cdot}00 \times 10^{-2}$	0·057
Ferric ammonium alum . .	$1{\cdot}55 \times 10^{-2}$	0·044
Chromic potassium alum .	$0{\cdot}66 \times 10^{-2}$	0·019
Titanium caesium alum .	$0{\cdot}13 \times 10^{-2}$	0·0037

Before considering the discrepancies between the thermodynamic temperature and the 'magnetic' temperature which
may occur at temperatures below 1° K let us consider the usual
methods of measuring the susceptibility.

Susceptibility measurement

Although the balance method (see Chapter V) of measuring
susceptibility was used in Leiden in their early experiments on

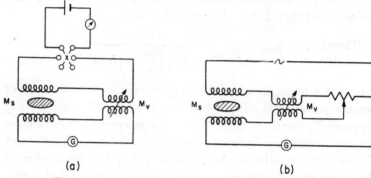

(a)   (b)

FIG. 110. (a) Ballistic bridge; (b) a.c. Hartshorn bridge.

demagnetization and has been used recently in Bristol (Mendoza
and Thomas, 1951) it has generally been superseded by the
induction bridge. Two obvious reasons are that measurement by
a microbalance of the force exerted on the salt pill by an inhomogeneous field requires (i) a comparatively strong magnetic
field so that the salt cannot be completely demagnetized,
and (ii) suspension of the pill from the balance which makes the
problems of thermal isolation rather difficult. As a result most
laboratories now use a mutual inductance method—a ballistic
bridge or a.c. Hartshorn bridge—or a self-inductance method
such as the a.c. Anderson bridge used at Berkeley.

In the ballistic method, a measured current supplied by an
accumulator (Figure 110(a)) is reversed through the primary
coil of a mutual inductance M_s around the salt pill; this induces a
current pulse through the secondary which is measured by the
deflexion of a ballistic galvanometer G—usually of period 10 to
20 seconds (e.g. a Tinsley Type 4500LS). The primary of M_s

consists of a few hundred turns of copper wire (say no. 30 B. & S. wire with 60 turns per inch over a length of 6 inches) wound onto the tail of the helium dewar and therefore immersed in liquid nitrogen, or it may be wound on the outer jacket of the experimental chamber and be in liquid helium; the secondary coil of some thousand or more turns of fine copper wire lies inside the primary. Part of the inductance may be cancelled by the variable inductometer M_v which is external to the cryostat. As discussed by de Klerk in his review (1956) practices differ in various laboratories: M_v may be used to create a null method whereby changes in the setting of M_v record the relative change in susceptibility of the salt pill; or M_v may be set so that the ballistic deflexion δ is approximately zero at say 4° K and as the temperature is lowered δ is recorded as a function of temperature.

In the latter case

$$\delta = \text{constant } \chi + b = \frac{a}{T-\Delta} + b.$$

The constants a, b which depend on the coil geometry and on the Curie constant are determined by plotting δ against the reciprocal of $(T-\Delta)$ in the range from 4° to 1° K, and then extrapolated at lower temperatures to obtain a value of $T^* = T^{(*)} - \Delta$. In using the ballistic method the writer has found it convenient to use an external inductometer consisting of a 0–1,000 μH variable inductance (e.g. Tinsley Type 4229 can be set to $\frac{1}{100} \mu$H) with a comparatively coarse mutual inductance capable of being set at approximate values in the range of 0–20 mH, in series.

With a little care in design this coarse balancing inductance can be avoided; it is common to wind two portions of the secondary of M_s in a region well above and well below the salt pill and wind them in opposition to the central portion. These are designed to partially or even completely annul the ballistic deflexion (or a.c. signal when using a bridge) in the region where the salt's susceptibility is small. For detailed references to the use of ballistic bridges (and also a.c. bridges) the reader is referred to de Klerk (1956) and also the comprehensive article by de Klerk and Hudson (1954) on the equipment for adiabatic demagnetization at the National Bureau of Standards.

The fact that the ballistic method has been used extensively in Oxford and the a.c. bridge (Figure 110(b)) has been used with only limited recourse to the ballistic bridge at centres such as Leiden and the National Bureau of Standards suggests that both have their merits and individual preference plays a large part in deciding which to use.

The Hartshorn bridge (Figure 110(b)) is operated with frequencies of thirty to a few hundred cycles supplied by an audiofrequency signal generator. The detector G is usually a vibration galvanometer or oscilloscope with preceding amplifier, and therefore can afford a greater sensitivity than the ballistic bridge; it is used as a null instrument and so requires a precision variable inductance. Details of such a mutual inductance have been given by de Klerk and Hudson (1954) and Erickson, Roberts, and Dabbs (1954). Apart from the more stringent requirements in the mutual inductance M_v, the a.c. method requires the apparatus inside the cryostat to be made of poorly conducting or insulating materials to avoid eddy currents; also at very low temperatures it may increase the heat inflow to the sample due to relaxation or hysteresis effects. This heat adsorption amounts to $\frac{1}{2}H_0^2 \omega \chi''$, where H_0 is the amplitude of the alternating field, ω is its angular frequency, and χ'' is the complex part of the susceptibility

$$\chi = \chi' - i\chi''.$$

For details of the use of the Anderson inductance bridge the reader is referred to Giauque and MacDougall (1935).

$T-T^{(*)}$ relations at very low temperatures

As yet we have not discussed the relation of the measured T^* or $T^* + \Delta = T^{(*)}$ to the thermodynamic temperature T. In the liquid helium region above $1°$ K, the temperature T of the salt is assumed to be that of the surrounding helium bath with which it is in thermal contact, and a very good estimate of T may be obtained from the helium vapour-pressure tables. Thus the constants in the equation $\chi_{\text{ext}} = \dfrac{C}{T - \Delta}$ (or in practice, perhaps

$\delta = \dfrac{a}{T-\Delta}+b\Big)$ may be determined assuming that the measured susceptibility or inductance is inversely proportional to $(T-\Delta)$. In this case we may assume that at temperatures just below $1°$ K, the magnetic temperature T^* determined from the measured susceptibility or inductance will, after addition of the quantity Δ, be a good estimate of T,

$$\text{i.e.}\quad T^{(*)} = T.$$

However, as the temperature is decreased further, and in particular as $T \to \theta_m$, this state of affairs may not be expected to continue.

From the second law of thermodynamics we define

$$T = \frac{dQ_{\text{rev}}}{dS} = \frac{dQ_{\text{rev}}/dT^{(*)}}{dS/dT^{(*)}};$$

it follows that by a series of demagnetizations from a known field H and known temperature T, and an allied series of specific heat determinations (warming the salt to determine $T^{(*)}$ as a function of Q), the numerator and denominator in this equation may be determined. Hence the relation between $T^{(*)}$ and T may be found for a particular salt.

Both the principles and the practice of the determination of the absolute scale below $1°$ K have been discussed at length by Kurti and Simon (1938 b), Simon (1939), Cooke (1949), Hull (1947), and in the reviews by Ambler and Hudson (1955), and de Klerk (1956). Figure 111 illustrates the principles of the determination. At temperature T_0 (in the liquid-helium region), the difference in entropy ΔS of the salt in fields H_1 and H_2 may be determined theoretically from the properties of the salt or directly by measuring ΔQ_0; heat ΔQ_0 is evolved in changing from H_1 to H_2 and may be determined from the quantity of helium evaporated. If two isentropic demagnetizations from H_1 and from H_2 to $H = 0$ take the salt to temperature T_1^* and T_2^* respectively, the difference in entropy is still ΔS between the positions A' and B'. Alternatively, by supplying heat ΔQ to the salt, it may be warmed from the temperature T_2^* to T_1^* and hence the difference $_1.T_2.\ = \Delta Q/\Delta S$ may be found in degrees absolute. This implies a knowledge of ΔQ which must be obtained by calibration of the heating source (γ-ray heating is used in Oxford and a.c. electrical heating at Leiden) at a temperature in the vicinity of T_0'; here the salt is known to obey Curie's law and hence the thermodynamic temperatures are known. By a series

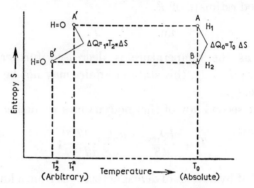

FIG. 111. Establishment of a thermodynamic temperature
scale below 1° K (after Kurti, 1952).

of demagnetizations, a fairly accurate picture of the T–T^* relation may be obtained.

In Figure 112 is shown the relation determined experimentally for potassium chrome alum (after Cooke, 1949) together with theoretical curves based on treatments of the internal inter-action field by Lorentz, Onsager, and Van Vleck. In Table XX are some values at various thermodynamic temperatures of the magnetic temperature $T^{(*)} = T^*+\Delta$, i.e. in terms of a spherical salt pill; these are based on data given by Ambler and Hudson (1955).

Before concluding this brief discussion of temperature measurement below 1° K, we should note that a number of secondary thermometers can be useful in this temperature range. These are in the electrical resistance category and have been discussed already (§§ 7.7, 7.8) in the section dealing with semi-conducting resistance thermometers and metallic alloy resistance thermometers. With any secondary thermometer, i.e. other than the susceptibility of the salt itself, the problems of thermal

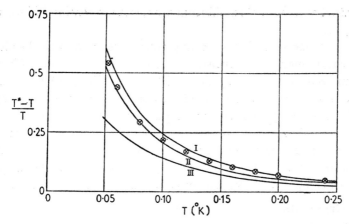

Fig. 112. Relation between magnetic temperature and absolute temperature for chromium potassium alum. Curve I, Onsager's theory; curve II, Van Vleck's theory; curve III, Lorentz's theory. Crosses are experimental results (after Cooke, 1949).

Table XX

T ($^{\circ}K$)	$T^{(*)}$ Iron ammonium alum	$T^{(*)}$ Chromium potassium alum	$T^{(*)}$ Manganese ammonium alum	$T^{(*)}$ Chromium methylamine alum	$T^{(*)}$ Cerium magnesium nitrate
0·4	0·40	0·406	0·43	0·408	..
0·3	0·30	0·310	0·336	0·311	..
0·2	0·229	0·215	0·245	0·215	..
0·18	0·214	0·195	..	0·196	..
0·16	0·198	0·174	0·20	0·180	..
0·14	0·183	0·156	..	0·160	..
0·12	0·168	0·138	..	0·139	..
0·10	0·149	0·121	..	0·124	..
0·08	0·127	0·103	..	0·113	..
0·06	0·105	0·086	..	0·098	..
0·05	0·097	0·079	..	0·094	..
0·04	0·0666	..	..	0·084	..
0·03$_5$	0·0666	..	..	0·076	..
0·03	0·067	..	..	0·066	..
0·02$_5$	0·068	..	..	0·057	..
0·02	0·070	..	..	0·051	0·02
0·01$_5$	0·072	..	..	..	0·01$_5$
0·006	..	..	..	..	0·0060
0·005	..	..	..	..	0·0052$_3$
0·004$_5$	..	..	..	..	0·0049$_0$
0·004	..	..	..	..	0·0045$_2$
0·003$_5$	..	..	..	..	0·0041$_5$

contact and thermal equilibrium arise, and are considered below in § 5.

A new method of correlating temperature scales with the aid of cerium magnesium nitrate as a 'secondary thermometer' has been used successfully by Cooke, Meyer, and Wolf (1956). This makes use of the fact that the susceptibility of cerium magnesium nitrate is highly anisotropic and χ is known to obey Curie's law down to about $0 \cdot 006°$ K; this salt forms a secondary thermometer to measure the susceptibilities and hence the $T^{(*)}$–T relations of a number of other salts, each of which can be made into a composite pill with a core of cerium magnesium nitrate.

4. Cryostats

Introduction

For effective cooling by demagnetization certain provisions must be met in the cryostat:

  (i) It must allow the salt to be cooled to $\sim 1°$ K by thermal contact with a pumped liquid-helium bath.

 (ii) At the salt there must be an adequate magnetic field to reduce the entropy appreciably, and thermal contact must be maintained to allow the heat of magnetization $(Q = T_0 \Delta S_m)$ to be transferred to the helium bath.

(iii) Before demagnetization this thermal contact must be broken, and after demagnetization thermal contact must be sufficiently bad that the leakage of heat to the salt pill is small compared with its heat capacity.

(iv) A mutual inductance in the cryostat should register the change in susceptibility of the salt and not be unduly influenced by other materials present.

In any laboratory the particular design of adiabatic demagnetization cryostat must depend somewhat on the means of attaining $T_0 \simeq 1°$ K, that is whether a small helium liquefier is incorporated in the cryostat or whether liquid helium may be transferred into it from a storage dewar. However, this is relatively unimportant in determining the general design of the experimental space around the salt pill and the method of suspending the pill.

Leiden and Oxford cryostats

In view of the long experience acquired at Leiden and Oxford the two cryostats illustrated in Figures 113 (*a*) and (*b*) are of particular interest. In the first figure (Figure 113 (*a*) of a Leiden cryostat) the ellipsoidal salt is mounted on a glass pillar within a small vacuum jacket, also of glass. The secondary coil of the

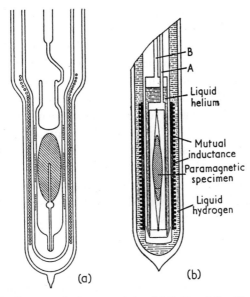

FIG. 113. Demagnetization cryostats. (*a*) Leiden (after Casimir, de Haas, and de Klerk, 1939); (*b*) Oxford (after Kurti, 1952).

mutual inductance is wound onto the vacuum jacket and is in the liquid helium contained by the inner dewar. The primary coil, wound onto the tail of the helium dewar, is immersed in the liquid hydrogen or liquid nitrogen of the outer dewar. Helium exchange gas is used in the vacuum jacket for cooling the salt pill and afterwards pumped away. The N.B.S. installation (de Klerk and Hudson, 1954) uses a very similar demagnetization cryostat, and in both Leiden and the N.B.S. the cryostat is suspended from a long rotatable arm so that the whole cryostat may be moved out of the poles of the magnet after demagnetization.

In the Oxford pattern (Figure 113 (b)) the salt pill is tautly suspended by silk or nylon threads inside a cylindrical metal cage; this cage fits into the German silver vacuum chamber which is sealed at the bottom by a greased cone and socket joint.† Formerly all these Oxford cryostats had a small Simon expansion liquefier in the upper part of the apparatus (see, for example, Hull, 1947, for description of whole cryostat and details of demagnetization procedure). The upper part of tube A (Figure 113 (b)) being soldered to the wall of the expansion vessel, allows helium gas to be cooled and condensed into the double-walled German silver chamber. The mutual inductance is wound onto a former of cloth-bonded bakelite or similar insulator, which fits over the outside wall of the vacuum case and is therefore surrounded by liquid hydrogen. The liquid helium is pumped through tube B and exchange gas is admitted and removed through tube A. It should be noted that if metal chambers surround the salt these should be of a metal such as German silver which does not become ferromagnetic at low temperatures. When an a.c. induction method is used for determining susceptibility it is preferable to use glass throughout the 'tail' assembly.

In Berkeley, Giauque and his collaborators have used spheroidal glass containers filled with powdered paramagnetic salts, the container being suspended by a glass tube inside a glass vacuum jacket (Fritz and Giauque, 1949). They have also used successfully plastic containers (Giauque *et al.*, 1952; Geballe and Giauque, 1952) in which the salt pills are mounted.

A metal cryostat

In Figure 114 (White, 1955) is a variation of the Oxford pattern in which the inner helium chamber C can be filled with liquid from the surrounding dewar through valve V, and may be reduced in temperature to about $1 \cdot 1°$ K by pumping. The inner

---

† As sealing agent for such a ground joint high-vacuum greases such as Apiezon L or Apiezon K are frequently used, but it has been found that fluids which form glasses may be more satisfactory. Hudson and McLane (1954) describe the use of an alcohol-glycerine (2 parts glycerine and 1 part of *n*-propyl alcohol) mixture which gives leakproof joints in the helium region, provided that it is cooled slowly to liquid-nitrogen temperatures.

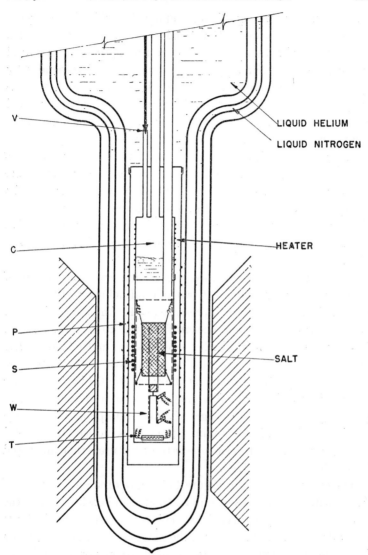

FIG. 114. Diagram of a demagnetization cryostat used for electrical resistance measurements (after White, 1955).

vacuum jacket is of German silver but has a copper flange at the top to facilitate soldering it with Wood's metal to the chamber C; vertical copper ribs are silver-soldered to the German silver to ensure temperature equilibrium, and yet avoid eddy currents being induced during the mutual inductance measurement. The salt pill of potassium chrome alum was pressed into a hard cylinder, painted with glyptal or nail varnish and suspended by nylon threads from a small German silver frame, made to slide inside the inner vacuum case. The primary P, of the mutual inductance is wound onto the outer brass vacuum jacket and the secondary S wound onto the inner German silver jacket. A modification (Dugdale and MacDonald, 1957) has been to place a platinum-glass seal in the bottom of the chamber C and take electrical leads out through this seal; the leads go through the pumped liquid helium and up the helium pumping tube rather than up the vacuum pumping tube; this provides more effective thermal anchoring and reduces the 'warming-up' rate considerably.

The experimental procedure with such a cryostat consists of (i) filling the inner chamber C with liquid helium and the space around the salt with a small pressure ($\sim 10^{-2}$ mm Hg) of helium exchange gas, (ii) cooling in steps from $4 \cdot 2°$ to $3°$, $2 \cdot 5°$, $2°$, $1 \cdot 5°$, $1 \cdot 1°$ K and measuring the ballistic deflexion or mutual inductance at each temperature, (iii) placing the dewar tail between the poles of a magnet, switching on the magnetic field and allowing a few minutes for heat of magnetization to be removed before pumping away the exchange gas, (iv) after pumping the exchange gas for a period of 10–30 minutes, the field is reduced to zero and the cryostat removed, (v) magnetic temperature is then measured by the inductance bridge.

The cryostat shown in Figure 114 is mounted on a relay rack which with the aid of wheels and a track, can be wheeled into the magnet gap very easily. The cryostats used at Oxford are generally fixed in position and the magnets are movable, being iron-core Weiss-type magnets on small trolleys or movable air-core solenoids which are capable of vertical movement.

Salt pills

The pressed variety may be easily made by partially filling a cylindrical hole in a steel block with the powdered salt, the bottom end of the hole being closed by a short length of steel rod which is free to slide in the hole. With a sliding steel piston inserted above the salt, a hand-operated or hydraulic press is then used to form a compact pill. The pill can then be pushed out fairly easily, although fracturing can occur during the removal which has led to the occasional use of a split steel block, in which the two halves are bolted together during the pressing operation. A little vacuum grease mixed with the powdered salt in a pestle and mortar before pressing often results in a stronger pill. With reasonable care, such salt pills may be ground or filed to a required shape and then surface-sealed with nail varnish or other cement to retard dehydration. Geballe and Giauque (1952) have described a technique of shaping salt pills into ellipsoids of revolution.

Alternatively, large single crystals of many paramagnetics may be grown from solution and can be formed onto a metal mesh or gauze in the process, e.g. onto silver, gold, or platinum gauze (Dugdale and MacDonald, 1957; Wheatley, Griffing, and Estle, 1956).

As may be seen from the figures in this section, narrow-tail glass dewars have been the usual containers for liquids in adiabatic demagnetization cryostats. The narrow tail allows the use of a smaller pole-gap in the magnet and hence higher fields for the same magnet current; the top section of the dewar is usually enlarged to give greater liquid-storage capacity. Multi-wall metal dewars designed for holding liquid helium in the inner dewar and liquid nitrogen in the outer dewar have now been produced commercially (e.g. Hofman Laboratories Inc., N.J.); these are tailed dewars, originally developed by W. E. Henry (Naval Research Laboratories, Washington) for use in magnetic fields.

5. Heat transfer and thermal equilibrium below 1° K
Introduction

Two major problems in carrying out measurements of physical properties at temperatures below 1° K are those of maintaining the temperature of a specimen sensibly constant and uniform, and knowing what the temperature is. Obviously this is particularly the case when the specimen under investigation is neither the cooling salt itself nor a paramagnetic salt whose temperature can be inferred from a susceptibility measurement. In most investigations on the properties of paramagnetic salts, the primary problem is to ensure a small heat leak and hence slow warming-up rate so that they are in thermal equilibrium during readings; they provide their own thermometer. But when investigating physical properties of materials which do not act as cooling agents themselves, the additional problem arises of thermal contact with the cooling agent and with the primary thermometer—the salt.

As we discussed in Chapter VI, the heat leakage is due largely to (i) radiation, (ii) residual gas conduction, (iii) conduction through solid supporting rods, wires, etc., (iv) gas desorption or adsorption, and (v) mechanical vibration. These factors have also been discussed in the review articles on adiabatic demagnetization. A very useful experimental study has been reported by Wheatley, Griffing, and Estle (1956).

Radiation

In so far as radiation is concerned, the heat leak is negligible if the salt is surrounded by a metal wall near 1° K, provided that no radiation from surfaces at higher temperatures can enter the 'salt' chamber via pumping tubes. In glass demagnetization cryostats, radiation protection is necessary in the form of a coating on the glass chamber which is at or near 1° K. Wheatley *et al.* found that an adsorbent film of 'Aquadag' and layer of aluminium foil was the most efficient; with this protection, rather than chemical silvering, a flashlight beam did not noticeably change the normal heat leak of 8 erg/min from other sources.

Gas adsorption

It seems somewhat dubious whether residual gas conduction and adsorption can be separated as heat-transfer factors, when a salt pill or specimen is at 0·01°–0·1° K and is surrounded by a 1° K enclosure. However, the dependence of heat-leak rate on the exchange-gas pressure† and pumping time before demagnetization is quite marked. Exchange-gas pressures of $\sim 10^{-4}$ mm appear to be too small for the heat of magnetization to be removed efficiently, and exchange-gas pressures of $\sim 10^{-2}$ mm are rather large as they result in large heat leaks (after demagnetization) even when pumping times of more than 1 hour are used. This is partly due to adsorption of helium on the surfaces at $1°$ K, which cannot be completely removed by pumping but which transfers slowly to the salt pill after demagnetization; such effects are much less marked with glass than with metal cryostats. In the 'baking out' or 'outgassing' technique for metal cryostats, often used at Oxford (Hull, 1947), the exchange gas is pumped away with the helium bath kept at $1·5°$ K rather than $1°$ K and the temperature is finally reduced to $1°$ K just before demagnetization. The effect of adsorbed exchange gas is most noticeable when salt pills or specimens have to be warmed up again to $0·5°$ or $0·6°$ K for the purpose of physical measurements, as the vapour pressure of liquid helium is relatively high ($\sim 10^{-4}$ mm Hg) at such temperatures, and the vacuum deteriorates rapidly due to desorption from the walls of the pill. In the experiments of Wheatley et al. with a glass cryostat, they confirmed that a suitable exchange-gas pressure is $\sim 10^{-3}$ mm and that to ensure minimum heat leak later, a pumping time of about 2 hours is needed. With a pumping time of 1 hour the heat leak 10 minutes after demagnetization was 18·5 erg/min compared with 2·3 erg/min when pumped for $2\frac{1}{4}$ hours.‡ For many experiments, such small heat leaks are an unnecessary luxury and a pumping of a few minutes followed by demagnetization (and the resulting adsorption of exchange gas on the salt pill) may be all that is necessary.

Heat conduction through glass and nylon supports

Available information is rather scarce on the heat conduction of glass or nylon—the principal supporting materials—below $1°$ K.

---

† For methods of removing heat of demagnetization, i.e. heat transfer, without the use of exchange gas, see discussion on two-stage processes in § 8.6.

‡ To achieve such small heat leaks a second 'guard-ring' salt pill was attached to the supporting glass tube.

The results of Berman and of Bijl (see review article by Berman, 1953, and compilation of Powell and Blanpied, 1954) on the heat conductivity of various glasses above 1° K suggest that in the temperature range between 1° and 3° K,

$$\lambda \simeq BT^{1\cdot3} \text{ erg/cm sec deg, where } B = 2,000\text{--}3,000.$$

Such an equation may be extrapolated to lower temperatures and would give results for heat flow very similar to those given by Berman, Foster, and Rosenberg (1955); these authors state that for a soft-glass rod of 10 cm length and 0·01 cm² cross-section with two ends at 0° K and 1° K respectively, the expected heat flow is 1·3 erg/sec. Wheatley, Griffing, and Estle find from their results on Pyrex glass below 1° K that $\lambda \simeq 1200T^{1\cdot6}$ erg/cm sec deg, which is a little smaller than the figures of Berman *et al*.

For nylon (from Berman, 1953, and Berman, Foster, and Rosenberg, 1955) we may assume $\lambda \simeq 250T^{1\cdot2}$ erg/cm sec deg and extrapolation to very low temperatures gives a figure of 0·14 erg/sec as the heat flow along a 10 cm thread of 0·01 cm² cross-section when the ends are at 0° K and 1° K respectively.

The heat leakage down glass supports may be reduced markedly by using a double-pill technique, mounting the second 'guard-ring' pill of a paramagnetic salt at a point on the supporting tube or thread. In a further refinement, Nicol (1955) and Dugdale and MacDonald (1957) thermally connected a light metal shield to the 'guard' salt so that a copper-plated German silver shield (at $T \simeq 0\cdot5°$ K) surrounded the other 'salt' pill or specimen being investigated. In this case not only is conduction down the supporting tube or thread reduced, but heat leaks due to gas conduction or adsorption are reduced also; by such means heat leaks of the order of 1–2 erg/min have been obtained.

Vibrations

The results of investigations of mechanical vibrations as a source of heat inflow have been discussed in Chapter VI. Suffice it to say that, with glass supports, the natural period of vibration is sufficiently high that normal laboratory or pump vibrations do not set the pill into vibrations of large amplitude, although heat leaks of a few ergs per minute might be traced to such a cause.

With salt pills suspended by threads, the resonant period is often much closer to or identical with the period of some local vibrations and may result in heat inputs of hundreds to thousands of ergs per minute; to counteract this, taut suspension threads, efficient damping of the pump vibrations and isolation of the cryostat from pumps and building vibrations may be used.

Thermal equilibrium and heat conduction in the salt

As most heat leaks to a salt are to the surface or to points on the surface, and any heat leaks arising from an attached specimen are also to isolated regions within the salt pill, their effect on the temperature equilibrium of the salt pill is important.

For a single crystal of an insulator we may assume fairly rapid establishment of thermal equilibrium; the thermal conductivity at these low temperatures is due to lattice waves of fairly long wavelength and is limited by crystal or grain boundaries. Casimir (1938) showed that

$$\lambda_B \simeq 1 \cdot 6 \times 10^3 D A^{2/3} T^3 \text{ W cm}^{-1} \text{ deg}^{-1},$$

where $C_v = A T^3$ J/cm^3 deg is the lattice specific heat and D the average grain size in centimetres. Thus in a paramagnetic of $\theta \simeq 200°$ K, density $\rho \simeq 2$ gm/cm^3, molecular weight $\simeq 500$, we may obtain

$$\lambda_B \simeq 6400 D T^3 \theta^{-2} = 1 \cdot 6 \times 10^6 D T^3 \text{ erg/cm sec deg}.$$

Although experiments on crystalline dielectrics above 1° K generally confirm Casimir's equation, experiments below 1° K— rather less accurate—suggest that the actual heat conductivity may be somewhat smaller. Thus Kurti, Rollin, and Simon (1936) found $\lambda \simeq 250$ erg/cm sec deg at 0·07° K for a ferric ammonium alum crystal of 0·7 cm diameter; this leads to a mean free path of about 1 mm rather than 7 mm (see Berman in his review of thermal conductivity in dielectric solids, 1953). For a potassium chromium alum crystal of the same dimensions, Kurti et al. found that $\lambda \simeq 1,000$ erg/cm sec deg at 0·18° K. Other results from the work of Bijl and of Garrett have been discussed in the review by Berman (loc. cit.).

In salt pills of compressed powder, we might expect the maximum thermal conductivity to be that calculated from Casimir's formula assuming a value for D approximating to the average size of the crystallites; Van Dijk and Keesom (1940) obtained $\lambda \simeq 13 \times 10^4 T^3$ erg/cm sec deg for compressed powdered ferric ammonium alum in the range $0.04°-0.3°$ K.

Turning to the contact thermal resistance between a paramagnetic salt and a solid, experiments by Mendoza (1948) indicated that for metal (copper) fins in a pressed pill of powdered salt, the heat flow

$$\dot{Q} \simeq 100A(T_1^3 - T_2^3) \text{ erg/sec cm}^2 \text{ deg}^3,$$

where A is the area of contact and T_1 and T_2 are the temperatures of salt and metal respectively; later Goodman (1953) found a rather higher value for the multiplicative constant. With crystals grown from solution onto silver wire mesh (Dugdale, MacDonald, and Croxon, 1957; see also Dugdale and Mac-Donald, 1957), experimental results suggest a heat flow across the metal-crystal interface which is about ten times larger than is deduced from the Mendoza equation. In the case of large single crystals cemented to quartz or copper, Wheatley et al. found the heat transfer to be about a hundred times better than that predicted by the Mendoza equation.

What is apparent from these various experiments on heat contact between the salt and embedded fins? Above about $0.1°$ K, as Mendoza suggested in 1948, the temperature of a specimen should be within a few hundredths of a degree of the temperature of the salt, provided that the specimen is connected via a good thermal link (copper wires), to extended fins which are firmly embedded in a compressed salt pill or are bonded to a single crystal. This presupposes that heat leaks to the specimen are maintained at a level of the order of 10 erg/min or less. The reader is also referred to two papers dealing with investigations of the electrical resistance of metals at temperatures below $1°$ K; these are by Mendoza and Thomas (1951) and Croft et al. (1953) and discuss the problems of temperature equilibrium in the very low-temperature region.

An interesting means for maintaining low temperatures despite an appreciable heat input is that of 'incomplete demagnetization'; this was originally suggested and used by Kurti, as far as the writer is aware. In this procedure the salt is first demagnetized to a field of, say, 1,000 oersteds. During the course of the experiment, the field is slowly reduced from 1,000 oersteds at a rate sufficient to keep the salt temperature sensibly constant; this takes advantage of the relatively large specific heat of the salt in a magnetic field (cf. Figure 106).

Two methods for improving thermal equilibrium within the cooling salt and between the salt and its surroundings have been used: these both involve the presence of liquid helium among the particles of salt using either a sealed capsule or an open capsule. In the former (Kurti, Rollin, and Simon, 1936; Hull, 1947; Hull, Wilkinson, and Wilks, 1951) a thick-walled metal tube containing a powdered salt is filled to 100 atmospheres with helium gas at room temperature and sealed off. For the latter technique (Hudson, Hunt, and Kurti, 1949) the salt container is connected by a capillary tube (0·2–0·3 mm inner diameter) to a helium supply from which helium is condensed into the container at 4° K; surface creep of the helium film at temperatures below the λ-point (2·17° K) and recondensation of the evaporating film causes an additional heat influx to the container which is approximately proportional to the diameter of the capillary tube. Although the resultant heat leak may be more than 100 erg/min, this open capsule technique has been useful for some investigations.

6. Two-stage cooling, cyclic magnetic refrigeration, and nuclear demagnetization

Thermal switches

Helium exchange gas has played a large part in the discussion of magnetic cooling. Its importance as an effective thermal link is obvious, and equally obvious are the disadvantages that it introduces; firstly, it takes some time to remove the exchange gas effectively and unless this is done, subsequent heat leaks are large; secondly, at temperatures below 0·5° K the vapour pressure of helium is less than 10^{-4} mm so that exchange gas is no longer a useful heat link.

For a thermal switch that can be opened or closed rapidly or which will operate at a temperature of $\frac{1}{10}°$ K or $\frac{1}{100}°$ K, a substitute for helium exchange gas is needed. The need for a substitute was emphasized by the following: Gorter (1934) and Kurti and Simon (1935) independently suggested that nuclear spin paramagnetism could provide a source of entropy at near $0.001°$ K, which if ordered by a magnetic field could be cooled by subsequent demagnetization to 10^{-5} to $10^{-6°}$ K. Due to the value of the nuclear moments in a nuclear paramagnetic being much smaller than the electronic moments in an 'ordinary' electronic paramagnetic, it is required that H/T_0 should be 10^6 to 10^7 oersteds/deg. Even with a field of 10^5 oersteds, this requires $T_0 \simeq 0.01°$ K so that a successful nuclear cooling experiment must depend on first reaching $\frac{1}{100}°$ by an electronic cooling stage. Therein lies the requirement of heat transfer.

Probably the most important form of thermal switch is the superconducting link suggested by Heer and Daunt (1949), Gorter (1948), and Mendelssohn and Olsen (1950) as a result of experiments on the heat conductivity of superconducting elements. This switch depends on the fact that the thermal conductivity λ_n of a superconducting element in the normal state (induced by a magnetic field exceeding the critical field), is larger than its conductivity λ_s in the superconducting state. In the normal state, conduction electrons are chiefly responsible for the conductivity and at temperatures near or below $1°$ K, λ_n is limited by physical or chemical impurities so that $\lambda_n \propto T$. For example, consider a metal of electrical resistivity $\rho_{295} \simeq 10^{-5}$ ohm cm and of sufficiently high purity that $\rho_r/\rho_{295} \simeq 10^{-3}$; from the Wiedemann–Franz–Lorenz law: $\rho\lambda/T = L \simeq 2.45 \times 10^{-8}$ W cm^{-1} deg^{-1}, it follows that $\lambda_n \simeq 2.45T$ W cm^{-1} deg^{-1} at low temperatures.

In the superconducting state, at temperatures well below the transition temperature, only the lattice waves are responsible for thermal conduction and λ_s is limited by presence of grain boundaries: then Casimir's formula gives
$$\lambda_s = 1.6 \times 10^3 A^{\frac{3}{2}} T^3 D,$$
where D is the average dimension of the crystal grains.

Since
$$C_v = AT^3 \text{ J/cm}^3 \text{ deg,}$$
$$= 1940 \frac{T^3}{\theta^3} \frac{\rho}{\text{at. wt.}},$$

therefore
$$\lambda_s = 2 \times 10^5 \left(\frac{\rho}{\text{at. wt.}}\right)^{\frac{2}{3}} \frac{T^3}{\theta^2} D \text{ W/cm deg.}$$

If, for example, $\theta \simeq 100°$ K,
$$\rho \simeq 10 \text{ gm cm}^{-3},$$

and the atomic weight $\simeq 100$, then
$$\lambda_s = 4DT^3 \text{ W/cm deg.}$$

Hence in a case where the grain dimensions are about 0·1 cm, it is clear that $\lambda_n/\lambda_s \simeq 6T^{-2}$; for $T = 0·1°$ K this gives $\lambda_n/\lambda_s \simeq 600$. Recent experimental work on heat conduction below 1° K (from a review by Mendelssohn, 1955, and also Mendelssohn and Renton, 1955, G. M. Graham—private communication) at the Clarendon and Mond laboratories has confirmed that $\lambda_s \propto T^3$ at very low temperatures in most specimens investigated, e.g. of Pb, Sn, In, Tl, Ta, Nb; the results also suggest that the constant of proportionality may often be smaller by a factor of two or three than is suggested by the grain size; this merely enhances the experimental value of the ratio λ_n/λ_s compared with that derived from Casimir's equation.

Such a thermal link whose conductivity may be changed by a factor of a thousand or more at 0·1° K by merely applying a field of a few hundred oersteds should therefore serve as an effective thermal switch in any two-stage cooling process, including nuclear cooling.

Other thermal switches are possible but have not proved as efficient as the superconducting link: Collins and Zimmerman (1953) tested a mechanical contact switch as part of a cyclic magnetic refrigeration process but found that the heat input due to friction at the switch was too large for its use below 1° K where heat leaks must be reduced to ergs rather than thousands of ergs. Fulton et al. (1957) at Duke University investigated a thermal link consisting of a vertical tube containing a liquid $He^3 + He^4$ mixture. With a carefully chosen geometry this vertical tube showed a heat conductivity in the downward direction some hundred or more times greater than in the upward direction. The fundamental processes underlying this 'heat flush' device are still somewhat obscure but it promises to be a useful form of heat linkage in the region near $1°$ K; it seems unlikely that it will prove useful in the lower temperature range of $0·1°–0·01°$ K.

Application of thermal switches

We may illustrate schematically the use of a thermal switch in a 'two-stage' magnetic cooling process (Figure 115) and

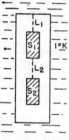

examine its application to three particular problems: (i) two-stage cooling involving electron paramagnetics, (ii) cyclic magnetic refrigeration, (iii) nuclear demagnetization. As illustrated, L_1, L_2 are thermal links, which when 'closed' allow heat flow; S_1 and S_2 are cooling salts.

In case (i) a two-stage demagnetization may be used to obtain temperatures of $\sim 0·001°$ K with comparatively small magnetic fields, e.g. 5,000 oersteds. A salt S_1 with a comparatively high characteristic temperature θ_m is magnetized with L_1 closed; L_1 is opened and S_1 is demagnetized to obtain a temperature of about $0·1°$ K. Salt S_2 of much lower θ_m (e.g. diluted salt) is in a magnetic field during this procedure and is therefore magnetized at $T_0 \sim 0·1°$ K. L_2 is now opened and S_2 is demagnetized to give a final temperature $T_1 \sim 0·001°$ K.

FIG. 115. The use of thermal switches in two-stage cooling processes.

In (ii) S_2 is a salt which acts as a thermal reservoir and is kept cool by cyclic removal of heat to S_1 and from S_1 to the helium bath: with L_1 closed, S_1 is magnetized; then after opening L_1, S_1 is demagnetized and L_2 is closed to partially cool S_2. Subsequently L_2 is opened and L_1 is closed and the process is repeated. Once the system has reached equilibrium, and provided that the heat leak to S_2 is small in comparison with its heat capacity, its temperature will oscillate with small amplitude about a mean temperature T with the period of the magnetic cycle.

In principle the nuclear cooling (iii) is similar to (i) but S_2 is now a nuclear paramagnetic while S_1 remains an electronic paramagnetic.

Two-stage cooling of electronic paramagnetics

Considering these processes in a little more detail, the first was ably demonstrated by the experiments of Darby *et al.* (1951) in

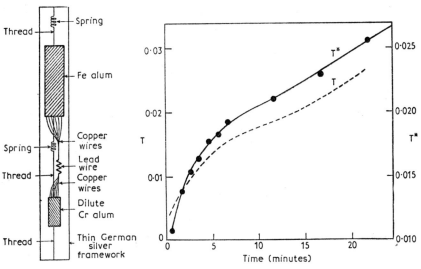

FIG. 116. Diagram of the arrangement used by Darby *et al.* (1951) in a two-stage cooling experiment; the temperature of the dilute chromium salt after demagnetization is shown in the graph (T^* = magnetic temperature, T = absolute temperature).

which a final thermodynamic temperature of about $0.003°$ K was obtained with a field $H \simeq 4{,}200$ oersteds; with $H \simeq 9{,}000$ oersteds, they reached $T \simeq 10^{-3°}$ K and maintained the temperature below $0.01°$ K for about 40 minutes.

In Figure 116 is shown their experimental arrangement and warm-up rate after demagnetization from 4,200 oersteds. In these experiments L_1 was helium exchange gas and L_2 a super-conducting thermal link of lead wire 3 cm long and 0·3 mm diameter. The consecutive processes of demagnetizing S_1 (iron ammonium alum), opening link L_2, and then demagnetizing S_2 (diluted mixed crystals of potassium chrome alum and potassium aluminium alum in the ratio of about 20:1) were achieved by gradual lowering of the magnet.

A further demonstration of this technique of reaching the millidegree region with small magnets has been given by Nicol (1955); in this case S_1 was manganous ammonium sulphate, and S_2 was chromium potassium alum. A temperature of a few millidegrees was reached, and by surrounding the second salt with a small radiation shield—cooled by the first salt—heat leaks of about 4 ergs/min were maintained to S_2.

Cyclic magnetic refrigeration

A notable technical advance has been the construction at Ohio State University (see Heer, Barnes, and Daunt, 1954, and Daunt, 1957 for details) of a cyclic magnetic refrigerator for maintaining temperatures in the range from $0 \cdot 2° - 1 \cdot 0°$ K. This continuously operated heat extractor is now being produced commercially by the A. D. Little Corporation (see, for example, Daunt *et al.*, 1955).

In Figure 117 (a) the salt R (potassium chrome alum), equivalent to S_2 in our earlier discussion, is the thermal reservoir which is cooled via the lead link (V_R) to salt A. The salt A consisting of iron ammonium alum is magnetized by magnet 2 with the link V_B to the 1° K helium bath closed and the link V_R open; V_B is then opened and A is demagnetized; V_R is now closed to cool R and then opened before the cycle of 2 minutes duration is repeated. Magnets 1 and 3 control the superconducting heat links. With the form of lead links used by Heer, Barnes, and Daunt the net rate of heat extraction obtained is about 70 erg/sec at $0 \cdot 26°$ K, 170 erg/sec at $0 \cdot 35°$ K, and 290 erg/sec at $0 \cdot 45°$ K.

Such a machine is particularly useful for investigating physical properties which necessitate continuous heat inputs of 1,000 erg/min or more. A salt container with internal copper fins is illustrated by Figure 117 (b); thermal equilibrium is assisted by mixing the salt with $\frac{1}{8}$ in. lengths of fine copper wire ($0 \cdot 002 - 0 \cdot 003$ in. diameter) and silicone vacuum grease; mixed in the ratio of 1 gm of wires and 1 gm of grease to 15 gm of salt, this is pressed under 3,000 lb/in² pressure into the container. The major difficulties associated with the design and construction of such a refrigerator would appear to be in the selection of optimum geometrical characteristics for the lead links and particularly in the timing equipment that controls the cyclic processes.

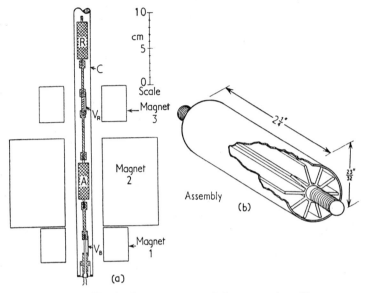

FIG. 117. (a) The basic components of the magnetic refrigerator. (b) The paramagnetic salt container of which the barrel is brass and the central rod and fins are copper (after Heer, Barnes, and Daunt, 1954).

Nuclear demagnetization

The possible attainment of the microdegree temperature region by demagnetization of nuclear spins was suggested by Gorter (1934) and by Kurti and Simon (1935), but the requirement that $H/T_0 \sim 10^7$ oersteds/deg appeared a considerable problem. Finally, in 1956, Kurti, Robinson, Simon, and Spohr (1956) successfully demagnetized copper from initial fields of between 20 and 28 kilo-oersteds and a temperature of $0 \cdot 012°$ K to reach about $20 \times 10^{-6°}$ K. The nuclear stage (equivalent to S_2 in the schematic diagram of Figure 115) is of a metal, copper, because of its nuclear spin—lattice relaxation time, which may be expected to be still of the order of minutes at $0 \cdot 01°$ K; 1,540 enamelled copper wires of only 0·005 in. diameter were used to reduce eddy-current heating. The wires, tied in a bundle, were folded over 4 times at the lower end to constitute the nuclear 'salt' and embedded at their top end in the electronic paramagnetic salt (S_1); this was chrome potassium alum mixed with some glycerol and water to promote thermal equilibrium and improve heat transfer to the copper wires, and was held in a Perspex container. The heat link L_2 thus consists of the copper wires themselves in order to avoid the complexity of a magnetically operated heat switch for these preliminary experiments. This whole assembly of $S_2+L_2+S_1$ was mounted inside a double-walled brass tube, the top part of which contained 25 g of manganous ammonium sulphate cooled by the initial demagnetization (when S_1 is demagnetized). The lower part of the double-walled shield was kept in good thermal contact with the manganous salt by liquid helium and thin copper wires between the brass walls. It appears likely that in the future the overcoming of problems of magnetic shielding will allow a superconducting heat link to be used between stages, and the warm-up rate will be reduced considerably below that in these initial experiments. Also, since only a small fraction of the nuclear magnetic entropy was removed by the initial conditions ($H/T_0 = 28000/0·012 \simeq 2\times10^6$ oersteds/deg), the possible future use of a somewhat smaller value for T_0 and increase in H to perhaps 50 or 60 kilo-oersteds will enable final temperatures of a few microdegrees to be reached.

7. Magnets

The design and construction of electromagnets is an extensive subject and it seems expedient here only to consider briefly the types of magnet normally used in paramagnetic cooling experiments and also some sources of information on their performance. The review articles (Ambler and Hudson, and de Klerk) have discussed this and such standard texts on magnetism as Bates (1948) give some details of and references to types of large electromagnets.

Most iron-core magnets are limited in their attainable field to about 20 kilo-oersteds by saturation, although with conical pole-tips of special alloys this may be increased somewhat. In an air-core solenoid this field may be considerably increased but power requirements are very much greater.

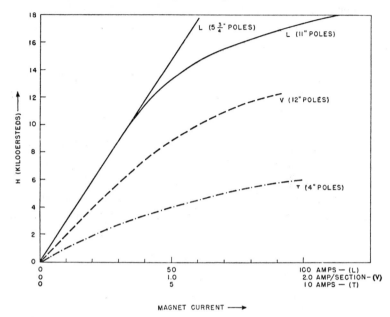

FIG. 118. Magnetic field as a function of current for three commercial electromagnets. (L = Arthur D. Little Corporation, V = Varian Associates, T = Tickford, Ltd.)

Of the iron-core magnets in use, the Weiss-type with coils wound on the poles and a U-shaped yoke is the most common. As an example, the small commercially available air-cooled magnet of the Clarendon Laboratory design (produced by Tickford, Ltd. of England) will yield fields of up to 6 kilo-oersteds in a 2 in. pole-gap with 4 in. diameter pole-faces; weighing only about 600 lb it can be easily mounted on a wheeled trolley. Larger iron-core magnets include those of Varian Associates (Palo Alto, California) and of the Arthur D. Little Corporation (Cambridge, Massachusetts). Some field-current curves for a 2 in. pole-gap are shown in Figure 118. With narrower pole-gaps and smaller pole-face diameters than those given in the figure, fields of up to 35 or 40 kilo-oersteds may be produced in these two magnets. The magnet produced by the Arthur D. Little Corporation is based on that designed and described by Bitter and Reed (1951) where details may be found. Earlier papers by Bitter (1936, 1937, 1939) have discussed some of the fundamental problems in magnet design.

Due partly to the work of Bitter and of Tsai (1947) greater attention has been paid to iron-free solenoid magnets in the past few years. A comparison between performance figures for a small Weiss-type electromagnet and an air-core solenoid has been given by Hudson (1949) which suggests that for producing fields below about 10 to 15 kilo-oersteds the iron-core magnet consumes considerably less power than the solenoid but above 20 kilo-oersteds the situation is reversed. An interesting and detailed account of the design and construction of the 100-kW water-cooled solenoid used by Kurti *et al.* (1956) for their nuclear demagnetization experiments has been given by Daniels (1950).

REFERENCES

Books and Review Articles

AMBLER, E., and HUDSON, R. P. (1955). *Rep. Progr. Phys.* **18**, 251, Phys. Soc., London.

BATES, L. F. (1948). *Modern Magnetism*, 2nd edn., Cambridge University Press.

BERMAN, R. (1953). *Phil. Mag. Suppl.* **2**, 103.

CASIMIR, H. B. G. (1940). *Magnetism and Very Low Temperatures*, Cambridge University Press.

COOKE, A. H. (1955). *Progr. Low Temp. Phys.* **1**, 224, North-Holland Publishing Co., Amsterdam.

GARRETT, C. G. B. (1954). *Magnetic Cooling*, Harvard University Press.

DE KLERK, D. (1956). *Handb. der Physik*, **15**, 38.

—— and STEENLAND, M. J. (1955). *Progr. Low Temp. Phys.* **1**, 273, North-Holland Publishing Co., Amsterdam.

KURTI, N. (1952). *Low Temperature Physics, Four Lectures*, p. 30, Pergamon Press, London.

MENDELSSOHN, K. (1955). *Progr. Low Temp. Phys.* **1**, 184, North-Holland Publishing Co., Amsterdam.

SIMON, F. E. (1937). *Very Low Temperatures*, p. 58, Science Museum Handbook, H.M.S.O., London.

—— (1939). *Science Progr.* No. 133, p. 31.

Papers

AMBLER, E., and HUDSON, R. P. (1956). *Phys. Rev.* **102**, 916.

BERMAN, R., FOSTER, E. L., and ROSENBERG, H. M. (1955). *Brit. J. Appl. Phys.* **6**, 181.

BITTER, F. (1936). *Rev. Sci. Instrum.* **7**, 479, 482.

—— (1937). Ibid. **8**, 318.

—— (1939). Ibid. **10**, 373.

—— and REED, F. E. (1951). Ibid. **22**, 171.

CASIMIR, H. B. G. (1938). *Physica*, **5**, 495.

—— DE HAAS, W. J., and DE KLERK, D. (1939). Ibid. **6**, 241.

COLLINS, S. C., and ZIMMERMAN, F. J. (1953). *Phys. Rev.* **90**, 991.

COOKE, A. H. (1949). *Proc. Phys. Soc.* **A62**, 269.

—— MEYER, H., and WOLF, W. P. (1956). *Proc. Roy. Soc.* A, **233**, 536.

CROFT, A. J., FAULKNER, E. A., HATTON, J., and SEYMOUR, E. F. W. (1953). *Phil. Mag.* **44**, 289.

DANIELS, J. M. (1950). *Proc. Phys. Soc.* **B63**, 1028.

—— and ROBINSON, F. N. H. (1953). *Phil. Mag.* **44**, 630.

DARBY, J., HATTON, J., ROLLIN, B. V., SEYMOUR, E. F. W., and SILSBEE, H. B. (1951). *Proc. Phys. Soc.* **A64**, 861.

DAUNT, J. G. (1957). Ibid. **B70**, 641.

—— HEER, C. V., McMAHON, H. O., REITZEL, J., and SIMON, L. (1955). 'Conférence de Physique des basses Températures', p. 362, *Suppl. Bull. Inst. int. Froid*, Paris.

DEBYE, P. (1926). *Ann. Phys.* **81**, 1154.

DUGDALE, J. S., and MacDONALD, D. K. C. (1957). *Canad. J. Phys.* **35**, 271.

—— —— and CROXON, A. A. M. (1957). Ibid. **35**, 502.

ERICKSON, R. A., ROBERTS, L. D., and DABBS, J. W. T. (1954). *Rev. Sci. Instrum.* **25**, 1178.

FRITZ, J. J., and GIAUQUE, W. F. (1949). *J. Amer. Chem. Soc.* **71**, 2168.

FULTON, C. D., HWANG, C. F., FAIRBANK, W. M., and VILAS, J. M. (1957). *Proc. 1956 Cryogenic Engng. Conf.* N.B.S., Boulder, Colorado, p. 220.

GEBALLE, T. H., and GIAUQUE, W. F. (1952). *J. Amer. Chem. Soc.* **74**, 3513.

GIAUQUE, W. F. (1927). Ibid. **49**, 1864.

—— GEBALLE, T. H., LYON, D. N., and FRITZ, J. J. (1952). *Rev. Sci. Instrum.* **23**, 169.

—— and MacDOUGALL, D. P. (1933). *Phys. Rev.* **43**, 768; **44**, 235.

—— —— (1935). *J. Amer. Chem. Soc.* **57**, 1175.

GOODMAN, B. B. (1953). *Proc. Phys. Soc.* **A66**, 217.

GORTER, C. J. (1934). *Phys. Z.* **35**, 923.

—— (1948). *Physica*, **14**, 504.

DE HAAS, W. J., WIERSMA, E. C., and KRAMERS, H. A. (1933). *Nature*, **131**, 719.

—— —— (1935). *Physica*, **2**, 335.

HEER, C. V., BARNES, C. B., and DAUNT, J. G. (1954). *Rev. Sci. Instrum.* **25**, 1088.

—— and DAUNT, J. G. (1949). *Phys. Rev.* **76**, 854.

HUDSON, R. P. (1949). *J. Sci. Instrum.* **26**, 401.

—— HUNT, B., and KURTI, N. (1949). *Proc. Phys. Soc.* **A62**, 392.

—— and McLANE, C. K. (1954). *Rev. Sci. Instrum.* **25**, 190.

HULL, R. A. (1947). *Rep. Cambridge Conf. Low Temp.*, p. 72, Physical Society, London.

—— WILKINSON, K. R., and WILKS, J. (1951). *Proc. Phys. Soc.* **A64**, 379.

DE KLERK, D., and HUDSON, R. P. (1954). *J. Res. Nat. Bur. Stand.* **53**, 173.

KURTI, N., ROBINSON, F. N. H., SIMON, F. E., and SPOHR, D. A. (1956). *Nature*, **178**, 450.

—— ROLLIN, B. V., and SIMON, F. E. (1936). *Physica*, **3**, 266.

—— and SIMON, F. E. (1934). *Nature*, **133**, 907.

—— —— (1935). *Proc. Roy. Soc.* **A**, **149**, 152.

—— —— (1938a). *Phil. Mag.* **26**, 849.

—— —— (1938b). Ibid. 840.

MENDELSSOHN, K., and OLSEN, J. L. (1950). *Proc. Phys. Soc.* **A63**, 2.

—— and RENTON, C. A. (1955). *Proc. Roy. Soc.* **A**, **230**, 157.

MENDOZA, E. (1948). *Les Phénomènes Cryomagnétiques*, p. 53 (Collège de France).

—— and THOMAS, J. G. (1951). *Phil. Mag.* **42**, 291.

NICOL, J. (1955). *Nat. Science Foundation Conf. Low Temp. Phys. Chem.* Paper K-4, Baton Rouge, Louisiana.

POWELL, R. L., and BLANPIED, W. A. (1954). *N.B.S. Circular* 556, U.S. Govt. Printing Office, Washington, D.C.

TSAI, B. (1947). *Rep. Cambridge Conf. Low Temp.* p. 89, Physical Society, London.

VAN DIJK, H., and KEESOM, W. H. (1940). *Physica*, **7**, 970.

WHEATLEY, J. C., GRIFFING, D. F., and ESTLE, T. L. (1956). *Rev. Sci. Instrum.* **27**, 1070.

WHITE, G. K. (1955). *Canad. J. Phys.* **33**, 119.

CHAPTER IX

VACUUM TECHNIQUES AND MATERIALS

1. Introduction

It is clear from a consideration of heat transfer that one of the most important requirements in low-temperature research is that of maintaining a high vacuum. Whether this vacuum be in a space around the refrigerant liquid or in an enclosure within the liquid, pressures of the order of 10^{-6} mm Hg or less must often be maintained to ensure thermal isolation or thermal equilibrium. The general techniques of producing high vacua have been discussed in such books as those by Dunoyer (1926), Dushman (1949), Yarwood (1955), Espe and Knoll (1936), Reimann (1952), Martin and Hill (1947), and other works including Strong (1938). Here we shall merely point out some features of a suitable pumping system and summarize the equations for the pumping speed of tubes and orifices, so that pumps and pumping-tube dimensions may be chosen which are commensurate with one another and which may meet such practical requirements as the removal of exchange gas from a cryostat.

The excellent book by Strong (1938) on laboratory techniques discusses the common methods of making seals, e.g. metal-glass seals, sealing cements, solders, etc. In low-temperature work some special problems arise as many cement seals and rubber gasket or rubber O-ring seals are no longer practicable for vacuum-tight assemblies. In § 3 of this chapter a brief account and discussion is given of available low-melting-point solders which are particularly useful in making vacuum-tight joints which can be cooled and can also be 'broken' and remade fairly readily. Some other types of vacuum seals and cements as well as the use of metal-glass seals at low temperatures are described later in the chapter.

2. Vacuum technique

High-vacuum system

In most low-temperature equipment, a vacuum system is

required to produce and maintain pressures of the order of 10^{-6} mm Hg in a relatively small chamber. As there are or should be no permanent gas leaks into the chamber (cf. a nuclear accelerator or ion source into which a small regulated leak of hydrogen, deuterium, or helium is maintained), pumping speeds are not of primary importance in maintaining a low pressure. However, in many cases a small pressure (say 10^{-1} mm Hg) of helium gas may be admitted to the chamber for purposes of obtaining thermal equilibrium. The time required for the subsequent removal of this exchange gas will depend on the effective speeds of the pumps and connecting tubes; unless an unusually short time of the order of seconds is required for this removal, the pumping speed of the system need only be of the order of a litre per second, i.e. much smaller than the speeds of hundreds or thousands of litres per second required in ion accelerators. It is fortunate that pumping speed requirements are rather modest, since the design of an experimental cryostat usually restricts the possible size of pumping tubes which connect the experimental chambers (enclosed as they are in a dewar vessel) to the pumping system. A conventional pumping system is illustrated in the schematic diagram of Figure 119. Pure helium for use as exchange gas (or for filling gas thermometers) is kept in the flask; this can be replenished by taking helium gas from a cylinder through a liquid-nitrogen-cooled charcoal trap or using evaporated helium gas from a liquid-helium storage dewar.

G_1 and G_2 are vacuum gauges for determining the approximate pressure in the system. G_1 is conveniently a discharge gauge in which a high voltage from a Tessla coil or a Ford coil produces a visible discharge at pressures from $\sim 10^{-2}$ mm Hg to ~ 10 mm Hg or higher depending on the gas present. The character of the discharge is determined by the gas pressure and type of gas. With a little experience, helium gas (giving a pinkish discharge turning pale green at lower pressures), nitrogen (reddish), oxygen (straw yellow), carbon dioxide (whitish blue), and water or organic vapours (bluish colour) can be distinguished. For measurement of lower pressures (the function of G_2 in Figure 119) a number of different types of gauge can be made or obtained from manufacturers of high-vacuum equipment. Among those commonly used are (i) the thermionic ionization gauge with a lower limit of 10^{-8} to 10^{-9} mm Hg, (ii) the mercury McLeod gauge which has a lower limit of about 10^{-6} mm Hg and does not register the pressure of condensable vapours, (iii) the Knudsen gauge which registers the true pressure of gas and vapour irrespective of their

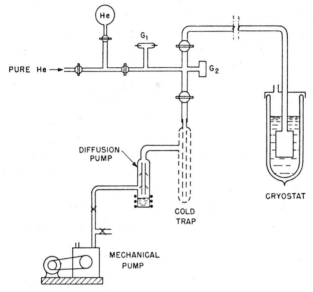

Fig. 119. Schematic diagram of a pumping system.

composition down to 10^{-6} mm Hg, (iv) the hot-wire Pirani gauge with a lower limit of 10^{-3} to 10^{-4} mm Hg, (v) the Phillips (or Penning) cold cathode ionization gauge which is available with a lower limit of 10^{-6} to 10^{-7} mm Hg. Of these the Phillips gauge has many advantages in range, simplicity, and reliability of operation but its sensitivity varies somewhat with the composition of the gas present so that it only provides an approximate measure of the pressure; the usual calibration supplied with a commercial model is approximately correct for air. Whichever gauge is used, a record of the pressure in the cryostat chamber is only obtained if the gauge is in a position close to the chamber, i.e. if the resistance of the pumping line (reciprocal of its pumping speed) is much less between the point of attachment of the gauge and the chamber than it is between this point and the throat of the diffusion pump. A further problem arises when the cryostat chamber is surrounded by liquid helium as the vapour pressure of gases other than helium will be negligible at this temperature. When the system is in equilibrium, and if there is no helium leak into the cryostat, the gauge may register a much higher pressure than exists in the cryostat chamber; the gauge is at room temperature, and is exposed to gases and vapours arising from the nearby tube walls, tap grease, back diffusion through the pump, etc., but these gases (other than helium) do not affect the static pressure in the chamber which is at liquid-helium temperatures. As Garfunkel and Wexler (1954) have pointed out, one of the only reliable means of measuring the helium-gas pressure in such a chamber, which may be as low as 10^{-8} or 10^{-9} mm Hg, is to connect a helium mass spectrometer leak detector on the high-pressure side of the diffusion pump and determine the rate at which helium gas is being 'ejected' by this pump.

The choice of metal or glass for the pumping system depends partly on the desired pumping speed and on individual preference as well as the availability of materials.

If large pumping speeds and hence large pumping tubes are required, metal tubes and large-bore metal valves—necessarily rather expensive or difficult to make—are needed. If neither a large pumping speed nor a mechanically robust system is necessary and a competent glass-blower is available, the entire pumping system (excepting the rotary mechanical pump) may be constructed relatively quickly from glass.

In Figure 119 a cold trap (usually liquid-nitrogen cooled) is shown in dashed lines. With a mercury diffusion pump, this trap is necessary to reduce the ultimate vacuum below the vapour pressure of mercury ($\sim 10^{-3}$ mm Hg) at room temperature. In an oil-diffusion pump the ultimate pressure without a cold trap varies from 10^{-4} mm Hg to about 10^{-7} mm Hg depending on the type of oil used and the design of the pump. Oil-diffusion pumps are, however, rather less robust in operation due to the danger of cracking the hot oil by exposure to air, and they generally require a somewhat lower backing pressure for efficient operation; while many mercury diffusion pumps operate satisfactorily with a maximum backing pressure in the range 1 to 5 mm, most oil diffusion pumps require that the backing pressure be kept well below 0·5 mm Hg.

These questions are discussed in much greater detail in the standard texts on vacuum technique by Yarwood, Dushman, Reimann, Strong, etc.

Pumping speed

The pumping speed of an orifice is expressed as the volume of gas passing through the orifice per unit time measured at the pressure which exists at the orifice; denoted by S this speed is usually expressed in litres per second. When the mean free path of the gas molecules is appreciably greater than the dimensions of the orifice or width of pumping tubes, so-called Knudsen conditions apply, i.e. the molecules diffuse without being affected by the presence of other gas molecules. Since the mean free path is inversely proportional to pressure and in most gases at room temperature is 100 cm for a pressure of 10^{-4} mm Hg, the condition for Knudsen flow is seen to be usually satisfied at the pressures produced by a diffusion pump, unless the dimensions of the pumping tubes and orifices are very great.

Under such high-vacuum conditions, the pumping speed or volume of gas escaping per unit time through an orifice is given by[†]

$$S = 3 \cdot 64 A \sqrt{(T/M)} \text{ l./sec,}$$

where A is the area in cubic centimetres, T is the absolute temperature, and M is the molecular weight of the gas. Hence, for air at room temperature

$$S = 11 \cdot 7 \text{ l./sec cm}^2.$$

Thus we may expect the pumping speed at the throat of a diffusion pump to be partly controlled by the available area of the annular aperture through which the gas diffuses before it is

[†] See, for example, a recent theoretical and experimental examination of the 'pumping speed of a circular aperture in a diaphragm across a circular tube' (Bureau, Laslett, and Keller, 1952).

entrapped by the streaming vapour of the pump. In fact the
efficiency of diffusion pumps is rather less than unity so that the
effective speed for air is given by

$$S_P = \text{speed factor} \times A \times 11.7 \text{ l./sec,}$$

where the 'speed factor' has a value of about 0·4 for a good oil
diffusion pump and about 0·2–0·3 for a mercury diffusion pump.

In the case of a cylindrical pumping tube for which the length l
is much greater than the diameter d, the speed or conductance
is given by

$$S_L = 3.82 \sqrt{\left(\frac{T}{M}\right)} \frac{d^3}{l} \text{ l./sec.}$$

For air at room temperature this reduces to

$$S_L \simeq 100 \frac{r^3}{l} \quad (\text{radius } r = \tfrac{1}{2}d)$$

$$= \frac{r^3_{\text{mm}}}{l_{\text{mm}}} \text{ l./sec.}$$

For helium gas, $M = 4$ and therefore the speed of an orifice,
pump, or tube is $\sqrt{(29/4)} \simeq 2.7$ times greater than for air. If a
section of the pumping tube is at a low temperature T the speed
of this section will be reduced proportionately to $T^{\frac{1}{2}}$ due to the
lower kinetic velocity of the gas molecules at this temperature;
this refers to the speed measured at the pressure existing in the
cold tube, not to the mass flow or equivalent room-temperature
speed which is increased as $T^{-\frac{1}{2}}$. Otherwise it might appear that
for a cryostat pumping system, tubes of larger bore are required
for the colder section than for the room temperature section.
This is, of course, not the case, as a detailed analysis shows,
since the pressure of a given mass of gas being taken through the
system will be proportional to the temperature at any point
assuming it is in equilibrium. Garfunkel and Wexler (1954) have
calculated the effective room-temperature speed S_r for a number
of tubes in series in a temperature gradient; if each of these tubes
is of length l_i and radius r_i and they are connected at one end to
an enclosure (temperature T_1, pressure P_1) and at the other to a

'pump' at room temperature T_r where it is assumed $P = 0$,

$$S_r = \frac{4(2\pi R T_r)^{\frac{1}{2}}}{3\sqrt{M}} \sum \frac{l_i}{r_i^3} \left(\frac{T_r}{T_1}\right)^{\frac{1}{2}}$$

which, if $T_r \simeq 295°$ K, reduces to

$$S_r \simeq \frac{9000}{\sqrt{(MT_1)} \sum \frac{l_i}{r_i^3}} \text{ l./sec,}$$

where l_i and r_i are in centimetres. In this derivation it is assumed that Knudsen conditions apply, that $l_i \gg r_i$, and that the gradient of P/T is small. Thus the effective speed varies inversely as the square root of the temperature T_1 at the cold end.

If we wish to calculate the time required to reduce the pressure in a volume V from P_1 to P_2, where the limiting low pressure that may be reached is P_0, time t is given by

$$t = \frac{V}{S} \ln \frac{P_1 - P_0}{P_2 - P_0};$$

and if we assume that $P_0 \ll P_1$, P_2,

$$t = 2 \cdot 3 \frac{V}{S} \log_{10} \frac{P_1}{P_2}.$$

For example, suppose P is initially 1 mm Hg in a volume of 1 litre and P_2 is to be 10^{-5} mm Hg, then if $S_P = 5$ l./sec and $S_L = 0 \cdot 5$ l./sec,

$$\frac{1}{S} = \frac{1}{5} + \frac{1}{0 \cdot 5}$$

$$= 2 \cdot 2$$

and

$$t = 2 \cdot 3 . \frac{1}{1/2 \cdot 2} . \log_{10}(10^5)$$

$$= 25 \text{ seconds.}$$

In practice the time required would be longer than this as the speed S_P of the diffusion pump would be small until the pressure was reduced to $\sim 10^{-3}$ mm Hg. From the initial pressure of 1 mm Hg down to 10^{-3} mm Hg, S_P would be largely governed by the speed of the backing pump and the tubing connecting the backing pump to the diffusion pump. Also, the speed S_L of the high-vacuum line would be much reduced in this higher pressure range as the conditions for Knudsen flow are not satisfied, i.e. collisions between gas molecules would reduce the diffusion rate.

At sufficiently high pressures that the mean free path is very much less than the lateral dimensions of the pumping tubes, we may assume normal laminar flow governed by Poiseuille's equation. In the intermediate region, usually corresponding to a pressure of 10^{-1} to 10^{-2} mm Hg, the mean free path and the lateral dimensions are comparable and precise calculation of the effective conductance of a tube is difficult.

We stated that the speed of a diffusion pump is controlled by the rate of diffusion of gas molecules through the throat of the pump into the vapour stream. In a rotary mechanical pump an oil-sealed eccentric rotor revolves in a cylindrical cavity 'sweeping' out the gas from the high pressure or entry side to the exhaust side at a speed depending on the number of revolutions per unit time and the volume of the space between the rotor and the fixed cylinder. In a pumping system, e.g. that of Figure 119, the speed of the mechanical pump need be much less than the speed of the diffusion pump. For example, if the speed of the diffusion pump is $S_P = 50$ l./sec at a pressure of 10^{-4} mm Hg, and the pump requires a backing pressure of 10^{-1} mm Hg, then the speed of the mechanical pump need be only

$$S_M = \frac{10^{-4}}{10^{-1}} \times 50 = 0{\cdot}05 \text{ l./sec}$$
$$= 3 \text{ l./min};$$

it is advisable in practice to increase this figure a few times to allow for the restricting effect of the tubing between the pumps. Backing pump speeds are often expressed in litres per minute rather than in litres per second.

It should be emphasized that in designing a pumping system, consideration should be given to the matching of the pumping speeds of the various components; therefore an approximate estimate should be made of the speed of the proposed pumping tubes between the diffusion pump and the cryostat. It is pointless to make or buy a large 200 l./sec diffusion pump, when it is to be connected by a length of 100 cm of 2-cm bore tubing (speed $S_L = r^3_{mm}/l_{mm} = 1$ l./sec) to the vacuum chamber of a cryostat; the total speed or conductance is the reciprocal of the sum of the reciprocals of the individual speeds, i.e. the resistances are additive so that $S = (\frac{1}{200}+\frac{1}{1})^{-1} \simeq 1$ l./sec in this example.

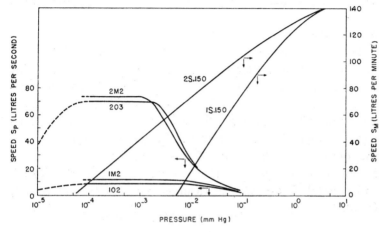

Fig. 120. Speeds of some commercial pumps (Edwards and Company, London) for dry air at room temperature. 1S150, Speedivac rotary pump: 1-stage; 2S150, Speedivac rotary pump: 2-stage; 1M2, mercury-diffusion pump: 2-stage; 2M2, mercury-diffusion pump: 2-stage; 1O2, oil-diffusion pump: 2-stage; 2O3, oil-diffusion pump: 3-stage.

Likewise it is rather wasteful to use a 450 l./min mechanical pump to back an 8 l./sec diffusion pump as a 50 l./min mechanical pump is just as effective.

An illustration of the dependence of pumping speed on pressure for some common mechanical and diffusion pumps is given in Figure 120. With dry air the one- and two-stage mechanical pumps should give ultimate vacua of about 10^{-2} and 10^{-4} mm Hg respectively. This assumes that no condensable vapours are present which may contaminate the oil. Mechanical pumps do not remove condensable vapours efficiently unless they are fitted with a gas ballast system, i.e. an automatic system which injects gas every cycle to aid in 'sweeping' away the condensable vapours. A diffusion pump does pump condensable vapours although the speed will vary with the molecular weight of the vapour. The mercury-diffusion pumps 1M2 and 2M2 will yield an ultimate vacuum of about 10^{-6} mm Hg if used with a cold trap. The oil-diffusion pumps 1O2 and 2O3 may be expected to give an ultimate vacuum (without cold trap) of 10^{-5} to 10^{-6} mm Hg, depending on the type of oil and the heating power used.

3. Solders

The most commonly used solders may be divided into three main classes: hard solders, soft solders, and low-melting-point solders. The latter have a frequent application in low-temperature equipment as they provide a means of making and breaking a vacuum joint without raising the temperature of the adjacent metals to more than about 100° C. More detailed information on the composition of hard and soft solders than is given below may be obtained from physical tables or a standard handbook such as the *Metals Handbook* (American Society of Metals, Cleveland, Ohio).

Hard solders

These solders generally melt between 600° and 1,000° C and are nominally a Cu–Zn brazing alloy with added silver; those having around 50 per cent silver content have the lowest melting-points. They are generally used with a borax or boric acid flux, the two components being commonly mixed to a paste with alcohol. Such fluxes are readily available commercially from firms which supply hard solders, e.g. Handy and Harman, Connecticut, or Johnson Matthey, London. Among the alloys are:

'Easy Flo' (Handy and Harman)—a strong solder melting at about 630° C, containing 50% Ag, 15·5% Cu, 16·5% Zn, 18% Cd.

'A.S.T.M. Grade 4'—a strong solder of relatively low melting range (675°–745° C) containing 45% Ag, 30% Cu, 25% Zn.

'A.S.T.M. Grade 2'—flows readily and melts over range 775°–815° C and contains 20% Ag, 45% Cu, 35% Zn.

'A.S.T.M. Grade 7'—high grade malleable and ductile solder containing 70% Ag, 20% Cu, 10% Zn which melts over the range 725°–755° C.

Silver—100% Ag melts at 960° C.

The three solders listed with A.S.T.M. (American Society for Testing Materials) specifications are fairly representative of commonly used silver solders, their compositions being taken from *Metals Handbook* (1939 edn., p. 1211).

Soft solders

Soft solders are generally tin-lead alloys, the eutectic mixture of 63 per cent Sn, 37 per cent Pb having a melting-point of 183° C. Mild fluxes such as rosin, rosin in alcohol or a paste of petroleum jelly, zinc chloride, and ammonium chloride are often used in radio soldering. When a flux with a stronger cleaning action is required as in many metal-metal junctions, a zinc chloride solution is formed by dissolving zinc in hydrochloric acid. For soldering to stainless steel excess hydrochloric acid is desirable or a strong solution of phosphoric acid may be used. Commercially available fluxes include 'Baker's Fluid' (Baker's Soldering Fluxes, Middlesex, England), Kester Soldering Salt (Kester Solder Co., Chicago, Illinois) and a stainless steel soldering flux (Dunton Company, Rhode Island).

The solders include:

37·5% Sn, 60% Pb, 2·5% Sb—melting over a range from 185°–225° C; this is generally used for joining lead pipes and cable sheaths.

40–45% Sn, 60–55% Pb—these are very ductile solders, melting over a range from about 183°–230° C and used generally in radio soldering.

50% Sn, 50% Pb—a good general purpose solder melting from 180°–225° C.

60% Sn, 40% Pb—a high quality general purpose solder melting from 183°–191° C.

100% Pb—pure lead is sometimes useful because of its higher melting-point of 327° C.

50% Sn, 32% Pb, 18% Cd—the addition of cadmium reduces the melting-point in this alloy ('low-temperature solder') to 145° C.

Low-melting-point solders

These solders, some of which melt well below 100° C, are alloys of bismuth with the elements lead, tin, cadmium (and indium

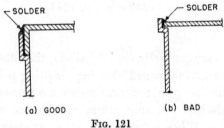

(a) GOOD   (b) BAD

FIG. 121

in some instances). Like pure bismuth, those alloys containing a high percentage of bismuth (usually more than about 50 per cent) expand on solidification. The alloys are rather weak and brittle and should be used for joints or seals where they are not subject to stress, particularly bending stress. If used in a situation illustrated by Figure 121 (a) with copper or brass, then Wood's metal (or other low-melting-point alloy) should give a completely satisfactory vacuum-tight joint, unaffected by repeated cooling to liquid-helium temperatures. It is advisable with these solders, particularly those with melting-points at 100° C or less, to 'pre-tin' the metal surfaces which are to be joined, with a soldering iron beforehand. These alloys do not generally 'tin' when at or just above their liquid points. Therefore parts should be pre-tinned before assembly using sufficient heat to activate the flux (zinc chloride solution, Kester's soldering salt, Baker's fluid are satisfactory).

Apart from Wood's metal, the alloys listed below are Cerroalloys, commercially available from the Cerro de Pasco Copper Corporation (New York). These latter alloys are chiefly produced for making moulds, castings, fillers to aid tube bending but provide a useful range of low-melting-point solders.

Wood's metal—50% Bi, 25% Pb, 12·5% Sn, and 12·5% Cd melts from 65° to 70° C.

Cerrobend—a eutectic alloy of 50% Bi, 26·7% Pb, 13·3% Sn, and 10% Cd melts at 70° C. It can be conveniently used as a substitute for Wood's metal and expands slightly on casting.

Cerrobase—a eutectic alloy of 55·5% Bi and 44·5% Pb melts at 124° C, contracts slightly on casting.

Cerrotru—a eutectic alloy of 58% Bi and 42% Sn melts at 138° C. This alloy expands slightly on casting but then shows very little further growth or shrinkage, unlike most of these alloys which continue to grow or shrink slightly for some hours after casting.

Cerrolow 117—a eutectic alloy of 44·7% Bi, 22·6% Pb, 8·3% Sn, 5·3% Cd, and 19·1% In melts at 47° C.

Cerrolow 136—a eutectic alloy of 49% Bi, 18% Pb, 12% Sn, and 21% In melts at 58° C and like Cerrolow 117 expands slightly on casting and later shows a slight shrinkage for some hours.

Cerroseal 35—containing approximately equal amounts of Sn and In, this is a special glass-wetting alloy which melts from 116°–126° C.

A large number of other low melting alloys, e.g. Rose's metal, Lipowitz's metal, are listed with their compositions and melting-points in the *Metals Handbook* (American Society of Metals) and many standard physical tables.

Special solders

Listed below are some less common solders of interest in low-temperature research:

Zinc-cadmium solder†—a eutectic alloy of 82·5% Cd and 17·5% Zn melting at 265° C is often used for attaching electrical potential leads to metal specimens as it is not super-conducting in the liquid-helium range of temperatures, unlike Wood's metal and most other soft solders which

---

† It is advisable to avoid overheating of the cadmium-rich solders as cadmium fumes are toxic.

are superconducting below 7° or 8° K. This Zn–Cd solder
flows quite freely on many metal surfaces when molten and
is used in a similar manner to a tin-lead soft solder.

Bismuth—this is a non-superconducting solder with melting-
point at 271° C which forms a rather mechanically weak
joint as it does not 'wet' a metal surface very thoroughly.

Bismuth–cadmium solder—a eutectic alloy of 60% Bi and
40% Cd melting at 140° C which does not become superconducting above 0·8° K (Cochran et al., 1956).

Indium—melting at 155° C; indium is a useful solder as it
bonds to many metals more thoroughly than does a tin-
lead solder. Due to its high ductility it does not form a very
strong joint; it has been used for soldering to many thin
metal films on glass (Belser, 1954).

Thermal-free solder—a solder containing 70·44% Cd, 29·56%
Sn, which gives a very low thermo-electric force with
respect to copper, is commercially produced by the Leeds
and Northrup Company, Philadelphia.

4. Vacuum seals and cements

Metal-glass seals

The technique of making glass–metal vacuum seals has been
discussed in many available texts (e.g. Strong, 1938; Reimann,
1952; Partridge, 1949). However, mention should be made here
of their ability to withstand frequent cooling to the temperatures
of liquid helium and remain vacuum-tight.

Copper-glass seals of the Housekeeper type appear to be
generally reliable and have been used, for example, in the 'tail'
of small Linde helium liquefiers at the Clarendon Laboratory for
long periods without any cracking. They have been used in sizes
at least up to 1-in. diameter and remain vacuum-tight in the
presence of liquid helium II, the 'super-fluid component' of which
has a vanishingly small viscosity and therefore magnifies the
effect of any small leak that is present.

Seals made with platinum wire or platinum tubing to soft glass
also seem to be quite satisfactory in maintaining complete
vacuum tightness at liquid-helium temperatures. If adequately

annealed they can withstand repeated cycling between room temperature and the lowest temperatures. Kovar-glass seals are generally less reliable. These are made with Pyrex and a Kovar sealing alloy (29% Ni, 17% Co, 53·7% Fe, 0·3% Mn) produced by the Stupakoff Ceramic and Manufacturing Company, Pennsylvania, and commercially made seals are also available from the same source. They are generally vacuum-tight at normal temperatures and Lane (1949) has described them as being suitable at liquid-helium temperatures. However, other experimenters (e.g. Corak and Wexler, 1953) have found these commercial Kovar seals somewhat unreliable when cooled to a low temperature, due to small gas leaks appearing in the seal.† Corak and Wexler have described sensitive leak tests at liquid-helium temperatures on tungsten-glass, zirconium-glass, and copper-glass seals which were all found to provide vacuum-tight seals under these stringent conditions.

Sealing cements and compounds

Apiezon Products, Ltd. supply through various distributing firms a large range of products useful in high-vacuum work. These products include: diffusion-pump oils Apiezon A, B, and C, a viscous low-vapour-pressure oil Apiezon J, a very viscous oil Apiezon K, greases L, M, and N for use in conical ground joints and taps, a tap grease T with a low temperature coefficient of viscosity useful for ground joints which may be raised above room temperature (maximum safe temperature of 110° C), and also a sealing compound and waxes. Silicone oils for diffusion pumps and silicone tap grease are also available from many suppliers of high-vacuum equipment.

The Apiezon sealing compound Q is a graphite-grease mixture with the consistency of plasticine which is very useful for temporary vacuum seals. Apiezon W, W100, and W40 are black waxes of low vapour pressure which flow easily onto a solid

---

† The experience of many low-temperature physicists seems to confirm the view that Kovar-glass seals are not always reliable. Many seals, particularly of the multi-lead commercial variety, have been found definitely unsatisfactory. Other seals, particularly 'home-made' single-lead seals, appear to have remained vacuum-tight after repeated use.

surface when molten and melt respectively at about 100° C, 80° C, and 45° C. Other common waxes which can be used for making vacuum-tight joints are shellac, beeswax-rosin mixture (m.p. 57° C), de Khotinsky Cement (shellac and wood tar mixture, m.p. 140° C), and Picein (black wax, melting at 80°–100° C depending on the variety used). Of these waxes, the Apiezon W series are very easy to use but are somewhat brittle and dissolve readily in a number of organic solvents. De Khotinsky wax is available in hard, medium, and soft grades (e.g. from Central Scientific Company) and is a little more difficult to apply than the W waxes but is less brittle and is not affected by many common organic liquids, including butyl phthalate.

These sealing compounds are not of much use in cementing materials which are to be cooled to low temperature, as they become brittle and tend to flake. For securing or thermally anchoring electrical wires to solid surfaces, some liquid cements —particularly those which can be cured by baking—provide a method of attachment which withstands repeated cooling quite well; bakelite varnish, Formel varnish, and glyptal lacquer may all be dried and hardened at a temperature of 120°–140° C and used for this purpose. Nail polish is also a useful cement for anchoring wires providing they are not subject to appreciable mechanical stress; it withstands low temperatures quite well.

However it is much more difficult to find a cement or sealing compound (apart from solders) which gives a strong vacuum-tight joint between metals or metal and glass, from room temperature down to the lowest obtainable temperatures. In the writer's experience, the Araldite resins (CIBA Company of Switzerland) provide good bonding agents for use over the low temperature range. These ethoxylene-resins are available in a number of forms including:

(i) Araldite type 1 available as a powder or in stick form (m.p. at about 100° C), can be flame cured but gives strongest bonding if baked at 180° C (2 hours) to 200° C (40 minutes). Joints made with this resin, including vacuum joints, appear to withstand repeated cooling satisfactorily (see, for example, Quarrington, 1954).

(ii) Araldite liquid adhesive type XV is similar to type 1 but is in liquid form; it is hot-setting.

(iii) Araldite cold-setting adhesives types 101 and 102 are a viscous liquid and a thin liquid respectively. With both a hardener is added just before use. These adhesives are useful in cases where the materials cannot be heated but do not give quite as strong a bond as Araldite type 1 and therefore are less suitable for low-temperature applications.

We have already mentioned in the section dealing with adiabatic demagnetization cryostats (§ 8.4) that ground cone and socket joints can remain vacuum-tight after cooling to liquid-helium temperatures if an Apiezon grease or a glass-forming liquid is used in the joint.

Other vacuum seals

Demountable vacuum seals used at or near room temperature are most frequently in the form of a rubber-ring seal. In recent years the ready availability of rubber O-rings and other forms of rubber gaskets, has made a seal of this type commonplace as it is reliable, does not require highly accurate machining of the parts which are to be sealed, and can be demounted and remade very quickly. When such a metal-metal or glass-metal joint has to be cooled to low temperatures, a rubber O-ring or rubber gasket is no longer practicable. For this reason solder-joints made with a low-melting-point alloy like Wood's metal have been commonly used by the low-temperature physicist. However, demountable joints sealed with a gasket of a ductile metal have proved quite successful. The use of a gold O-ring made from 0·020 in. gold wire has been described by Wexler, Corak, and Cunningham (1950) and careful tests showed that such a seal between metal surfaces remained vacuum-tight at temperatures down to and below the λ-point of liquid helium.

Although other metals, e.g. indium, aluminium, lead, copper, lead plus a few per cent tin, may also be used as metal gasket materials, gold (or silver) appears to be the most suitable as it is quite ductile in the annealed condition and work hardens as it is strained. Gold, silver, and copper are metals of face-centred cubic structure which work harden on straining, and the flow stress and rate of work hardening increase as the temperature is lowered. Gold and silver are the more suitable of these three due to their greater ductility and relative freedom from tarnishing.

REFERENCES

BELSER, R. B. (1954). *Rev. Sci. Instrum.* **25**, 180.

BUREAU, A. J., JACKSON LASLETT, L., and KELLER, J. M. (1952). Ibid. **23**, 683.

COCHRAN, J. F., MAPOTHER, D. E., and MOULD, R. E. (1956). *Phys. Rev.* **103**, 1657.

CORAK, W. S., and WEXLER, A. (1953). *Rev. Sci. Instrum.* **24**, 994.

DUNOYER, L. (1926). *Vacuum Practice*, Bell & Sons, London.

DUSHMAN, S. (1949). *Scientific Foundations of Vacuum Technique*, Wiley & Sons, New York.

ESPE, W., and KNOLL, M. (1936). *Werkstoffkunde der Hochvakuum Technik*, Springer, Berlin.

GARFUNKEL, M. P., and WEXLER, A. (1954). *Rev. Sci. Instrum.* **25**, 170.

LANE, C. T. (1949). Ibid. **20**, 140.

MARTIN, L. H., and HILL, R. D. (1947). *A Manual of Vacuum Practice*, Melbourne University Press.

PARTRIDGE, J. H. (1949). *Glass-to-Metal Seals*, Society of Glass Technology, Sheffield.

QUARRINGTON, J. E. (1954). *J. Sci. Instrum.* **31**, 387.

REIMANN, A. L. (1952). *Vacuum Technique*, Chapman & Hall, London.

STRONG, J. (1938). *Modern Physical Laboratory Practice*, Blackie & Son, London.

WEXLER, A., CORAK, W. S., and CUNNINGHAM, G. T. (1950). *Rev. Sci. Instrum.* **21**, 259.

YARWOOD, J. (1955). *High Vacuum Technique*, 3rd rev. edn., Chapman & Hall, London.

PART III

PHYSICAL DATA

CHAPTER X

HEAT CAPACITY AND EXPANSION COEFFICIENT

1. Heat capacity of solids

IT is well known (see, for example, texts by Mott and Jones, 1936; Kittel, 1953) that the specific heat at constant volume of most solids may be represented tolerably well by the Debye function

$$C_v = 9Nk(T/\theta)^3 \int\limits_0^{\theta/T} \frac{x^4}{(e^x-1)(1-e^{-x})}\, dx$$

$$= 9R(T/\theta)^3 J_4(\theta/T).$$

The derivation of such a formula is based on the elastic continuum model of a solid for which the number of modes of vibration in a frequency interval ν, $\nu+d\nu$ is given by

$$f(\nu)\, d\nu = bV\nu^2\, d\nu = 4\pi\left(\frac{1}{v_l^3}+\frac{2}{v_t^3}\right)V\nu^2\, d\nu;$$

V is the volume of the solid and v_l, v_t are the wave propagation velocities for longitudinal and transverse waves respectively. Since according to quantum statistics the average energy in each mode at temperature T is

$$\tfrac{1}{2}h\nu + \frac{h\nu}{e^{h\nu/kT}-1},$$

we expect the total internal energy U to be given by

$$U = \int\limits_0^{\nu_m} \frac{h\nu}{e^{h\nu/kT}-1}\, bV\nu^2\, d\nu.$$

The maximum frequency ν_m is given by the normalizing condition that in a volume V containing N atoms, there are only $3N$ modes:

$$3N = \int_0^{\nu_m} f(\nu)\, d\nu = \tfrac{1}{3} b V \nu_m^3.$$

Introducing the Debye characteristic temperature

$$\theta_D = h\nu_m/k,$$

and writing $x = h\nu/kT$, we find that

$$U = 9NkT(T/\theta)^3 \int_0^{\theta/T} \frac{x^3\, dx}{(e^x - 1)}$$

and

$$C_v = \left(\frac{\partial U}{\partial T_v}\right) = 9R(T/\theta)^3 \int_0^{\theta/T} \frac{x^4}{(e^x - 1)(1 - e^{-x})}\, dx.$$

In Table XXVII (at the end of Chapter XI) are given values of C_v computed from Debye's expression for various values of θ/T.[†] Note that for $T > \theta_D$, $C_v \to 3R = 5\cdot98$ cal/g-atom deg, and for $T \leqslant \theta_D/20$, $C_v = 465(T/\theta_D)^3$ cal/g-atom deg.

As might be expected, experimental values for C_v often depart quite considerably from those given by the Debye model, a large part of the discrepancy arising from the fact that the real frequency spectrum in the atomic lattice is very different from the $f(\nu) \propto \nu^2$ spectrum assumed by Debye. These questions have been discussed in detail over the past three decades and a recent review by Blackman (1955) gives an excellent account of the present situation.

What is perhaps surprising is that the discrepancies in most solids are so small. Usually they are represented by deriving an appropriate value of θ_D from each experimental value of C_v (using the tabulated Debye function) and drawing a graph of θ_D versus T; in such a graph the Debye theory would demand complete constancy of θ from $T = 0°$ K upwards. Figure 122 shows experimental θ_D plots for a number of solids, and it may be noted how relatively constant θ_D is as a function of temperature.

† These values are taken from the Landolt–Bornstein physical tables. A more complete tabulation of the Debye energy and specific heat functions to six places has been given by Beattie (1926).

At high temperatures, that is at temperatures comparable with θ_D, the value of θ_D calculated from experimental data appears to be fairly constant for any particular solid, and the major variations usually occur at temperatures below about $\theta_D/5$. Because of a lack of positive experimental information that still exists with respect to many elements and for reasons of

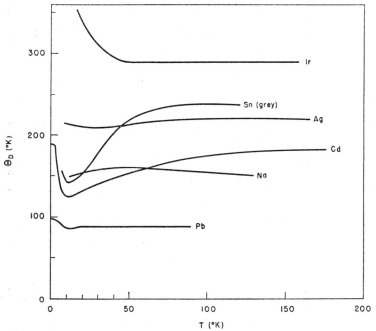

FIG. 122. Variation of θ_D with temperature.

space it is impracticable to list details of the observed specific heat data. However, for purposes of cryogenic design it is usually sufficient to assume the validity of the Debye approximation and calculate for any solid in question the specific heat on the basis of the values of θ_D listed in Table XXVIII (end of Chapter XI) and the tabulated Debye function (Table XXVII); values of θ_D shown for the various elements are values calculated from specific heat data obtained in the region between $\theta_D/2$ and θ_D, and are from the following sources of information: (i) compilation by Shiffman (1952), (ii) reviews by Blackman (1955), Keesom and Pearlman (1956), Bijl (1957), and some papers published since the writing of these reviews.

The values of specific heat discussed above are values, C_v, of the specific heat at constant volume. C_v is related to the quantity which is usually measured, namely the specific heat at constant pressure C_p, by the thermodynamic equation

$$C_p - C_v = VT\beta^2/\chi; \qquad (51)$$

here β is the volume expansion coefficient and χ is the compressibility. It follows to a first approximation that

$$C_p - C_v = AC_v^2 T,$$

where the constant A may be calculated by (51) at one temperature. The difference $C_p - C_v$ is negligible at low temperatures but usually becomes of the order of 1 per cent at temperatures in the vicinity of $\frac{1}{2}\theta_D$.

In some solids there are other substantial corrections to be made to the lattice specific heat to give coincidence with experimental values. In metals the free electrons contribute to the specific heat, their contribution being proportional to the absolute temperature. The electronic specific heat is usually expressed as

$$C_e = \gamma T,$$

where the constant γ varies from $\sim 10^{-4}$ cal/g-atom deg^2 for monovalent metals to $\sim 10^{-3}$ for transition metals.

Clearly the temperature dependence indicates that C_e becomes important at very low temperatures, being comparable with the lattice specific heat at $\sim 5°$ K for many metals; it should also become important again at very high temperatures, e.g. $T = 1,000°$ K or more. However, for cryogenic design the electronic heat capacity is not of major importance, and the reader is referred to the review by Daunt (1955) for more detailed information.

Among technical materials whose heat capacity is important in calorimetry and has been measured are the following:

Glyptal (air dried at room temperature): 4°–100° K by Pearlman and Keesom (1952).

Araldite (type 1 baked at 180° C); 1·5°–20° K by Parkinson and Quarrington (1954).

Wood's metal (12·5% Sn, 12·5% Cd, 25% Pb, 50% Bi): 1·5°–20° K by Parkinson and Quarrington (1954).

Formite bakelite varnish (baked): 4°–90° K by Hill and Smith (1953).

Pyrex glass: 2°–20° K by Smith and Wolcott (1956).

It is interesting to note from the observations of Parkinson and Quarrington that the heat capacities per gram of Araldite and Wood's metal are both far greater than that of copper at temperatures from 2°–20° K, and a similar observation may also be made for glyptal and bakelite varnish. Thus even small quantities of these cements or solders used in the assembly of a calorimeter contribute appreciably to its heat capacity and therefore must not be neglected.

Very frequently in low-temperature design we need to know approximate values for the heat capacity of a given weight of a metal, in order to calculate the approximate volume of liquid refrigerant required for cooling it. Obviously, a knowledge of the total heat, or enthalpy, H enables us to calculate this more readily. The enthalpy may be derived by integrating the C_p–T curve:

$$H(T) = U + PV = \int_0^T C_p \, dT.$$

Since $C_p - C_v$ is not a unique function of T/θ but depends on the expansion coefficient and compressibility of a substance, a general table of H as a function of T/θ cannot be compiled. However, for our practical purposes it may be assumed that $U = \int C_v \, dT$ will be sufficient approximation to $H = \int C_p \, dT$. Table XXI below, abbreviated from the Landolt–Bornstein physical tables, gives values of $(U - U_0)/T$ as a function of θ/T. It should be remembered that this tabulation in the form $U - U_0$ neglects the presence of any specific heat anomalies due to order-disorder transitions or other excitation processes which will contribute to the internal energy and the enthalpy of a substance in which they occur. However, these are relatively uncommon in the range below 300° K.

TABLE XXI

$$Some\ values\ of\ \frac{U-U_0}{T} = \frac{1}{T} \int_0^T C_v\ dT\ in\ cal/g\text{-}atom\ °K$$

θ/T	$\dfrac{U-U_0}{T}$	θ/T	$\dfrac{U-U_0}{T}$	θ/T	$\dfrac{U-U_0}{T}$
0·2	5·522	2·2	2·409	6·0	0·461
0·4	5·111	2·4	2·205	6·5	0·379
0·6	4·723	2·6	2·018	7·0	0·313
0·8	4·359	2·8	1·847	7·5	0·260
1·0	4·018	3·0	1·689	8·0	0·218
1·2	3·698	3·5	1·352	9·0	0·156
1·4	3·400	4·0	1·082	10·0	0·115
1·6	3·123	4·5	0·869	11·0	0·087
1·8	2·866	5·0	0·701	12·0	0·067
2·0	2·628	5·5	0·568	15·0	0·034

As an example consider the cooling from 90° to 4° K of 1 g-atom of copper (63·6 g), for which $\theta_D \simeq 310$.

At 90° K, $T/\theta = 0·290$ ($\theta/T = 3·44$), therefore

$$U-U_0 = 90 \times 1·37 = 123\ cal/g\text{-}atom.$$

At 4° K, $T/\theta = 0·012_9$ ($\theta/T = 77·5$), therefore

$$U-U_0 \simeq 0·01\ cal/g\text{-}atom.$$

Hence $U_{90}-U_4 \simeq 123$ cal/g-atom.

This indicates that about 180 cm³ of liquid helium would be required to cool 63·6 g of copper from 90° to 4° K, using only the latent heat of vaporization of the helium.

2. Coefficient of thermal expansion

When making low-temperature equipment it is usual to select the same material for the different pumping tubes. Not only is this simpler for reasons of availability but it lessens the risk of strains arising from differential expansion or contraction between different parts of the system. As an example, it is ill-advised to use a thin-walled inconel tube as the material for a metal sleeve running through the centre of a brass chamber, if the tube is constrained by being soldered to the chamber at each end. The difference in contraction of the materials imposes considerable strain on the light inconel tube when both are cooled from room temperature to say 4° K.

Frequently in cryogenic design, some knowledge is required of the expansion coefficients of the commonly used materials. Direct measurements of the expansion or contraction of many solids have been made in the past few years from room temperature down to about 4° K, although accurate information about the low-temperature end of this range is limited. The expansion coefficient of a solid has a temperature dependence very similar to that of the specific heat, so that at temperatures well below the Debye temperature the linear expansion coefficient (which we shall denote by α) becomes very small and extremely difficult to measure with any degree of accuracy.

The expansion coefficient α and the specific heat at constant volume may be related by the Grüneisen expression (see, for example, Mott and Jones, 1936, or Kittel, 1953)

$$3\alpha = \gamma \chi C_v / V,$$

where χ is the compressibility and C_v/V is the specific heat per unit volume; the proportionality constant γ is known as Grüneisen's constant, and may be alternatively defined by

$$\gamma = -\frac{d \log \theta}{d \log V}.$$

The Grüneisen relation is derived on the basis of certain assumptions and is not necessarily valid at all temperatures (Barron, 1957). At normal temperatures, however, γ appears to be sensibly constant, the value for many elements being in the range 1·5–2·5. At low temperatures it appears possible for γ (or the experimentally observed ratio α/C_v) to vary, and some recent experimental work (Bijl and Pullan, 1955; Nix and Mac-Nair, 1941; Figgins et al., 1956; Balluffi and Simmons, 1957) has examined this. However, as we mentioned above, accurate knowledge of α is very difficult to obtain when it has become very much smaller than its room temperature value. From the technical aspect, the values of α at temperatures in the vicinity of 10° or 20° K are of much less interest as the major part of the thermal contraction on cooling has already taken place in the range from 300° K to 40° or 50° K. Hence a change in the Grüneisen γ from say 2·1 to 1·7 which only occurs for $T < \theta/5$ would have negligible practical effect on the total change in dimensions of a solid which is being cooled from 300° K to 10° or 20° K.

In Table XXVIII (at the end of Chapter XI) are given experimental values for the linear expansion coefficient of a large number of elements at room temperature, compiled chiefly from the *Smithsonian Physical Tables* (9th edn., 1954). If approximate values for $\alpha = \alpha(T)$ are required for a particular element at low temperatures, we assume

$$\frac{\alpha(T)}{\alpha(295)} \simeq \frac{C_v(T)}{C_v(295)}.$$

A value for $\alpha(295)$ is obtained from Table XXVIII and $C_v(T)/C_v(295)$ is obtained using a θ_D value from this table and the Debye function (Table XXVII); of course, if experimental values of C_v at the required temperatures are available, these should be preferred.

For example: In the case of copper, α at 295° K is $0·167 \times 10^{-4}$ per ° C; since $\theta_D = 310°$ K, $\theta/T = 1·05$ at 295° K from which

$$C_v \simeq 5·64 \text{ cal/g-atom deg.}$$

At a temperature T, $\alpha(T) = \dfrac{C_v(T)}{5·64} \times 0·167 \times 10^{-4}$;

at 50° K, $\theta/T = 6·2$ and hence $C_v = 1·48$,

therefore $\qquad\qquad \alpha = 0·044 \times 10^{-4}$;

and at 100° K, $\theta/T = 3·1$ and hence $C_v = 3·85$,

therefore $\qquad\qquad \alpha = 0·115 \times 10^{-4}$ per °C.

In many instances, experimental information on the temperature variation of the expansion coefficient is available. Table XXII below shows experimental values of the change in the length at a temperature $T°$ K from the length at the ice point, divided by the length at the ice point, i.e. values of

$$(L_T - L_{273})/L_{273},$$

for a number of commonly used metals. More complete data for the thermal contraction of these and other metals have been given by:

Nix and MacNair (1941) for Cu, Al, Au, Ni, and Fe from about 77° to about 670° K.

Nix and MacNair (1942) for Mo, Pd, Ag, Ta, W, Pt, and Pb from 77° to 670° K.

Rubin, Altman, and Johnston (1954) for copper from 15° to 300° K.

Bijl and Pullan (1955) for Cu and Al from 20° to 273° K.

Beenakker and Swenson (1955) for brass, German silver, beryllium, copper, cupro-nickel, cast iron, invar, and stainless steels (nos. 302, 304, 316) from 4·2° to 300° K.

H. L. Johnston and collaborators from Ohio State University (unpublished)† for nickel, monel, inconel, contracid, stainless steels (nos. 304, 410), low carbon steel, and free machining yellow brass from liquid-helium temperatures to 305° K.

TABLE XXII

$$10^4 (L_T - L_{273})/L_{273}$$

Element	$T°$ K								
	0	25	50	75	100	150	200	250	300
Copper . .	−29·3	−29·3	−28·8	−27·2	−24·9	−18·8	−11·6	−3·6	+4·5
Aluminium .	37·4	37·4	37·0	34·8	32·4	25·0	15·6	−4·9	+6·6
Nickel . .	20·4	20·4	20·2	19·5	18·0	14·0	8·65	−2·9	+3·5
Iron . .	..	..	..	..	15·8	12·4	7·8	−2·45	+3·2
Silver . .	..	..	..	..	29·8	22·0	13·4	−4·2	+5·1
Tungsten . .	..	..	..	..	6·7	5·0	3·1	−1·0	+1·3
Platinum . .	..	..	..	..	14·3	10·6	6·4	−2·1	+2·5
Lead . .	..	..	..	..	46·7	33·8	20·3	−6·7	+7·9
Brass . .	34·5	34·5	33·7	31·6	28·8	21·6	13·4	−4·2	+5·0
German silver .	33·9	33·9	33·2	31·3	28·7	21·6	13·4	−4·2	+5·0
302 Stainless steel . .	28·4	28·4	28·1	26·9	24·6	18·5	12·0	−4·2	+4·7
304, 316 Stainless steel . .	26·3	26·3	26·2	25·2	23·2	17·5	10·8	−3·8	+4·2
Invar . .	4·6	4·6	4·6	4·6	4·2	3·1	1·8	−0·6	+0·7
Monel (cold-rolled) . .	22·4	22·4	22·0	21·1	19·5	15·0	9·4	−3·1	+3·7
Cupro-nickel (70 Cu, 30 Ni) .	25·2	25·2	24·8	23·8	22·2	17·2	10·8	−3·5	+4·2
Inconel . .	20·4	20·4	20·1	19·4	18·0	13·9	8·7	−2·8	+3·4

† I am grateful to Dr. C. A. Swenson of Iowa State College for supplying me with these data.

REFERENCES

BALLUFFI, R. W., and SIMMONS, R. O. (1957). *Bull. Amer. Phys. Soc.* ser. II, **2**, 137.

BARRON, T. H. K. (1957). *Ann. Physics*, **1**, 77.

BEATTIE, J. A. (1926). *J. Math. Phys.* **6**, 1.

BEENAKKER, J. M., and SWENSON, C. A. (1955). *Rev. Sci. Instrum.* **26**, 1204.

BIJL, D. (1957). *Progr. Low Temp. Phys.* **2**, 395, North-Holland Publishing Co., Amsterdam.

—— and PULLAN, H. (1955). *Physica*, **21**, 285.

BLACKMAN, M. (1955). *Handb. der Physik*, **7**, 325.

DAUNT, J. G. (1955). *Progr. Low Temp. Phys.* **1**, 202, North-Holland Publishing Co., Amsterdam.

FIGGINS, B. F., JONES, G. O., and RILEY, D. P. (1956). *Phil. Mag.* **1**, 747.

HILL, R. W., and SMITH, P. L. (1953). Ibid. **44**, 636.

KEESOM, P. H., and PEARLMAN, N. (1956). *Handb. der Physik*, **14**, 282.

KITTEL, C. (1953). *Introduction to Solid State Physics*, Wiley & Sons, New York.

MOTT, N. F., and JONES, H. (1936). *The Theory of the Properties of Metals and Alloys*, Clarendon Press, Oxford.

NIX, F. C., and MACNAIR, D. (1941). *Phys. Rev.* **60**, 597.

—— —— (1942). Ibid. **61**, 74.

PARKINSON, D. H., and QUARRINGTON, J. E. (1954). *Brit. J. Appl. Phys.* **5**, 219.

PEARLMAN, N., and KEESOM, P. H. (1952). *Phys. Rev.* **88**, 398.

RUBIN, T., ALTMAN, H. W., and JOHNSTON, H. L. (1954). *J. Amer. Chem. Soc.* **76**, 5289.

SHIFFMAN, C. A. (1952). *Heat Capacities of the Elements below Room Temperature*, General Electric Research Publication Services, Schenectady.

SMITH, P. L., and WOLCOTT, N. M. (1956). *Phil. Mag.* **1**, 854.

Added in Proof. Additional data and references concerning thermal expansion of solids at low temperatures are given in two very useful reports by H. L. Laquer and E. L. Head of the Los Alamos Scientific Laboratory. Issued by the United States Atomic Energy Commission in 1952, they have been available from the Office of Technical Services, Department of Commerce, Washington, D.C. Report AECU-2161 gives data for many common plastics and AECD-3706 deals with other materials and includes an extensive bibliography of work on elements, alloys, and compound.

CHAPTER XI

ELECTRICAL AND THERMAL RESISTIVITY

1. Electrical resistivity

Introduction

ALTHOUGH this book does not pretend to deal with the theory of transport properties of metals, a brief discussion of electron transport processes and the mechanisms which limit them, may help our appreciation of the value of certain physical data and of the extent to which these data may be extrapolated.

In an element which is a metallic conductor, some electrons are free or quasi-free so that they can be accelerated by the action of an applied electric field. The conductivity remains finite due to the influence of various electron scattering processes, chiefly thermal vibrations of the metallic ions in the crystal lattice and the chemical or physical impurities present in the lattice. If these processes are such as to produce a finite mean free time τ or mean free path l for the electrons, we should expect classically that the electrical conductivity

$$\sigma = \frac{Ne^2\tau}{m} = \frac{Ne^2l}{mv},$$

where N is the number of conduction electrons per cubic centimetre, e the electronic charge, m the electronic mass, and v their average velocity in the absence of an applied field.

On the quantum mechanical band model, the position is rather more restrictive. There must be vacant energy states into which an electron can make a transition after exchanging energy with the applied field or scattering centres; when scattered by a vibrating ion the energy exchanged is only of the order of kT so that only those electrons with energies near the top of the conduction band can take part in the conduction process. This restricts electronic conduction to elements in which the highest energy band is not completely filled, or some equivalent situation, e.g. a filled band which just touches or is overlapped by an empty band. In the monovalent metals (Cu, Ag, Au, and the alkalis) the s-band is half filled; in the divalent metals Mg, Zn, Cd, etc., conductivity is assured by overlapping of the s- and p-bands. Another important class are the transition elements in which an unfilled d-band overlaps with a succeeding s-band and produces a complex situation in which about 0·5–1 free electron per atom in the s-band appears to account for the electrical conductivity.

As in the classical picture, we can define an effective mean free path on the band model and deduce that

$$\sigma = \frac{Ne^2l}{mv}.$$

Now v is the average velocity of the electrons at the top of the band, i.e. near the Fermi surface. The electrons involved are only those within a region of the order of the thermal energy kT from the Fermi surface; their energy at the surface is 1–7 eV (equivalent to thermal energy at $\geqslant 20{,}000°$ K), therefore the velocity v at ordinary temperatures is practically temperature independent; also N, e, and m are constants. Calculation of the electron free path, however, is difficult except perhaps at high temperatures $(T \geqslant \theta)$ and at low temperatures $(T \ll \theta)$: when $T \geqslant \theta$ the wave number $\mathbf{k}$ of the electron and wave number $\mathbf{q}$ of the lattice wave or phonon with which it interacts are comparable in magnitude. Therefore the change in direction or momentum of an electron at a collision with a vibrating ion is considerable and l is simply the average distance an electron travels between collisions. When $T \ll \theta$, $\mathbf{q}$ is very small and collisions with phonons become rare and less important since static imperfections (chemical impurity atom, dislocation, grain boundary) are still present and cause elastic scattering.

So that:

(i) For $T > \theta$, resistivity is due chiefly to scattering by phonons, which is denoted by ρ_i.

Now $\rho_i \propto l^{-1}$

$\propto$ mean square amplitude of vibration of ions

$\propto T/Mk\theta^2$ ($M =$ atomic weight).

(ii) For $T \ll \theta$, $\rho_i \to 0$

and $\rho \simeq \rho_r$

therefore $\rho \simeq$ constant, since $l =$ constant.

In practice we may expect that at moderately high temperatures the electrical resistance of a fairly pure metallic element is due to thermal vibrations and that the resistivity ρ_i should be proportional to T. Except in the ferromagnetic elements Fe, Ni, and Co, and in the complex element Mn, this generally holds to a first approximation. Change in the Fermi surface with temperature and thermal expansion do affect the linearity of $\rho_i(T)$, but for many cryogenic calculations it is sufficient to assume $\rho_i \propto T$ over a range from $T \sim \frac{1}{2}\theta$ up to a temperature approaching a phase change or the melting temperature. At temperatures sufficiently low that $\rho_r \gg \rho_i$, the resistance becomes sensibly constant unless a superconducting transition occurs; in this context the phrase 'sufficiently low' depends on the purity of the element. Elements such as Na, Sn, and In may be readily obtained with a chemical purity exceeding 99·999 per cent and since they anneal at or near room temperature, specimens of such elements may have a residual resistivity ρ_r, nearly ten thousand times smaller than their resistivity at room temperature; in such instances ρ_r only becomes dominant for $T < \frac{1}{20}\theta$.

We have not discussed the behaviour of ρ_i at temperatures below the region $(T \geqslant \theta)$ where scattering is elastic. Detailed accounts of this subject as well as the general theoretical background to this section may be found in such sources as Mott and Jones (1936), Wilson (1953), Fröhlich (1936), Jones (1956), MacDonald (1956). The direction of motion and the energy of an electron before and after a collision with a phonon are governed by the conservation laws:

$\mathbf{k'} = \mathbf{k} + \mathbf{q}$ (conservation of momentum or wave number)

and $E' = E \pm h\nu$ (conservation of energy).

As $h\nu \sim kT$ and $E' \simeq E$ is the Fermi energy, the change in energy at a collision is small However, at temperatures $T \sim \theta_D$, $|\mathbf{q}| \sim |\mathbf{k}|$ and the change in direction or momentum is large. As the temperature decreases, the wave number $\mathbf{q}$ or the dominant lattice waves decreases, unlike the electron wave number $\mathbf{k}$ which is sensibly constant. Since $h\nu \sim kT$, therefore $\mathbf{q} \propto T$ and it follows that to a first approximation the angle of deflexion of an electron by interaction with a lattice wave is given by

$$\phi \sim |\mathbf{q}|/|\mathbf{k}| \sim T/\theta.$$

At temperatures quite low in comparison with the Debye temperature we expect the lattice specific heat to vary as T^3 and the density of phonons to vary as T^3. This suggests that the probability of scattering of an electron should be proportional to T^3 but the angle ϕ may be so small as to make a single scattering a very inefficient resistive process. If, indeed, a series of scatterings of an electron is required to deflect it from its 'conduction path', then the probability of its being scattered through a large angle in a series of random scattering processes will vary as $(T/\theta)^2$.

Hence

$$\rho_i \propto T^3 . (T/\theta)^2$$
$$\propto T^5.$$

On a more mathematical plane, Bloch obtained theoretically that the resistivity due to electron-ion interaction should be

$$\rho \propto \frac{T^5}{\theta^6} \int_0^{\theta/T} \frac{x^5 \, dx}{(e^x - 1)(1 - e^{-x})} \tag{52}$$

$$= C \frac{T^5}{\theta^6} J_5(\theta/T) \quad (C \text{ is a constant}).$$

Bloch suggested this equation should be suitable in the low-temperature limit as it reduces to

$$\rho = 124 \cdot 4 \frac{C}{\theta} \left(\frac{T}{\theta}\right)^5 \quad \text{for } T \ll \theta.$$

Grüneisen recognized that (52) might be applicable not only at low temperatures but also at intermediate temperatures, since it reduces to the required linear function of T at high temperatures:

$$\rho \simeq \frac{C}{4} \frac{T}{\theta^2} \quad \text{for } T/\theta \geqslant 0 \cdot 5;$$

he showed that for many metallic elements a suitable choice of

θ allowed experimental results to be represented by this Grüneisen–Bloch expression (52).

Note that the ratio of resistance at a low temperature, $T_1 < \frac{1}{10}\theta$, to that at a 'high' temperature, $T_2 \geqslant 0.5\theta$, is

$$\frac{\rho_1}{\rho_2} = \frac{497 \cdot 6}{\theta^4} \frac{T_1^5}{T_2}.$$

The validity of identifying θ in the above discussion with θ_D may be questioned. For an ideal metal, in which the conduction electrons are completely free (energy $E \propto k^2$) or in which the Fermi surface is perfectly spherical, it is expected theoretically that electrons may only interact with longitudinal lattice waves; hence an appropriate characteristic temperature might be $\theta = \theta_L$ where it has been shown that $\theta_L \simeq 1.5\theta_D$. However, if both transverse and longitudinal waves interact with the electrons the Debye characteristic temperatures θ_D, taken from specific heat data might be more appropriate. Experimental evidence suggests that this is probably so in many instances; certainly, values of θ (or θ_R) obtained from substituting experimental values of electrical resistance into the Grüneisen–Bloch expression lie much closer to θ_D than to $1.5\theta_D$. However, this is perhaps a rather naïve comparison as the transport theory, on which the Grüneisen–Bloch formula is based, neglects other important processes such as dispersion, i.e. variation of phonon velocity with frequency, and Umklapp processes, i.e. effective Bragg reflections of the electron by the lattice.

Even in the monovalent elements no unique choice of θ gives very good agreement between the Grüneisen–Bloch equation and experimental data over a range of temperature from around θ down to $\frac{1}{20}\theta$. Sodium is an exception as choosing $\theta_R = \theta_D$ enables quite good agreement to be established down to temperatures of $7°$ or $8°$ K.†

2. Data on electrical resistivity
Metallic elements

As we have a rather better knowledge of the Debye characteristic temperature (θ_D), from specific heat data, than of any

† Below $8°$ K it appears (Woods, 1956) that $\rho_i \propto T^6$ rather than T^5.

other characteristic temperature, it is instructive to compare experimental values for the variation of reduced resistivity ρ_i/ρ_θ as a function of reduced temperature T/θ_D with some

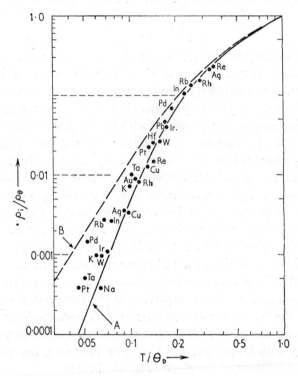

FIG. 123. Reduced electrical resistivity (ρ_i/ρ_θ) as a function of reduced temperature (T/θ_D).

$$\text{───── Curve } \rho_i/\rho_\theta = 4{\cdot}226(T/\theta_D)^5 \int_0^{\theta/T} \frac{x^5\,dx}{(e^x-1)(1-e^{-x})}.$$

$$\text{- - - Curve } \rho_i/\rho_\theta = 2{\cdot}084(T/\theta_D)^3 \int_0^{\theta/T} \frac{x^3\,dx}{(e^x-1)(1-e^{-x})}.$$

theoretical functions. Figure 123 shows on a logarithmic graph the reduced resistivity as a function of reduced temperature together with two theoretical curves of which curve A represents the Grüneisen–Bloch equation (52):

$$\frac{\rho_i}{\rho_\theta} = \left(\frac{T}{\theta}\right)^5 \int_0^{\theta/T} \frac{x^5\,dx}{(e^x-1)(1-e^{-x})} \Big/ \int_0^1 \frac{x^5\,dx}{(e^x-1)(1-e^{-x})}$$

$$= \left(\frac{T}{\theta}\right)^5 J_5(\theta/T) \div J_5(1)$$

$$= 4\cdot226(T/\theta)^5 J_5(\theta/T).$$

Sondheimer (1950) has tabulated values of the integral $J_5(\theta/T)$ for a limited number of θ/T values ranging from 0 to 1·25. Earlier, Grüneisen (1933) gave a fuller table in the form

$$F(\theta/T) = 4(T/\theta)^4 J_5(\theta/T),$$

from which one may write

$$\rho_i/\rho_\theta = 1\cdot056(T/\theta)F(\theta/T). \tag{53}$$

Curve A and the values for ρ_i/ρ_θ given in Table XXVII (col. 4) were obtained from Grüneisen's tabulation using equation (53).

The second theoretical curve (B in Figure 123) is based on a $J_3(\theta/T)$ function and is the type of functional relation between electrical resistance and temperature which Wilson (1938) has suggested might be valid for transition elements, at least over a restricted temperature range. Briefly, the reason for this is as follows: the transition elements all show a high electrical resistivity at room temperature in comparison with monovalent metals, despite a not very different effective number of free electrons, i.e. the parameter $\rho_{295}\,M\theta_D^2$ varies from 50 to 250 among the transition elements[†] whereas for Cu, Ag, and Au, $\rho M\theta^2 \simeq 10$ and for the alkali metals $\rho M\theta^2 \simeq 4$. Mott (1935, 1936) suggested that this results from the additional high probability of s-electrons being scattered into the d-band by interaction with thermal vibrations rather than merely being scattered to other available states in the s-band. Wilson proposed that this preponderance of s–d transitions over s–s transitions arising from the high density of states in the d-band, could continue down to lower temperatures but that the s–d transitions must eventually

[†] Excepting manganese for which this parameter has a value of about 1,400, ρ being expressed in ohm cm units and θ_D in °K.

be forbidden as the wave number of the interacting phonons becomes small. He deduced a resistive contribution due to s–d scattering to be given by

$$\rho_{sd} = b(T/\theta)^3 \int\limits_{\theta_E/T}^{\theta/T} \frac{x^3\,dx}{(e^x-1)(1-e^{-x})}.$$

If this were true we might expect ρ_{sd} to decrease exponentially for $T \leqslant \theta_E$. However, lacking any knowledge of θ_E we may derive a relation $\rho_i/\rho_\theta = f(\theta/T)$ based on the dubious assumptions that

$$\rho_i \simeq \rho_{sd}$$

and

$$\rho_{sd} = b(T/\theta)^3 \int\limits_{0}^{\theta/T} \frac{x^3\,dx}{(e^x-1)(1-e^{-x})}.$$

Hence

$$\frac{\rho_i}{\rho_\theta} = (T/\theta)^3 J_3(\theta/T)/J_3(1)$$

$$= 2{\cdot}084\left(\frac{T}{\theta}\right)^3 J_3(\theta/T). \qquad (54)$$

Curve B and some values of this function (54) tabulated in Table XXVII (col. 5), have been calculated from the tables of J_3 values given by MacDonald and Towle (1956).

A detailed comparison of experimental evidence with (53) or (54) requires a more accurate knowledge of the appropriate θ-values that are used. It may suffice to point out that the experimental values of ρ_i/ρ_θ generally lie in the region between curves A and B (Figure 123). Also, at low temperatures ($T \leqslant \frac{1}{10}\theta$) equations (53) and (54) lead to T^5 and T^3 relations: for monovalent metals and some divalent metals we find $\rho_i \propto T^5$ at sufficiently low temperatures but for the transition elements the index of T in this region varies from 3 to 5, and in some transition elements there is evidence that $\rho_i \propto T^2$ for $T \sim \frac{1}{50}\theta$, which suggests that electron-electron interactions become important at these very low temperatures. For the experimental points in Figure 123, values of $\theta = \theta_D$ from Table XXVIII have been used; and values of electrical resistivity have been taken from Gerritsen (1956), Meissner and Voigt (1930), and a number of papers by the writer and his collaborators (for example White, 1953; Kemp et al., 1955, 1956a; Harper et al., 1957;

MacDonald, White, and Woods, 1956; White and Woods, 1957 a, b, c, d, e). The values of ρ_i at room temperature $(T = 295°\,\text{K})$ given in Table XXVIII are also taken from these sources; they are values of the 'ideal' electrical resistivity $(\rho_i = \rho - \rho_r)$ due to scattering by thermal vibrations and are probably correct to within 1 or 2 per cent. For K, Ru, Mn, and Os the margin of error may be appreciably greater due to uncertainty in the dimensions of the specimens measured.

On Figure 123 are drawn three horizontal lines representing three different values of the residual electrical resistance, namely $\rho_r/\rho_\theta = 10^{-3}, 10^{-2}, 10^{-1}$. This and the assumption that $\rho = \rho_i + \rho_r$ (Matthiessen's rule) suggest that our ability to predict correctly a value for ρ at temperature T on the basis of values for $\rho_r = \rho$ (at $T_1 \ll \theta$) and $\rho_i \simeq \rho$ (at $T_2 \geqslant \theta$), depends on the ratio ρ_r/ρ_θ (or ρ_r/ρ_{295}) for the metal in question. For impure or badly strained specimens ρ_r/ρ_θ may be as high as 10^{-1} and we may estimate ρ fairly accurately at all temperatures without knowing in detail the behaviour of $\rho_i(T)$ at low temperatures, for at such temperatures $\rho_r \gg \rho_i$. When, however, we wish to know ρ at a temperature $T \leqslant \frac{1}{10}\theta$ for a very pure specimen in which $\rho_r/\rho_\theta \sim 10^{-3}$, the task is more difficult unless experimental data on $\rho_i(T)$ are available. To assist in this situation Table XXIII gives experimental values for ρ_i in micro-ohm cm for some common elements at various temperatures. The sources of data for this table have again been those of the writer and his collaborators (loc. cit.) and Van den Berg (1948) for Pb, Meissner and Voigt (1930) for Al, de Haas and Van den Berg (1936) for Au and Ag.

TABLE XXIII

T	Na	Cu	Au	Ag	Al	Pb	Fe	Ni	Pt	W
295	4·84	1·69	2·21	1·64	2·76	21·0	9·8$_0$	7·0$_4$	10·42	5·32
273	4·40	1·55	2·04	1·50	2·50	19·3	8·69	6·2$_0$	9·59	4·80
200	2·9$_5$	1·05	1·4$_5$	1·04$_5$	(1·6$_4$)	..	5·34	3·7$_5$	6·76	3·20
150	2·1$_0$	0·71	1·0$_5$	0·73$_5$	(1·0$_6$)	..	3·1$_5$	2·2$_5$	4·78	2·11
100	1·2$_0$	0·35	0·65	0·42$_5$	0·4$_8$	..	1·2$_4$	1·0$_2$	2·74	1·03
75	0·7$_4$	0·18	0·42	0·26$_5$	0·21	4·59	0·5$_2$	0·46	1·70	0·51
50	0·3$_4$	0·04$_9$	0·20	0·11	..	2·76	0·1$_2$	0·14	0·72	0·150
40	0·18	0·02$_3$	0·12	0·058	..	2·04	0·06	0·07	0·40	0·070
30	0·072	0·006$_1$	0·05$_9$	0·020	..	1·26	0·02$_3$	0·03$_1$	0·16	0·022
20	0·015	0·001$_0$	0·01$_3$	0·0042	0·0036	0·56	0·00$_7$	0·00$_9$	0·044	0·0057
15	0·0058	0·0002	0·003$_7$	0·0011	..	0·25	0·003$_8$	0·004$_4$	0·012	0·0027
10	0·0008$_4$	..	0·0006	0·0002	..	..	0·001$_5$	0·002$_0$	0·0029	(0·0009)

Procedure for calculating values of ρ

Given a bar or wire of a metallic element—purity unknown—we may require an estimate of its electrical resistance at temperatures from 4° to 300° K. The simplest procedure is then to measure the electrical resistance R_{295} at room temperature, and measure R_4 by dipping it into a dewar of liquid helium. If the specimen is a fine wire having a resistance of 10^{-2} ohm or more, this may be measured with potentiometer or resistance bridge. If it is a solid bar of copper of resistance 10^{-5} or 10^{-6} ohm then some form of galvanometer amplifier is more suitable (see review by MacDonald, 1956, for details of a galvanometer amplifier).† Then, knowing R_{295} and $R_4 = R_r$, we can deduce R_i at room temperature $(= R_{295} - R_r)$; if desired the shape factor $l/A = R/\rho$ may also be calculated, using a value of $\rho(295°$ K$)$ from Table XXVIII. Then, at temperatures between 4° and 300° K,

$$\rho = \rho_i(T) + \rho_r$$

or
$$R = R_i(T) + R_r,$$

where the constant R_r (or ρ_r) is known. $R_i(T)$ or $\rho_i(T)$ may be found, using a value of $\theta = \theta_D$ from Table XXVIII, from (i) the Grüneisen–Bloch equation, (ii) Figure 123, or (iii) experimental values of ρ_i in Table XXIII. It follows from our earlier remarks that method (i) may be in serious error at temperatures $T \leqslant \frac{1}{10}\theta$ unless we apply a prior knowledge of the departures from the Grüneisen–Bloch equation for the metal in question.

Example: Given a rod of copper, it is found that $R_{295} = 0.016$ ohm, $R_4 = 0.00027$ ohm, and it is required to know R at 110° K. Firstly, $R_i(295) = 0.0160_0 - 0.00027 = 0.0157_3$ ohm. Assuming $\rho_i/\rho_\theta = (T/\theta)^5 J_5(\theta/T) \div J_5(1)$ we have

$$\frac{\rho_i(110)}{\rho_i(295)} = \frac{\rho_i(110)}{\rho_i(\theta)} \frac{\rho_i(\theta)}{\rho_i(295)}.$$

For $\dfrac{T}{\theta} = \dfrac{110}{310}$ Table XXVII gives $\dfrac{\rho_i(110)}{\rho_i(\theta)} = 0.249$ and for

---

† A commercial galvanometer-amplifier is now produced by Tinsley Ltd. of London.

$$\frac{T}{\theta} = \frac{295}{310} \text{ gives } \frac{\rho_i(295)}{\rho_i(310)} = 0\cdot945; \text{ hence}$$

$$\frac{\rho_i(110)}{\rho_i(295)} = 0\cdot263$$

and $R_i(110) = 0\cdot263 \times 0\cdot016 = 0\cdot00414$ ohm.

Now $R = R_i(110) + R_4$

$$\simeq 0\cdot0044 \text{ ohm at } 110° \text{ K.}$$

Data on metallic alloys

   In most alloys, excepting those very dilute alloys which may be regarded as slightly impure metallic elements, the residual or impurity resistance is relatively high. In many important alloys such as the stainless steels, monel, cupro-nickel, etc., ρ_r is much greater than the resistivity due to thermal vibrations and hence $\rho \simeq \rho_r$ and is practically independent of temperature. As we mentioned earlier (§ 4.7) some alloys (manganin and constantan) show an anomalous decrease in resistance as the temperature falls below 100° K, but the total change in resistance in cooling from 300° to 4° K is still less than 20 per cent of the total.

   For some of the alloys used commonly in low-temperature equipment, Table XXIV gives values of the electrical resistivity at room temperature, at 77° or 90° K, and at 4° K.

   It is interesting to note the general effect of different impurity atoms present in solid solution in a parent metal (see, for example, Friedel, 1956, for discussion, and also Mott and Jones, 1936; Gerritsen, 1956). As stated by Norbury's rule, the increase in residual resistivity due to the addition of a specific impurity, varies approximately as the square of the valency difference (Z) between the constituents, i.e. the matrix and impurity; the addition to copper of 1 atomic per cent of Zn $(Z = 1)$, Ga $(Z = 2)$, Ge $(Z = 3)$, As $(Z = 4)$ increases the resistivity by approximately $0\cdot3$, $1\cdot4$, $3\cdot8$, $6\cdot8$ micro-ohm cm respectively. Generally for metals such as Al, Cu, Ag, Au the increase, $\Delta\rho$, in micro-ohm cm per atomic per cent is $0\cdot1$–$0\cdot5$ for a homovalent impurity, and increases to 5 or more for a valence difference of 3 or more.

   Up to a fairly large concentration of impurity—provided it is within the range of solid solubility—the increase in resistance varies nearly linearly with concentration in many binary systems. This is to be expected from Nordheim's rule which states that for a disordered solid solution $\Delta\rho$ varies with concentration c as

$$\Delta\rho = ac(1-c)+bc.$$

TABLE XXIV

Electrical resistivity in micro-ohm cm

Sample	Physical condition	295° K	90° K	77° K	4° K
Brass (30 Zn, 70 Cu)	strained	7·2	5·0	..	4·3
(Kemp *et al.* 1957) .	annealed	6·6	4·2	..	3·6
Cupro-nickel (90 Cu, 10	strained				
Ni) (Estermann & Zim-	or	14·7	..	12·7	12
merman, 1952) . .	annealed				
Cupro-nickel (80 Cu, 20	as				
Ni) (Hulm, 1951) . .	received	26	..	24	23
Manganin (Kamerlingh	as				
Onnes & Holst, 1914) .	received	40	39	..	37
German silver (Berman,	as				
1951). . . .	received	30	27·5	..	26
Constantan (Berman, 1951)	wires as				
	received	52·5	45	..	44
Monel (Estermann & Zim-	strained				
merman, 1952) . .	or	50	..	32	30
	annealed				
Stainless steels (Berman,	as				
1951) . . .	received	71	52·5	..	49
Stainless steels (Ester-	as				
mann & Zimmerman,	received	74	..	52	51
1952) . . .					
Inconel (Estermann &	strained	94	..	91	90
Zimmerman, 1952) .	annealed	103	..	100	102
Inconel (White & Woods,					
unpublished, 1956) .	half-hard	107	104	104	104

This is a parabola and since usually the constant $a \gg b$, we have that approximately $\Delta\rho \propto c$ provided $c \leqslant 0\cdot2$. Nordheim's rule is not always obeyed as in some alloy systems the band structure and effective number of conduction electrons may be sensitive to certain added impurities. In both Ag–Cd and Cu–Zn a non-linear variation of $\Delta\rho$ with concentration is found, even for concentrations as low as 2 per cent. Also, in alloys involving a transition element, the unfilled d-band has a profound effect on the resistance of the alloy; the type of relation between $\Delta\rho$ and c which is expressed in Nordheim's rule is then no longer obeyed (see, for example, Mott and Jones, 1936; Wilson, 1953; also Kemp *et al.*, 1956 *b*).

It is profitless to consider the quantitative theory of scattering of electrons by physical imperfections. The theory of such scattering processes is of rather uncertain validity, particularly in the case of stacking faults, so that any hope of predicting an electrical residual resistivity from a prior knowledge of dislocation density, density of vacancies, or stacking faults seems singularly groundless. What may be noted is that severe cold working of a pure metal will generally affect its residual resistance quite markedly, in silver, for example, to the extent of about 0·2 micro-ohm cm; however, the effect of such working may be quite lost in an alloy for which the residual resistance is already 10 micro-ohm cm or more. Incidentally, this is not necessarily the case when considering the heat conduction in an alloy of high electrical resistance, e.g. stainless steel, because an appreciable part of the heat is carried by lattice waves at low temperatures; the lattice waves are much more sensitive at low temperatures to the presence of line or plane imperfections such as dislocations or boundaries than they are to point imperfections. The heat conductivity at $10°$ K of a stainless steel rod may be decreased appreciably by cold work while its electrical resistance is not noticeably altered.

3. Discussion of thermal resistivity

Electronic thermal conduction

In those pure metallic elements for which there is approximately one charge carrier per atom, i.e. excepting elements such as bismuth, the electronic thermal conductivity λ_e is much larger than the lattice conductivity λ_g. The same scattering processes limit λ_e as limit the electrical conductivity. We may adopt a simple kinetic model for which $\lambda_e = C_e vl/3$, where the electronic specific heat C_e is proportional to T and v is practically constant.

Then at temperatures for which the mean free path l is the

same for electrical or thermal transport we expect theoretically
that

$$\rho\lambda_e = \frac{\lambda_e}{\sigma} = \frac{\pi^2}{3}\left(\frac{k}{e}\right)^2 T = LT. \tag{55}$$

The Lorentz constant L has the value $2{\cdot}45\times10^{-8}$ W Ω deg^{-2}.

At high temperatures ($T \geqslant \theta_D$), large angle elastic scattering
of the electrons by thermal vibrations occurs, and we expect the
effective mean free path l to vary as T^{-1} and to have the same
magnitude for thermal or electrical transport; hence just as we
expect $\rho \propto T$, so should λ_e be constant and

$$\frac{\rho\lambda_e}{T} = L \quad (T \geqslant \theta_D).$$

Experimental values for a number of metals at or near room
temperature indicate that this Wiedemann–Franz–Lorenz law
is moderately well obeyed.

At sufficiently low temperatures where impurity scattering is
dominant, the mean free path should be constant so that
$\rho \simeq$ constant, and $\lambda \propto T$. Measurement at liquid-helium
temperatures on a large number of metallic elements have confirmed the validity of the equation (55), namely that

$$\frac{\rho_r\lambda_r}{T} = \frac{\rho_r}{W_r T} = 2{\cdot}45\times10^{-8} \text{ W }\Omega\text{ deg}^{-2}$$

within the limits of experimental accuracy which are about
± 1 per cent; here λ_r and $W_r (= 1/\lambda_r)$ are respectively the electronic
thermal conductivity and electronic thermal resistivity limited
by static impurities.

At all temperatures we expect the thermal resistivity due to
impurities W_r, and that due to thermal vibrations W_i, to be
additive, at least to a first approximation; that is, the thermal
equivalent of Matthiessen's rule should be approximately
correct:
$$1/\lambda = W = W_r + W_i,$$
where $\qquad W_r = A/T \quad (A \text{ is a constant})$
and $\qquad W_i = W_i(T)$
$$= W_\infty, \text{ a constant, for } T \geqslant \theta_D.$$

The theoretical solutions of the transport equation which gives $W_i(T)$ have been discussed in detail by Wilson (1953) and Klemens (1956). Suffice it to say that the agreement between experiment and theory is not good, which is not altogether surprising in view of the neglect in the theory of Umklapp processes and dispersion at high temperatures. However, it has

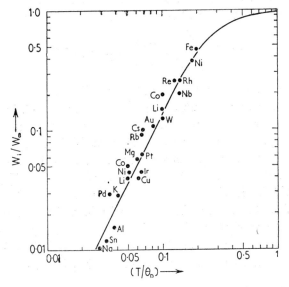

FIG. 124. Reduced thermal resistivity (W_i/W_∞) as a function of reduced temperature (T/θ_D)

$$\underline{\qquad} \quad W_i/W_\infty = 2(T/\theta)^2 \int\limits_0^{\theta/T} \frac{x^3\,dx}{(e^x-1)(1-e^{-x})}.$$

been shown (MacDonald, White, and Woods, 1956) that a function of the form $(T/\theta)\,J_3\,(\theta/T)$ appears to fit the observations of $W_i(T)/W_\infty$. The graph in Figure 124 illustrates the degree of correlation between observations and this empirical function. The curve represents the variation of

$$2(T/\theta)^2 \int\limits_0^{\theta/T} \frac{x^3\,dx}{(e^x-1)(1-e^{-x})}$$

with the reduced temperature T/θ. The experimental values of

W_i/W_∞ are calculated from data on W_i given in Klemens's review article, in Rosenberg (1955), Powell and Blanpied (1954), and work by the writer and collaborators (see § 2 and references at the end of this chapter). The values of W_∞, the fairly constant thermal resistivity at temperatures $T \geqslant \theta_D$, and of θ_D are taken from Table XXVII, W_∞ being the approximate reciprocal of λ_{295}. The J_3 function tabulated by MacDonald and Towle (1956) has been used to obtain the values of

$$2(T/\theta)^2 \int\limits_0^{\theta/T} \frac{x^3 \, dx}{(e^x-1)(1-e^{-x})} \simeq W_i/W_\infty$$

used in Figure 124 and given in Table XXVII.

This partial agreement suggests that with a knowledge of the thermal resistivity of a metallic element at room temperature and at liquid-helium temperatures, both $W_i(T)$ and $W_r = A/T$ can be calculated approximately at any intermediate temperature; hence the electronic thermal conductivity, $\lambda_e = (W_i + W_r)^{-1}$, can be obtained. More simply, the Wiedemann–Franz law allows us to calculate an approximate value for W_∞ and a good value for $A = W_r T$ directly from electrical resistance measurements made at room temperature and at the temperature of liquid helium. This procedure is outlined in more detail in § 4 below.

Lattice thermal conductivity

In insulators all the heat current is carried by lattice waves; in semi-conductors and in semi-metals like bismuth, graphite, or antimony, lattice conductivity is usually dominant at low temperatures; while in many disordered alloys the lattice heat conductivity may be at least comparable with the electronic heat conductivity at low temperatures so that $\lambda = \lambda_e + \lambda_g$. The temperature dependence of the lattice conductivity is rather more complex and therefore less predictable than that of the electronic conductivity; this arises from the variation in frequency or wavelength of the dominant lattice waves with temperature which results in a very different temperature dependence for scattering by the different classes of lattice imperfections.

At high temperatures the lattice conductivity λ_g, is chiefly limited by thermal vibrations, i.e. interaction between the waves (or phonons) themselves due to the anharmonic nature of the coupling between the vibrating atoms. If we denote this thermal resistance by W_u, then it is dominant at temperatures $T \geqslant \theta_D$ except in highly disordered solids.

The effect of physical and chemical impurities on lattice waves is complicated because the important frequencies are temperature sensitive. As we should expect from physical intuition it is found that at very low temperatures, where only long waves are excited in the solid, planar irregularities scatter the waves much more effectively than do small point defects. As discussed in detail by Berman (1953) and Klemens (1956) grain boundaries (resistivity W_B), dislocations (W_D), and vacancies or impurity atoms (W_P) provide three distinct scattering processes for which the proportionality relations between effective mean free path and frequency ν are as follows:

(i) grain boundaries: l_B is frequency independent, generally

$$\lambda \simeq \tfrac{1}{3}Cvl;$$

therefore, since $C \propto T^3$ for $T \ll \theta_D$,

$$\lambda_B \propto W_B^{-1} \propto T^3 \quad \text{for } T \ll \theta_D$$

as the phonon velocity v is constant;

(ii) dislocations: $l_D \propto \nu^{-1}$

and, since $\nu \propto T,$

therefore $\lambda_D \propto W_D^{-1} \propto T^2;$

(iii) point defects: $l_P \propto \nu^{-4} \propto T^{-4}$ (Rayleigh scattering);

therefore $\lambda_p \propto W_p^{-1} \propto T^{-1}.$

It is only in the case of boundary scattering that we can make any reliable *a priori* estimate of the mean free path of the lattice waves. Casimir (1938) has deduced that in an extended crystalline solid $\lambda_B = 2 \cdot 31 \times 10^3 RA^{\frac{1}{3}}pT^3$ W/cm deg,

where R is the radius of the crystal, assumed to be of circular cross-section; p is approximately a constant which depends on the ratio of sound velocities in different directions, the usual value being $p \simeq 1 \cdot 4$. A is the constant in $C_v = AT^3$ J/cm³ deg.

Formulae for λ_D and λ_p have been deduced by Klemens (1956) but their applicability is limited to isotropic crystals and we must know the number of dislocations present or the particular number and form of the impurities. It does appear that in some simple cubic solids the formula given by Klemens for the resistivity due to point defect scattering W_p is substantially verified by experiment.

The temperature dependence of the phonon-interaction term W_u, which is important at higher temperatures, may be given by

$$W_u \propto T \text{ for } T \geqslant \theta.$$

It has been shown by Peierls that at low temperatures (see reviews of Berman, 1953, and Klemens, 1956) the interactions between lattice waves which are responsible for a thermal resistance (called Umklapp processes by Peierls) become increasingly improbable; these Umklapp processes involve a type of Bragg reflection of the lattice wave which becomes energetically improbable at T falls below some characteristic temperature θ_u.

Thus, for $T \ll \theta_D$, we might expect

$$W_u \propto e^{-\theta/aT}.$$

A confirmatory exponential dependence has been observed in such crystals as diamond, sapphire, solid helium, bismuth, and quartz at temperatures $T \simeq \frac{1}{20}\theta_D$.

The treatment by Peierls does not give the absolute magnitude of the interaction process but at higher temperatures (region where $W_u \propto T$) a simplified model of a cubic crystal has been used by Leibfried and Schlömann (1954) and also by Dugdale and MacDonald (1955) to obtain

$$\lambda_u = 12k^3 M A_0 \, \theta^3/5h^3\gamma^2 T \qquad \text{(L.–S.)}$$

or $\qquad \qquad \lambda_u = vCA_0/3\beta\gamma T \qquad \qquad \text{(D.–M.)}$

v is the velocity of the lattice waves, C is the specific heat per unit volume, A_0 is the lattice constant, β is the cubic expansion coefficient, γ is the Grüneisen parameter, M is the atomic mass, h and k are Planck's and Boltzmann's constants respectively. These two formulae may be shown to be approximately equivalent and have been verified experimentally within expected

limits of accuracy (i.e. limits of accuracy arising from uncertainty in the Grüneisen parameter γ and other constants),
for a number of alkali halide crystals, solid argon, and solid
helium.

Thus far we have neglected the scattering that is due to free
electrons, a process which is a major factor in limiting the lattice
thermal conductivity of metals. Makinson (1938) showed that
this thermal resistance (W_E) is proportional to T^{-2} at low
temperatures and (see also Klemens, 1956) is related to the
electron-phonon coupling which is responsible for ρ_i and W_i in
the respective electron transport processes.

An earlier figure (Chapter VI, page 184) illustrates the differing temperature dependences of the total thermal conductivity
in a pure metallic element, a crystalline dielectric solid, an alloy,
and a glass.

4. Thermal-resistivity data

Pure metallic elements

A practical example of the folly of assuming particular values
of thermal conductivity for a material merely because it is
labelled by the name of a certain element is illustrated by
Figure 125. These curves are experimental values for various
samples of copper and show the tremendous variation of conductivity, particularly from $10°$–$30°$ K, that arises with slight
change in chemical or physical purity.

At high temperatures $\lambda \simeq \lambda_\infty$ is relatively insensitive to purity
or temperature; the values of λ_{295} which are listed in Table
XXVIII are intended to represent the best experimental esti-
mates of the conductivity of the metallic elements in states of
high purity and at a temperature sufficiently high that $\lambda \to \lambda_\infty$.

When the practical problem arises of calculating approximate
values of $\lambda(T)$ for a particular sample of a metallic element the
suggested procedure is:

(i) Measure its electrical resistance at room temperature
and in liquid helium to obtain R_{295} and R_4; by comparing
$R_{295} - R_4$ with ρ_i at $295°$ K given in Table XXVIII, the shape
factor l/A may be calculated.

(ii) Then calculate $W_\infty = \rho_i(295° \text{ K})/2\cdot45\times10^{-8}$. 295 cm deg W^{-1} or obtain W_∞ direct from Table XXVIII, assuming $W_\infty = 1/\lambda_{295}$. Also obtain $W_0 T = \rho_4/2\cdot45\times10^{-8}$ cm deg W^{-1}.

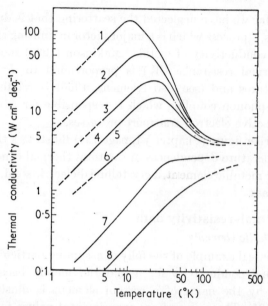

FIG. 125. Thermal conductivity of copper samples. 1, pure (99·999%, annealed, American Smelting and Refining); 2, pure (99·999%, annealed, Johnson Matthey); 3, coalesced (99·98%, oxygen free annealed, Phelps Dodge); 4, pure (99·999%, cold worked, Johnson Matthey); 5, electrolytic tough pitch (99·9+%, representing some tubes, much sheet and plate); 6, free-cutting tellurium (99%+0·6% Te, representing machining rods and bar); 7, pure Cu+0·056% Fe (annealed); 8, phosphorus deoxidized (99·8%+0·1% P, representing some tubes, pipe, sheet and plate). Curves 1, 3, 5, 6, and 8 from Powell, Rogers, and Roder (1957); curves 2 and 4 from White (1953), and 7 from White and Woods (1955).

(iii) At each temperature T, calculate $W_0 = \rho_4/2\cdot45\times10^{-8}T$; and using Table XXVII or Figure 123 calculate

$$W_i = 2W_\infty(T/\theta_D)^2 . J_3(\theta_D/T).$$

(iv) Then at each temperature $W \simeq W_0 + W_i$.

For example: Consider a bar of iron; measurements with a galvanometer amplifier give $R_{295} \simeq 0\cdot00141$ ohm and $R_4 \simeq 0\cdot00011$ ohm.

Step (i) gives $R_i(295) = 0.00130$ ohm and since
$$\rho_i(295) = 9.8 \times 10^{-6} \text{ ohm},$$
$l/A = 133$.

Hence $\rho_4 = 0.83 \times 10^{-6}$ ohm cm.

Step (ii). We may calculate
$$W_\infty = 9.80 \times 10^{-6}/2.45 \times 10^{-8} . 295 = 1.36,$$
or obtain a more reliable value†
$$W_\infty = 1/\lambda_{295} = 1.25 \quad \text{(from Table XXVIII)},$$
and
$$W_0 T = \rho_4/L = 34.$$

Step (iii). Using $\theta_D = 400° K$ we may proceed to calculate W or λ at, say, $40° K$.

For $T/\theta = 0.1$, Figure 124 (Table XXVII) gives $W_i/W_\infty = 0.144$, therefore
$$W_i = 0.18 \quad \text{and} \quad W_0 = 34/40 = 0.85.$$

Step (iv). Thus at $40° K$, $W = 0.85 + 0.18 = 1.03$, hence
$$\lambda \simeq 0.97 \text{ W cm}^{-1} \text{ deg}^{-1}.$$

The chief inaccuracy in this method of predicting λ lies in the possible departure of W_i from the assumed $T^2 . J_3(\theta/T)$ relation. This semi-empirical relation leads to $W_i/W_\infty = C(T/\theta)^2$ for $T \leqslant \frac{1}{10}\theta$ where $C = 14.4$, whereas experiment shows that C may vary from 10 to about 25; in general a range of 12–20 covers most metallic elements. Again at temperatures $T < \frac{1}{10}\theta$, W_i appears to fall more rapidly than T^2 in many elements, so that an index of 2.3–2.5 (rather than 2.0) is not unusual. At worst such discrepancies may result in our estimate of λ being wrong by 30 or 40 per cent in the vicinity of the conductivity maximum. A much better estimate may be obtained if we merely use our electrical resistance data to estimate $W_0 T$ and use existing experimental data on λ (for other samples of the element) to give values of W_i.

Either procedure is usually more reliable than to attempt to guess the physical or chemical purity of a specimen, since residual electrical resistance and low temperature heat conductivity are

† For a ferromagnetic element like iron, this is only a crude approximation since W_∞ is not truly constant but steadily increases with temperature.

very sensitive to specific impurities and their state of segregation in the metal.

For those interested in more detailed information about the thermal conductivity of the elements and other solids, the following references are useful:

(i) The compilation of R. L. Powell and Blanpied (1954) contains fairly complete graphs of the thermal-conductivity measurements available in 1954 of solids below room temperature.

(ii) Review articles by Berman (1953) on dielectric solids and by Olsen and Rosenberg (1953) on metals, surveyed much of the available low-temperature data (see also Rosenberg, 1955).

(iii) Another useful review of some experimental data on the thermal conductivity of metals and alloys has been given by R. W. Powell (1955).

(iv) More recently Klemens (1956) has reviewed both the theoretical and experimental aspects of heat conduction in solids at low temperatures.

(v) Reviews dealing more exclusively with heat transport in superconductors are those of Mendelssohn (1955 and 1956).

Metallic alloys

As we discussed above for pure metallic elements, a relatively easy measurement, that of $\rho_4 = \rho_r$, allows a rough estimate of the electronic thermal conductivity λ_e, to be made. In cases where the impurity scattering is not excessive, for example wherever $\rho_r/\rho_{295} < 0.5$, it may be assumed that electronic conductivity λ_e, is the dominant mechanism,

i.e.
$$\lambda = \lambda_e + \lambda_g$$
$$\simeq \lambda_e.$$

It is in the technically important alloys such as monel, stainless steel, and cupro-nickel that the residual resistance is very high and λ_e is reduced to become comparable with λ_g. Estimation or prediction of λ_g from other physical data appears extremely difficult at the present time. By making certain assumptions about the process of phonon-electron interaction, a relation between W_E (or λ_E) and W_i can be deduced which enables us to estimate crudely the lattice conductivity in annealed alloys at temperatures below about $\frac{1}{20}\theta$, where λ_g is chiefly limited by the presence of free electrons (see White and Woods, 1957 f):

$$\lambda_E = \frac{0 \cdot 53 T_1 \times 10^{-6}}{\rho_i(T_1)} (T/\theta)^2 \quad \text{for } T \leqslant \tfrac{1}{20}\theta,$$

where temperature T_1 is comparable with θ_D and may be conveniently 295° K or thereabouts.

In most instances, the ideal electrical resistivity ρ_i at 295° K for the major constituent of an alloy is known,

then $$\lambda_E \simeq 157 . 10^{-6}(T/\theta)^2/\rho_i(295).$$

As an example we may choose annealed inconel and assume, since nickel is the major constituent, that

$$\rho_i(295) = 7 \cdot 1 \times 10^{-6} \text{ ohm cm} \quad \text{and} \quad \theta_D \simeq 390° \text{ K};$$

then λ_E, the thermal conductivity due to phonons when scattering by free electrons is dominant, is

$$\lambda_E \simeq \frac{157 \times 10^{-6}}{7 \cdot 1 \times 10^{-6}} (T/390)^2 = 1 \cdot 4 \times 10^{-4} T^2 \text{ W/cm deg.}$$

This result appears to approximate to the experimentally determined values for the lattice conductivity of annealed inconel at temperatures below 20° K (see, for example, Estermann and Zimmerman, 1952).

However, even if this estimate of W_E were always correct, it could only yield a value of λ_g over a narrow temperature range and be correct for annealed alloys in which dislocation scattering is unimportant.

Because of these difficulties, data are given below (Table XXV) for measured values of total heat conductivity in a number of common alloys, some of them in both annealed and cold-worked conditions. The data have been largely taken from Powell and Blanpied (1954) with the exception of data on brass, beryllium, copper, soft solder, and Wood's metal which were published by Berman, Foster, and Rosenberg (1955), and the non-magnetic alloy silicon bronze (Powell, Rogers, and Roder, 1957).

TABLE XXV

λ in $W\ cm^{-1}\ deg^{-1}$ for technical alloys

Alloy	Physical condition	2° K	4° K	6° K	10° K	20° K	40° K	80° K	150° K	300° K
24-S Aluminium.	as received	..	..	..	..	0·17	0·36	0·60	0·88	1·1
Cu+2 Be .	annealed, 300° C	0·009	0·019	0·029	0·049	0·107	0·215	0·371	..	..
Cu+10 Ni .	annealed	..	0·011	0·023	0·055	0·16	0·32	0·38	..	..
Constantan .	as received	..	0·008₄	0·016	0·035	0·088	0·13	0·18	0·18	0·23
German silver .	as received	..	0·007	0·013	0·028	0·074	0·13	0·17	0·18	0·2
Monel .	annealed	..	0·008₆	0·015	0·030	0·070	0·120	0·16	0·2	0·24
Monel .	drawn	..	0·005	0·008₇	0·018	0·044	0·084	0·14	0·18	0·22
Inconel .	annealed	..	0·004₅	0·008	0·017	0·041	0·080	0·11	0·13	0·14
Inconel .	drawn	..	0·002₇	0·004₇	0·0093	0·023	0·050	0·092	0·12	0·14
Stainless steel .	as received	..	0·002₅	0·004	0·007	0·020	0·046	0·080	0·11	0·15
Brass (Cu+40 Zn) (+3 Pb) .	annealed	0·015	0·034	0·054	0·096	0·193	..	..	..	..
Brass (Cu+40 Zn) (+3 Pb) .	as received	0·013	0·029	0·046	0·082	0·175	0·33	0·53	0·9	1·0
Wood's metal		0·010	0·040	0·073	0·120	0·17	0·20	0·23	..	..
Silicon bronze (Cu+3 Si, 1 Mn) .	as received	..	..	..	..	0·034	0·069	0·140	..	0·3
Soft solder (60 Sn+ 40 Pb) .		0·050	0·160	0·265	0·425	0·560	0·525	0·525	0·5	0·5

Dielectric crystals

These are of only limited interest in cryogenic design and the Figure 126 showing data from Powell and Blanpied (1954) and some more recently published work, seems sufficient to illustrate the brief discussion above of $\lambda_g(T)$ in crystalline insulating materials.

Glasses, nylon, Teflon, etc.

Glass is a highly disordered substance, and the conductivity, which is due to lattice waves, might be expected to be given by the product $Cvl/3$ where the mean free path l is of the order of the interatomic distance. This seems to be approximately true at least down to temperatures of 20°–30° K, below which longitudinal lattice waves of long wavelength make a significant contribution to λ_g (see Klemens, 1951, 1956). Table XXVI gives experimental results for Pyrex and 'Phoenix' taken from Powell and Blanpied (1954) and for soft glass from White and Woods (unpublished);

for want of a better location, results for nylon (Berman, Foster, and Rosenberg, 1955), Perspex (measurements by Berman shown in Powell and Blanpied, 1954), and Teflon (Powell and Rogers, 1955) are given here also.

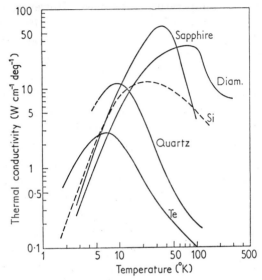

FIG. 126. Thermal conductivity of some crystalline dielectric solids.

TABLE XXVI
Thermal conductivity in mW deg^{-1} cm^{-1}

Material	2° K	4° K	6° K	10° K	20° K	40° K	80° K	150° K	300° K
Soft glass .	0·52	1·15	1·55	1·9	2·0	2·6	4·6	..	..
Pyrex glass .	..	..	1·1	..	..	..	4·8	7·6	11
'Phoenix' glass .	0·4	0·9	1·1	1·1$_5$	1·3$_5$	2·1	3·9	..	..
Perspex . .	0·4	0·5$_7$	0·6	0·6$_2$	0·7$_4$	..	..	..	..
Teflon . .	..	0·4$_5$	0·67	0·9$_5$	1·4$_2$	1·9$_6$	2·3	..	..
Nylon . .	0·06$_5$	0·12$_5$	0·20	0·3$_9$	0·9$_8$	..	..	..	..

Powder insulators

The importance of some powdered materials in providing thermal insulation for liquid-air vessels has already been mentioned (§ 2.1).

The effective thermal conductivities of many powder insulators and cellular glass or cellular plastic insulators are very similar at room temperature in the presence of an atmosphere of air. Due partly to the effect of radiation as a mode of heat transfer, some experimental values suggest that the thermal conductivity may not be uniquely defined in such materials but depends slightly on thickness or temperature difference. However, to a first approximation, the apparent thermal conductivities of a broad group of insulators such as Zerolite, rock-wool, corkboard, cellular glass blocks, Styrofoam, Santocel (silica aerogel), and fibre-glass wool all lie in the range of 300–600 μW cm^{-1} deg^{-1}. If the mean temperature is reduced, the conductivity decreases in an almost linear fashion which is consistent with the fact that a large part of the conductivity is apparently due to the air or gas present in the porous medium, and a lesser fraction is due to radiation. A very marked decrease in thermal conductivity occurs for the powder insulators when the gas pressure is reduced. For example, for silica aerogel (White, 1948) at a mean temperature of 183° K, the thermal conductivity has the following values.

Pressure	100	1	10^{-2}	10^{-3}	10^{-4}	10^{-5}	mm Hg
λ	125	53	17	13	11	11	μW/cm deg.

If the pressure is kept below 10^{-3} mm Hg, λ is relatively insensitive to pressure (see, for example, Johnston, Hood, and Bigeleisen, 1955). Figure 127 below, taken from the work of Fulk *et al.* (1957) at the National Bureau of Standards, illustrates the dependence of λ on pressure. This latter group of workers has also shown that the conductivity decreases when finely divided aluminium is added to a powder insulator. Figure 128 shows the extent to which the addition of aluminium powder reduces the apparent thermal conductivity in Perlite or Santocel, presumably by reducing the radiation transfer.

Other data on heat flow in powder insulators have been given by Palmer and Taylor (1948), Bradley and Stone (1948), Reynolds *et al.* (1955), and Van Gundy and Jacobs (1957).

Of the cellular or foamed plastic insulators, perhaps the most commonly used in recent years has been Styrofoam, an exploded polystyrene which has a conductivity of about 430 μW cm^{-1} deg^{-1} at room temperature. From data given for Styrofoam by Waite (1955) we may obtain: λ is 430 at a mean temperature of 300° K,

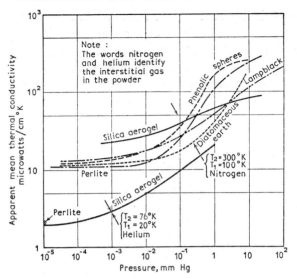

Fig. 127. Apparent mean thermal conductivity of some powder insulators as a function of gas pressure (after Fulk, Devereux, and Schrodt, 1957).

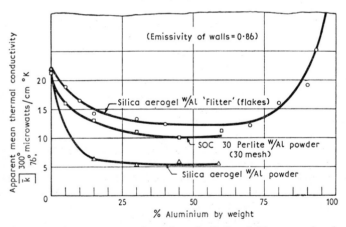

Fig. 128. Apparent mean thermal conductivity of silica aerogel and Perlite as a function of added aluminium content (after Fulk, Devereux, and Schrodt, 1957).

290 at 227° K, 220 at 173° K, and 160 at 116° K. Such figures indicate that Styrofoam insulation is comparable with Santocel insulation when air at or near atmospheric pressure is present in

the Santocel. If, however, the interstitial air is removed from the Santocel its conductivity becomes appreciably lower; if the pressure is lower than 10^{-2} mm Hg, then the effective thermal conductivity is reduced by an order of magnitude and can be even further reduced by the addition of a finely divided reflecting powder (e.g. aluminium).

REFERENCES

BERMAN, R. (1951). *Phil. Mag.* **42**, 642.

—— (1953). *Phil. Mag. Suppl.* **2**, 103.

—— FOSTER, E. L., and ROSENBERG, H. M. (1955). *Brit. J. Appl. Phys.* **6**, 181.

BRADLEY, C. B., and STONE, J. F. (1948). *Chem. Engng. Progr.* **44**, 723.

CASIMIR, H. B. G. (1938). *Physica*, **5**, 495.

DUGDALE, J. S., and MACDONALD, D. K. C. (1955). *Phys. Rev.* **98**, 1751.

ESTERMANN, I., and ZIMMERMAN, J. E. (1952). *J. Appl. Phys.* **23**, 578.

FRIEDEL, J. (1956). *Canad. J. Phys. (Suppl.)* **34**, 1190.

FRÖHLICH, H. (1936), *Elektronentheorie der Metalle*, Springer Verlag, Berlin.

FULK, M. M., DEVEREUX, R. J., and SCHRODT, J. E. (1957). *Proc. 1956 Cryogenic Engng. Conf.* N.B.S., Boulder, Colorado, p. 163.

GERRITSEN, A. N. (1956). *Handb. der Physik*, **19**, 137.

GRÜNEISEN, E. (1933). *Ann. Phys.* **16**, 530.

DE HAAS, W. J., and VAN DEN BERG, G. J. (1936). *Physica*, **3**, 440.

HARPER, A. F. A., KEMP, W. R. G., KLEMENS, P. G., TAINSH, R. J., and WHITE, G. K. (1957). *Phil. Mag.* **2**, 577.

HULM, J. K. (1951). *Proc. Phys. Soc.* **B64**, 207.

JOHNSTON, H. L., HOOD, C. B., and BIGELEISEN, J. (1955). *Proc. 1954 Cryogenic Engng. Conf.* N.B.S. Report No, 3517, p. 139.

JONES, H. (1956). *Handb. der Physik*, **19**, 227.

KAMERLINGH ONNES, H., and HOLST, G. (1914). *Leiden Comm.* 142a.

KEMP, W. R. G., KLEMENS, P. G., SREEDHAR, A. K., and WHITE, G. K. (1955). *Phil. Mag.* **46**, 811.

—— —— and WHITE, G. K. (1956a). *Aust. J. Phys.* **9**, 180.

—— —— SREEDHAR, A. K., and WHITE, G. K. (1956b). *Proc. Roy. Soc.* A, **233**, 480.

—— —— TAINSH, R. J., and WHITE, G. K. (1957). *Acta. Met.* **5**, 303.

KLEMENS, P. G. (1951). *Proc. Roy. Soc.* A, **208**, 108.

—— (1956). *Handb. der Physik*, **14**, 198.

LEIBFRIED, G., and SCHLÖMANN, E. (1954). *Nachr. Ges. Wiss. Göttingen*, IIa, 71.

MacDonald, D. K. C. (1956). *Handb. der Physik*, **14**, 137.

—— and Towle, L. (1956). *Canad. J. Phys.* **34**, 418.

—— White, G. K., and Woods, S. B. (1956). *Proc. Roy. Soc.* A, **235**, 358.

Makinson, R. E. B. (1938). *Proc. Camb. Phil. Soc.* **34**, 474.

Meissner, W., and Voigt, B. (1930). *Ann. Physik*, **7**, 761, 892.

Mendelssohn, K. (1955). *Progr. Low Temp. Phys.* **1**, 184, North-Holland Publishing Co., Amsterdam.

—— (1956). *Canad. J. Phys. (Suppl.)* **34**, 1315.

Mott, N. F. (1935). *Proc. Phys. Soc.* **47**, 571.

—— (1936). *Proc. Roy. Soc.* A, **153**, 699.

—— and Jones, H. (1936). *The Theory of the Properties of Metals and Alloys*, Clarendon Press, Oxford.

Olsen, J. L., and Rosenberg, H. M. (1953). *Phil. Mag. (Suppl.)* **2**, 28.

Palmer, B. M., and Taylor, R. B. (1948). *Chem. Engng. Progr.* **44**, 652.

Powell, R. L., and Blanpied, W. A. (1954). *Nat. Bur. Stand. Circular* 556, U.S. Govt. Printing Office, Washington, D.C.

—— and Rogers, W. M. (1955). *Nat. Science Foundation Conf. Low Temp. Phys. and Chem.* 1955, Baton Rouge, Louisiana.

—— —— and Roder, H. M. (1957). *Proc. 1956 Cryogenic Engng. Conf.*, N.B.S., Boulder, Colorado, p. 166; *J. Appl. Phys*, **28**, 1282.

Powell, R. W. (1955). *Bull. Inst. int. Froid*, Annexe 1955–2, p. 115.

Reynolds, M. M., Brown, J. D., Fulk, M. M., Park, O. E., and Curtis, G. W. (1955). *Proc. 1954 Cryogenic Engng. Conf.* N.B.S. Report No. 3517, p. 142.

Rosenberg, H. M. (1955). *Phil. Trans. Roy. Soc.* A, **247**, 441.

Sondheimer, E. H. (1950). *Proc. Roy. Soc.* A, **203**, 75.

Van den Berg, G. J. (1948). *Physica*, **14**, 111.

Van Gundy, D. A., and Jacobs, R. B. (1957). *Proc. 1956 Cryogenic Engng. Conf.* N.B.S., Boulder, Colorado, p. 156.

Waite, H. J. (1955). *Proc. 1954 Cryogenic Engng. Conf.* N.B.S. Report No. 3517, p. 158.

White, G. K. (1953). *Aust. J. Phys.* **6**, 397.

—— and Woods S. B. (1955.) *Canad. J. Phys.* **33**, 58.

—— —— (1957a). Ibid **35**, 248.

—— —— (1957b). Ibid. 346.

—— —— (1957c). Ibid. 656.

—— —— (1957d). Ibid. 892.

—— —— (1957e). *Rev. Sci. Instrum.* **28**, 638.

—— —— (1957f). *Proc. 1956 Cryogenic Engng. Conf.* N.B.S., Boulder, Colorado, p. 120.

White, J. F. (1948). *Chem. Engng. Progr.* **44**, 647.

Wilson, A. H. (1938). *Proc. Roy. Soc.* A, **167**, 580.

—— (1953). *The Theory of Metals*, Cambridge University Press.

Woods, S. B. (1956). *Canad. J. Phys.* **34**, 223.

TABLE XXVII

Some important physical functions (see Chapters X and XI)

T/θ	θ/T	C_v cal/mol deg	ρ_i/ρ_θ $(\alpha T^5 J_5)$†	ρ_i/ρ_θ $(\alpha T^3 J_3)$‡	W_i/W_∞ $(\alpha T^2 J_3)$§
(∞)	0	5·957	∞	..	..
(10)	0·1	5·954	10·55	10·4	1·00
(5)	0·2	5·945	5·268	..	..
(2·5)	0·4	5·909	2·617	..	..
(2·0)	0·5	5·833	2·083	2·062	0·990
(1·667)	0·6	5·851	1·725	..	..
(1·25)	0·8	5·770	1·274	..	..
(1·0)	1·0	5·669	1·000	1·000	0·960
(0·833)	1·2	5·549	0·813	0·8186	0·942
(0·714)	1·4	5·412	0·678	..	..
(0·667)	1·5	5·337	0·623	0·6341	0·912
(0·625)	1·6	5·259	0·574	..	..
(0·556)	1·8	5·094	0·493	..	..
(0·500)	2·0	4·918	0·426	0·4444	0·853
(0·400)	2·5	4·444	0·3043	..	..
(0·333)	3·0	3·947	0·2220	0·2478	0·714
(0·286)	3·5	3·459	0·1639	..	..
(0·250)	4·0	2·996	0·1216	0·1491	0·572
(0·222)	4·5	2·573	0·0906	..	..
(0·200)	5·0	2·197	0·0679	0·09360	0·449
(0·1667)	6·0	1·582	0·03849	0·06082	0·350
(0·143)	7·0	1·137	0·02220	..	..
(0·125)	8·0	0·8233	0·01308	0·02832	0·217
(0·111)	9·0	0·6041	0·00791	..	..
(0·100)	10·0	0·4518	0·00492	0·0149	0·143
(0·0833)	12	0·2667	0·002071	..	..
(0·0769)	13	0·2109	0·001401	0·00684	0·085
(0·0714)	14	0·1688	0·000972	..	..
(0·0625)	16	0·1133	0·000500	..	..
(0·0556)	18	0·0796	0·000278	..	..
(0·0500)	20	0·0580	0·000164	0·00188	0·036
(0·0400)	25	0·0298	0·0000526	..	..
(0·0333)	30	0·0172	0·0000220	..	..

† ρ_i/ρ_θ tabulated as $(T/\theta)^5 J_5(\theta/T) \div J_5(1)$.
‡ ρ_i/ρ_θ tabulated as $(T/\theta)^3 J_3(\theta/T) \div J_3(1)$.
§ W_i/W_∞ tabulated as $2(T/\theta)^2 J_3(\theta/T)$.

Notes and references for the table overleaf

(i) Values of atomic weight, density, coefficient of linear thermal expansion and structures have been taken from standard physical tables, e.g. *Smithsonian Physical Tables* (9th revised edition, Smithsonian Institution, 1954), *Rare Metals Handbook* (Reinhold Publishing Corporation, N.Y. 1954), and *Manual of Lattice Spacings and Structures of Metals and Alloys* (W. B. Pearson, Pergamon Press, 1958).

(ii) Values for the Debye characteristic temperature θ_D, have been obtained from specific-heat data given in the reviews (Shiffman, 1952; Blackman, 1955; Keesom and Pearlman, 1956) listed in Chapter X, from references listed in these reviews, and from some more recent papers.

(iii) Many values for electrical resistivity have been calculated from the ice-point values given in the review by Gerritsen (1956), although in the case of most transition elements, recent experimental data obtained by the writer and his collaborators (references in Chapter XI) have been used.

(iv) Thermal conductivity data are taken partly from the compilations by R. L. Powell and Blanpied (1954) and R. W. Powell (1955). Some other references reviewed by Klemens (1956) have been used; the data for transition elements and alkali metals have been obtained in some cases by extrapolation of the low-temperature measurements of the writer and his collaborators (references in Chapter XI). Those values of thermal conductivity in the table which are enclosed in brackets are obtained by extrapolation.

(v) Experimental values of T_c, the superconducting transition temperatures, are those listed in the review by B. Serin ((1956) *Handb. der Physik*, **15**, 210, 1956) except in the case of niobium (White and Woods, 1957d, Chapter XI). T_c for hafnium is in some doubt (see R. A. Hein (1956) *Phys. Rev.* **102**, 1511).

TABLE XXVIII

Physical properties of some elements at room temperature (295° K). For anisotropic elements the values listed are generally appropriate to the polycrystalline form

Element	Atomic weight	Structure	Density (g cm⁻³)	θ_D (°K)	Coefficient of linear thermal expansion × 10^4 per °K	Electrical resistivity (μ ohm cm)	Thermal conductivity (W cm⁻¹ deg⁻¹)	Superconducting transition temperature (°K)
Aluminium	26·97	f.c.c.	2·70	380	0·24	2·76	2·4	1·20
Antimony	121·76	rhombohedral	6·68	210	0·11	36	0·2–0·3	..
Arsenic	74·91	,,	5·73	290	0·05	29	..	..
Barium	137·36	b.c.c.	3·5	110	0·18–0·26	41	..	..
Beryllium	9·013	h.c.p.	1·84	920	0·12	≃ 3·6	≃ 2·0	..
Bismuth	209·0	rhombohedral	9·8	120	0·13	115	0·1	..
Boron	10·82	hexagonal (?)	2·34	1,300	0·08	≃ 10^{12}	(0·2)	..
Cadmium	112·41	h.c.p.	8·65	175	0·30	7·4	0·92	0·56
Calcium	40·08	f.c.c.	1·55	210	0·22	4·1	..	..
Carbon:								
(graphite)	12·01	hexagonal	2·22	≃ 400	..	$\left.\begin{array}{c}10^2 \\ 10^6\end{array}\right\}$	~2	..
(diamond)		diamond	..	≃ 2,000	..	> 10^{12}	6·5	..
Caesium	132·91	b.c.c.	1·9	45	0·97	20·8	(0·4)	..
Chromium	52·01	b.c.c.	7·2	480	0·044–0·075	12·9	0·8₆	..
Cobalt	58·94	h.c.p.	8·92	380	0·13–0·16	5·80	(1·2)	..
Copper	63·54	f.c.c.	8·96	310	0·167	1·68	4·2	..
Gallium	69·72	orthorhombic	5·97	240	0·18	15	..	1·103
Germanium	72·60	diamond	5·32	400	0·06	~ 5×10^7	≃ $180/T$	..
Gold	197·2	f.c.c.	19·3	185	0·14	2·21	3·1	..
Hafnium	178·6	h.c.p.	13·09	210	0·06	30·6	(0·22)	0·37 (?)
Indium	114·76	tetragonal	7·31	110	0·30	8·8	(0·8)	3·40
Iridium	193·1	f.c.c.	22·5	290	0·065	5·05	1·45	..
Iron	55·85	b.c.c.	7·87	400	0·12	9·80	0·80	..
Lead	207·21	f.c.c.	11·34	≃ 88	0·29	21	0·35	7·18
Lithium	6·94	b.c.c.	0·53	360	0·45	9·4	0·72	..

Element								
Magnesium	24·32	h.c.p.	1·74	330	0·25	4·3	1·6	..
Manganese	54·93	cubic (complex)	7·44	410	0·37	140	..	..
Mercury (near 220° K)	200·61	rhombohedral	14·2	110	0·61	≈ 21	≈ 0·3 (200°K)	4·17
Molybdenum	95·95	b.c.c.	10·2	380	0·052	5·33	$1\cdot4_5$	..
Nickel	58·69	f.c.c.	8·9	390	0·13	7·05	$0\cdot9_0$	..
Niobium	92·91	b.c.c.	8·57	250	0·071	14·4	0·53	9·2
Osmium	190·2	h.c.p.	22·48	..	0·048	9·1	(0·9)	0·71
Palladium	106·7	f.c.c.	12·02	290	0·12	10·55	$0\cdot7_2$	..
Platinum	195·23	f.c.c.	21·45	225	0·089	10·42	$0\cdot7_0$	..
Potassium	$39\cdot09_6$	b.c.c.	0·86	98	0·83	7·1	0·98	..
Rhenium	186·31	h.c.p.	21·0	275	0·066	18·7	(0·5)	1·70
Rhodium	102·91	f.c.c.	12·44	350	0·084	4·78	1·50	..
Rubidium	85·48	b.c.c.	1·53	61	0·66	13·6	(0·6)	..
Ruthenium	101·7	h.c.p.	$12\cdot2_5$	..	0·08	7·4	(1·0)	0·47
Selenium	78·96	vitreous	4·30	..	..	$>10^{12}$	0·002–0·003	..
		hexagonal	4·80	250	0·49	..	..	..
Silicon	28·06	diamond	2·32	700	0·4	$\approx 10^7$	5/T	..
Silver	107·88	f.c.c.	10·49	220	0·024	1·64	≈ 400/T	..
Sodium	$22\cdot99_7$	b.c.c.	0·97	160	0·19	4·84	4·2	..
Strontium	87·63	f.c.c.	2·6	140	0·71	23	1·4	..
Tantalum	180·88	b.c.c.	16·6	230	0·065	13·0	..	4·38
Tellurium	127·61	hexagonal	6·24	180	0·17	$0\cdot4 \times 10^6$	0·55	..
Thallium	204·39	h.c.p.	11·85	94	0·29	17	(10/T)	2·39
Thorium	232·12	f.c.c.	11·7	140	0·11	15·6	≈ 0·5	1·37
Tin	118·7	tetragonal	7·3	160	0·25	11·1	0·7	3·73
		(diam. cubic) (Grey tin)	5·76	260	..	..	..	..
Titanium	47·90	h.c.p.	4·5	360	0·085	≈ 43·0	0·20	0·39
Tungsten	183·92	b.c.c.	19·3	315	0·046	5·32	1·6	..
Uranium (α)	238·07	orthorhombic	19·05	160	0·13	25	0·28	0·8
Vanadium	50·95	b.c.c.	6·11	380	0·08	20·0	0·36	4·89
Zinc	65·38	h.c.p.	7·14	240	0·27	$5\cdot9_5$	1·2	0·91
Zirconium	91·22	h.c.p.	6·5	250	0·059	42·4	0·21	0·55

AUTHOR INDEX

SUBJECT INDEX